THE ROYAL SOCIETY: CONCEPT AND CREATION

TO D. J. W.

THE ROYAL SOCIETY:
CONCEPT
AND CREATION

MARGERY PURVER

WITH AN INTRODUCTION BY
H. R. TREVOR-ROPER

THE M.I.T. PRESS

Massachusetts Institute of Technology, Cambridge, Massachusetts

First published in 1967
by Massachusetts Institute of Technology
Cambridge, Massachusetts

© *Margery Purver 1967*

Library of Congress Catalog Card Number 66–25631

Printed in Great Britain

CONTENTS

ILLUSTRATIONS

ACKNOWLEDGMENTS

I first wish to thank Miss Dorothy Wheal, to whom this book is dedicated, for her generous help and support and constant interest in the work, which have sustained me throughout the long period of research involved.

I wish to thank Professor H. R. Trevor-Roper for his advice over a considerable period in the later stages and in connexion with the publication of the book.

I should like to express my appreciation of the Royal Society's permission to use its archives, and of the courteous help of the Librarian.

I owe a particular debt to Dr. E. J. Bowen, F.R.S., whose interest in the subject has been a continual source of encouragement.

I should like to express my thanks to Fr. Thomas Corbishley, S.J., former Master of Campion Hall, Oxford, who read the text of the work and has given me the benefit of his wisdom.

I wish to thank the Emeritus Curator of the Museum of the History of Science, Oxford, Dr. C. H. Josten, for his long and helpful interest in the subject, and the present Curator, Mr. F. W. Maddison, for whose help in obtaining some of the photographs I am most grateful.

I should like to express my thanks to Mrs. Hester Jenkins, who has helped me in many ways, out of her own experience of research, with much practical kindness.

My thanks are also due to Dr. Anne Whiteman of Lady Margaret Hall, Oxford, and Miss Rosemary Syfret of Somerville College, Oxford.

I owe particular thanks to Dr. Butzmann, Keeper of Manuscripts of the Herzog August Bibliothek, Wolfenbüttel, for a transcript (in addition to the microfilm) of a manuscript used in this book.

I am grateful for the courteous help of the British Museum; the Bodleian Library, Oxford, especially Mr. W. G. Harris and Miss Patricia Brown, of Duke Humphrey's Library; the National Portrait Gallery, especially Miss Caroline Brown;

the Warburg Institute; the Scottish National Portrait Gallery; the Royal Library, Stockholm; and the Library of the University of Uppsala.

I should like to express my appreciation of the prompt and kind help, in my inquiries, of the following Oxford colleges: Wadham, Trinity, Merton, Brasenose, Christ Church and All Souls.

I am glad to have this opportunity of thanking the Leverhulme Trustees for a research award which helped me to carry out the part of this work concerned with the 'Invisible College' and 'Pansophia'.

INTRODUCTION

The foundation of the Royal Society in London in 1660 is an important episode in intellectual history: in the history of philosophy no less than in that of science. At the time of its foundation, the Royal Society embodied a new philosophy and a new scientific attitude; and its prompt recognition by the restored monarchy of Charles II, which gave it its royal charter in 1662, showed a new attitude on the part of the monarchy. For not only was the patronage of scientific research by the Stuart monarchy something new in itself: it was also, in this instance, politically surprising. The body to which Charles II gave a royal charter and royal patronage was a private body which had been formed during 'the late usurpation'. Charles II repudiated, emphatically, most of the work of Oliver Cromwell. He cancelled the legislation of the 'interregnum', reversed its social policy, repurged the universities, swept away the national Puritan Church. Only the informal scientific society which owed its impulse to Cromwell's own brother-in-law John Wilkins was singled out for positive royal favour. This is evidence of the position which that society had already, by that time, acquired.

How did this society emerge? By what process, and out of what elements, was it formed? What was its distinguishing philosophy? To these questions an answer has long ago been given. The prototype of the Royal Society, we are told, was an informal body of men who met together in London in or slightly before 1645, in order to foster experimental science. Time and the historians have added detail and definition to this body. Its members have been identified as 'puritan' in religion, utilitarian in secular aims. They have been given a centre in Gresham College, a mercantile institution whose professors (it is said) emphasized practical rather than speculative knowledge. Their philosophy, we are told, was the philosophy of Francis Bacon, the advocate of such utilitarianism. This 'puritan' group, we are told, migrated, about 1648, to Oxford where it continued to thrive under the leadership of

John Wilkins, then Warden of Wadham College. In 1658-9 it returned to London and to Gresham College. After the Restoration it adroitly contrived to secure royal patronage and so to continue into the new age as a royal foundation.

Such is the account of the origins of the Royal Society which, with whatever variations of detail, has been received since 1756, when Thomas Birch, F.R.S., published the first volume of his *History of the Royal Society*. It is an account which has been consecrated by time, blessed by the Society itself, incorporated in official histories and reigning textbooks. It has also, more recently, given support to, and received support from those historians who see a socially determined connexion between 'puritanism' and scientific innovation. With such literary credentials, and such sociological support, the account is by now an established orthodoxy.

When any historical interpretation has become an orthodoxy, it is useful to dismantle the structure and look again at its constituent parts, lest immobility lead to petrifaction, orthodoxy to dogma. This is what Miss Margery Purver has done in this important book. Taking nothing on trust, she has re-examined the early history of the Royal Society in detail. With a fine, exact scholarship, she has scrutinized all the old sources and discovered many that are new. And when she has re-assembled the machine, how different it looks! Much of the structure is the same, but the functions are different: so different that serious revisions may be necessary in other departments of history too.

In order to see what Miss Purver has done, it is convenient to consider the basis of the established interpretation. We can then see at what points Miss Purver has challenged it, and judge the validity of her challenge.

The first historian of the Royal Society was Thomas Sprat, then a Fellow of Wadham College, Oxford, afterwards Bishop of Rochester. Sprat had been an undergraduate at Wadham College in the 1650s and was a disciple and *protégé* of John Wilkins, the Warden. His *History of the Royal Society* was written over the period 1664-7 and published in 1667. In it, he clearly ascribes the origin of the Society to the Oxford meetings of the 1650s. To any previous meetings in London he makes no reference at all. He either knew of no such meetings or did not regard them as relevant to his subject.

How, then, did the utilitarian Londoners come in? They first appeared in literature in 1678, when John Wallis, a distinguished mathematician, in the course of a private controversy, implicitly contradicted Sprat and declared that the first beginnings of the Royal Society were in London in the 1640s. Since Wallis was twenty years older than Sprat and had been a member both of the London and of the Oxford groups, his authority naturally seemed strong. And if it should be objected that Sprat's personal inexperience is irrelevant, since his authority is not his own but that of Wilkins, then it could be answered that in such matters Wilkins himself may not have been reliable. As a former 'puritan', brother-in-law to the usurper, he had a past to bury, and prudence might dictate selection of evidence. For a royal society, Oxford in the 1650s might seem a less tainted source than London in the 1640s.

For these reasons Birch and all later historians have preferred the authority of Wallis to that of Sprat, or at least have subsumed Sprat in Wallis. They have supposed that the London group was an earlier extension of the Oxford group which Sprat, through ignorance or prejudice, failed to notice. And in order to justify this decision, they have passed retrospective judgment on the two authorities. They have ascribed to Wallis a veracity of which his contemporaries, at least, were doubtful, and they have refused to Sprat even the humblest virtues of a historian. To the latest official historian of the Royal Society, writing on the occasion of its tercentenary, Sprat is 'an unfledged writer', 'ill-equipped and ill-informed', a 'time-server', 'ambitious for literary distinction', whose views may be dismissed without consideration or ceremony.

The implications of this view are considerable. It presupposes not merely that the Royal Society had a slightly longer history than it at first avowed but also that there is a continuity of philosophy between the two groups. But this is not a necessary supposition. It is perfectly possible that Wilkins and Sprat chose to ignore the London meetings not through Sprat's ignorance or Wilkins' prejudice but because they did not recognize such continuity: because they believed that the London meetings of the 1640s differed in character from the Oxford meetings of the 1650s and so, in spite of an undeniable overlap in membership, could not be lineally connected with the Royal Society.

Once this is recognized, it becomes necessary to re-examine the evidence. First, we must ask, what is the independent historical value of Sprat's *History*? Is it fair to dismiss it simply because Sprat, by his own admission, was writing under supervision, or because his supervisors may have had reasons for reticence? Is Sprat necessarily to be rejected in favour of Wallis? Secondly, we must ask, what was the peculiar 'concept' of the Royal Society, and how far had that concept been pursued either by the London group of the 1640s or by the Oxford group of the 1650s? In thus re-examining the evidence, and in asking these questions, we must be careful to discriminate. We must not assume connexions before they are proved. The fact that Robert Boyle in the 1640s, wrote of an 'invisible college' does not necessarily shed any light on the Oxford society of the 1650s, of which Boyle would admittedly be a member; the fact that Samuel Hartlib and many others professed themselves Baconians in the 1640s does not necessarily mean that their aim was identical either with that of Bacon or with that of Wilkins; and the fact that Wallis was himself a member both of the London group and of the Oxford group does not necessarily mean that the two groups had the same intentions or that Wallis's later account is unquestionably true. When we are seeking to define or establish a connexion, the connexion cannot at any point be presumed.

Miss Purver has presumed nothing. She starts from the beginning, and tests every piece of evidence before using it. First, she examines the statements of both Sprat and Wallis and the circumstances in which each was made. The result of this examination is to clear away many of the objections made to Sprat's authority. She shows, from the records of the Royal Society, that Sprat was not merely the mouthpiece of Wilkins: he was employed and supervised by the whole Society; and there is no reason to suppose either that Wilkins had any desire to bury his 'puritan' past (which was anyway well known), or that such a past would be buried by merely ignoring the first three years of the Society's history. Moreover, Sprat's account is supported by independent contemporary testimony. On the other hand, Wallis's account was first uttered by him incidentally eleven years later, is unconfirmed by any contemporary writer, and was afterwards abandoned even by him. Miss Purver therefore argues that any re-examination of the early history of the Society must begin from the assumption that Sprat's authority is to be preferred to that of Wallis. This means that Sprat's refusal to recognize the London group of the 1640s as a direct ancestor of the Royal Society cannot be dismissed as mere ignorance or prejudice: it must be taken seriously. We must reckon at least with the possibility that the two groups were conceptually different.

Once this possibility is admitted, it becomes necessary to isolate the Royal Society's concept of science and to see this concept undistorted by evidence concerning the earlier group. Miss Purver's analysis of the work of the two groups suggests that it was in fact qualitatively different. All the evidence which relates to the earlier group shows that that group was concerned rather with particular discoveries, already made by others, than with conceptual change. It was Baconian indeed, at least in its own eyes, but with a vulgar Baconianism, the Baconianism of Hartlib, not of Francis Bacon. The real Baconianism, the Baconianism of Francis Bacon, was something very different.

It is the fate of all great men to be quickly vulgarized. In the generation after Bacon's death, many men called themselves Baconians who grasped only the external details of his work. His *experimenta fructifera* were seized upon by utilitarian gadgeteers, his *experimenta lucifera* by millenarian visionaries. Whoever attacked the authority of the past, the philosophy of Aristotle, or the organization of the universities, whoever looked forward to an advance of learning or a new utopia, saw himself as a 'Baconian'. This was especially so in the 1640s, which can be described as the heyday of vulgar Baconianism. It took time and the recovery of critical standards to restore the devalued name; and it was the Oxford group which restored it, recovering it alike from London artisans and technical experimenters on one hand and from radical or visionary puritans on the other.

And what was the true Baconianism that Wilkins and his friends restored? In one of her most illuminating chapters Miss Purver has re-created the 'new philosophy' of Bacon, redeeming it not only from the puritan vulgarization of Hartlib and his friends but from the Victorian vulgarization of Macaulay. She has shown that Bacon's message to his contemporaries was not merely remote philosophizing or a recommendation to 'proficiency in utilitarian skills'. It was not 'the experimental method' or even 'the inductive method', or indeed any mere method. It was a 'new philosophy', a 'true and active philosophy' which was to replace the received 'idols of the market-place' and 'idols of the theatre', 'building in the human understanding a true model of the world'. Within the context of this new philosophy, new methods could be usefully employed. These new methods included experiment but did not consist in experiment. They consisted rather in a continuous process of interaction between experiment and reasoning, 'a true and perfect marriage between the empirical and the rational faculty'. Such methods, in such a context, by transforming observation into new general laws, would be capable of gradual but perpetual expansion. The 'new philosophy' unlike the old, which was merely a system for 'the nice ordering and setting forth' of things already discovered, was a philosophy of new discovery 'promising infinite utility hereafter'.

Such, according to Miss Purver, was the true Baconian philosophy which was revived, after its temporary vulgarization, by the founders of the Royal Society. In starting to build on that base they recognized, and asserted, that they were doing something new, unprecedented in the history of science. The Royal Society, declared its first President, when formally receiving its royal charter in 1662, was 'the first foundation of the greatest improvement of learning and the arts that they are capable of, and which hath never heretofore been attempted by any'; it was an attempt, wrote Sprat, several years later, 'which all ages had despair'd of'; and it owed its inspiration to 'the one great man who had the true imagination of the whole extent' of it, Francis Bacon. It may be said that, in this, Sprat idealized Bacon: that he abstracted him from his social ambience as a more modern historian would not do. But this does not affect the Society's direct indebtedness to him rather than to any intervening source.

The Royal Society's repudiation of 'vulgar Baconianism' for true Baconianism is illustrated incidentally in its attitude to religion, to which Miss Purver devotes a chapter. The puritan vulgarizers had attached their fragmentary interpretations of Bacon's thought to an exclusively Protestant ideology. Bacon's study of Nature had been subordinated to the Protestant pantheism of the puritan sects, his anti-Aristotelianism to their social radicalism, his new 'metaphysic' to the millenarism of their prophets. His *experimenta lucifera* had degenerated into the *Via Lucis* of Comenius. But the Oxford group contrived to disengage his philosophy from these new doctrinal restraints. They disengaged it so successfully from the distorting protestantism of the 1640s that its two original leaders, Wilkins and Ward, could both become Anglican bishops and the Society itself could be accused by its enemies of 'reducing England unto Popery'. In this disengagement, this emancipation of science and philosophy from the coercion of particular religious systems, they showed themselves, once again, true disciples of Bacon.

Such is the general argument of Miss Purver's book. So brief a summary cannot possibly do justice to the detailed research which has resolved so many lingering doubts, to the fine scholarship which has separated the concretions of past evidence, or to the analytical power which has enabled the author to command her own industry and scholarship and clarify large issues as well as small. These enviable qualities will be obvious to the reader and will earn the respect even of those who may be reluctant to yield to her conclusions. For it can hardly be expected that such a reinterpretation will be easily admitted by scholars committed to the old orthodoxy. The quotation which she has chosen as an epigraph to her book may be applied to the New Philosophy of the seventeenth century. It may also be read as evidence that her own conclusions (first presented in an Oxford doctoral thesis in 1959) have already been resisted, and resisted strongly, before they could be presented, as they now are, to the fair and open criticism of scholars.

H. R. TREVOR-ROPER

It hath alwaies beene the unhappinesse of new truths in Philosophy, to be derided by those that are ignorant of the causes of things, and rejected by others, whose perversenesse ties them to the contrary opinion . . .

John Wilkins,
The Discovery of a World in the Moone,
1638

THE PROBLEM OF THE ORIGIN

OF THE ROYAL SOCIETY

Since the middle of the eighteenth century, when Thomas Birch published his *History of the Royal Society*, various theories have been put forward on problematic aspects of the Royal Society's origin, but baffling and irreconcilable elements remain. It may therefore be asked whether the central problem has been recognized, and whether the basic assumptions, invariably made, ought not to be examined.

In the minds of all historians of the Royal Society from Birch onwards, the essential foundation of the Society has been the series of meetings described by John Wallis, the mathematician, which began in about 1645 in London. It has followed as a matter of course that these meetings constituted not only a precursor, but also the prototype of the Oxford meetings of about 1648–59, which were stated by Thomas Sprat, the Society's first historian, to be the source of the Royal Society.

On the assumption that Sprat's account was the expression of a private opinion, modern historians have either failed to give it sufficient weight, or have dismissed it altogether. Contemporary evidence is here brought to show that Sprat's *History of the Royal Society*, published in 1667, was compiled under the surveillance of the Council of the Royal Society, which set up special committees to advise Sprat on all matters relating to its origin, purpose and progress.

Bound up with this traditional assumption about the origin of the Royal Society are various other theories: one that

Gresham College was the Society's place of origin; some concerned with the identity of 'the Invisible College'; another that 'the Puritan ethic' was the underlying impulse which produced the Royal Society, and so on.

But all these conjectures on the origin of the Royal Society have the same fundamental limitation: they deal with selected aspects of the problem without ever engaging the problem as a whole or asking the real question, so the main issue has been left untouched. At the same time, an immense preoccupation with marginal considerations, lacking a central point of reference, has produced 'findings' which are largely irrelevant and have themselves contributed to the general state of confusion on this subject.

The first step towards a solution, therefore, must be the thorough examination of the nature and purpose of the Royal Society itself, before attempting to compare it with earlier societies, especially if the aim is to consider its position in relation to these societies. Preoccupation with the identities and dates of such societies, rather than with the essential nature of their purposes and activities, has helped to prolong the deadlock, for the core of the whole matter is one of definition. Thus, although the origin of the Royal Society appears to turn on date and place, these facts are really of small importance. The real problem concerns the fundamental concept of the Royal Society and its claim to uniqueness.

During the three hundred or so years since the Society's inception, retrospective assumptions, gathering weight from continual repetition, distortion and embellishment, have imposed a pattern of their own. Like a lost city buried beneath the gradual deposit and landslides of the centuries, the Society's original *raison d'être* has vanished from sight. In the following chapters I shall attempt to uncover what the founders of the Royal Society intended when they 'first conceiv'd it in their minds',[1] and what, in fact, they were doing when they 'put it in execution'.[2]

The central question considered here is whether the Royal Society was merely an unconscious product of its time, distinctive only in the measure of its success and fame; or whether

[1] Thomas Sprat, *The History of the Royal Society of London, for the Improving of Natural Knowledge*, London, 1667, p. 53.
[2] Ibid., p. 52.

it deliberately set out to initiate the means which, transcending all individual discoveries, focused and stimulated scientific endeavour—the construction of a new system of natural sciences—and thus played a major part in bringing about an effective scientific revolution.

Historians of science of this period, intent on following the development of particular lines of discovery, or even of particular sciences, have seldom seen those individual developments in relation to their much larger scientific, and, ultimately, philosophical context; so the enormous pressures of prevailing systems of thought, whether towards retarding and repressing, or towards accelerating and expanding the growth of the discovery-nodes within, have been largely ignored. The assumption has generally been that particular discoveries, together with a certain amount of practical know-how at an ordinary day-to-day level, somehow resulted in the replacement of a fossilized, medieval system of sciences by a live modern one, and that this was bound to happen. But that is almost to reverse cause and effect in this situation; for while, obviously, scientific progress could not be made without particular discoveries, these did not constitute, and of themselves were incapable of producing a new, comprehensive system of sciences.

It is the main contention of this thesis that the effective scientific revolution of the seventeenth century owed a considerable debt to an intellectual revolution of a far more conscious kind than has hitherto been indicated, whose practical application was the deliberate inauguration of a new system of sciences: a system which in its working released, stimulated and, above all, organized and related scientific discovery in a way, and on a scale, never before attempted, at the same time establishing basic principles which have governed the development of the sciences ever since.

A definition of what the early Royal Society was, implicitly involves comparison, and requires a statement of what it was not. As Francis Bacon said of experimental science, 'no one successfully investigates the nature of a thing in the thing itself; the inquiry must be enlarged, so as to become more general'.[3] So some examination is necessary of societies which bore a superficial likeness to the Royal Society, or for one reason or another have been thought to constitute its source. It therefore

[3] Francis Bacon, *Novum Organum* I, Aph. LXX, London, 1620.

seemed best to treat the subject in two parts. Part One is concerned with the intellectual source, the inception and the development of the Royal Society up to the period immediately following its own publication of its history, in 1667. Part Two deals with some of the more serious misconceptions which obscured the essential nature of the early Royal Society, and is therefore different in character from Part One. The various expositions in Part Two have no sequence or cohesion as a whole, each section resembling an appendix rather than a chapter.

The first of these expositions is an examination of John Wallis's account of the origin of the Royal Society, which differs from all other contemporary accounts and opinions. This account has constituted the main stumbling block to historians, but that could scarcely have happened if the real issue had not already become obscured. So any worthwhile appraisal of the problem must take into account not only a careful analysis of what Wallis actually said—and this has never been done—but, even more important, a comparison with the contemporary Royal Society's own exposition of its nature and purpose, which has also been entirely disregarded by modern historians. It is therefore necessary to inquire into the methods used by those who support what has become the traditional view.

A number of factors have masked the evidence, and these are not altogether simple, as they have tended to react on one another and to combine in a tangle of misapprehensions. To begin with, uncritical acceptance of Wallis's account of the origin of the Royal Society automatically discredits Sprat's, and the rejection of Sprat's account impinges on the validity, some even think the veracity, of the rest of his evidence, which is of far greater importance than a mere matter of time and place.

On the question of Wallis's evidence, there has not only been no analysis of the two versions of his account, but the fact that he emended his first version has been overlooked. Composite accounts have been made from details put together from his two versions, and the knowledge that Wallis later omitted certain statements has therefore been lost.

Another factor which has further confused the issue is that historians, making the assumption that the meetings at Oxford of about 1648–59 were only a continuation of those in London which began in 1645, have applied to the London meetings evidence and contemporary opinions which relate only to the Oxford meetings, thus attributing to the London meetings characteristics which they did not have, and obscuring the essential differences between these and those at Oxford.

The fact that Wallis later abandoned the case that the Royal Society originated in these earlier meetings in London, and wrote an account entirely in accordance with Sprat's, confirming the origin of the Royal Society at Oxford, is here brought to light in this context for the first time.

The theory that Gresham College was the source of the Royal Society depends not only on acceptance of John Wallis's earlier opinion against all evidence to the contrary, but, in addition, on a misreading of that account, whereby it is supposed that the London meetings he described began at Gresham College. But these, and other arguments for Gresham College are only marginal: again the real question is one of definition; so the nature, outlook and pursuits of Gresham College are discussed in their relevance to the purpose of the Royal Society.

The activities of Samuel Hartlib and his 'pansophic' associates must be considered in some detail, not because they have much real bearing on the subject of the early Royal Society, but because misunderstanding about them has caused so much confusion; at the same time, knowledge of the way in which this group's own misconceptions concerning the nature of the Society arose and persisted, helps to illuminate the true nature of the Society.

In general the evidence on this whole subject has neither been examined closely nor integrated. In this study, although some fresh manuscript material has been brought to light, and some already known has been brought to bear on the subject for the first time, the collation and re-interpreting of contemporary printed sources has been the most important factor in arriving at what may appear to be a new definition of the early Royal Society, but is in fact only a restatement of that conceived by the originators.

The main case in point here is the nature of the Royal Society's debt to Francis Bacon. Sprat said that Bacon was the 'one great Man, who had the true Imagination of the whole extent of this Enterprize, as it is now set on foot';[4] yet historians of science, looking at Bacon's own contribution as a scientist, and confused by persisting Victorian misapprehensions about his concept of science, have exclaimed that it was a mercy that the Royal Society went its own way. Correlation of Sprat, speaking with the authority of the Royal Society as an institution, and Bacon, particularly in his *Novum Organum*, shows that the debt to Bacon was overwhelmingly philosophical rather than scientific, but that, notwithstanding this, Bacon was the great formative influence on the Society's concept of science.

This correlation of sources also discloses the measure of Bacon's influence on the Royal Society's religious and linguistic policies, at the same time revealing each in a new light.

It is generally accepted that the early Royal Society was an institution whose influence extended far beyond the normal boundaries of a private society, and that its activities were prominent in the scientific eruption which occurred in the second half of the seventeenth century. There is therefore, perhaps, some historical justification for endeavouring to discover the impetus which produced this society, the real nature of its contribution to modern science, and its place in the history of its time.

[4] Thomas Sprat, *History*, p. 35.

PART ONE

I

THE VALIDITY AND
SIGNIFICANCE OF SPRAT'S
HISTORY AS A SOURCE

Since Thomas Sprat's *History of the Royal Society* was published in 1667,[1] only five years after the Society's existence had received the hall-mark of incorporation by Royal Charter, many publications on the subject have appeared. Yet Sprat's exposition of the conception and beginning of the Royal Society remains the only one which tells us, in any detail, not only what the founders were doing, but, even more important, what they *thought* they were doing.

As Sprat's testimony is so important it is necessary to know whether his account represents the Royal Society as a body, or whether it is merely, as is generally assumed, an expression of his own or of John Wilkins's private opinion.

When, in 1663, the Royal Society's Charter of incorporation had finally been adjusted to its satisfaction,[2] its desire to publish an authorized record of its origin, purpose and achievement

[1] Thomas Sprat, *The History of the Royal Society of London, for the Improving of Natural Knowledge*, London, 1667.
[2] Below, pp. 136–40.

was a natural corollary of its newly acquired status. In fact Sir Robert Moray, who had been mainly responsible for obtaining the Royal Letters Patent and now headed the list of the Council nominated in the Charter,[3] and William Brereton, also a member of the Council, confirmed that the Royal Society had already taken steps towards publishing an official history which would give information on all that concerned the Society.[4] Although Sprat, defending the Society against attacks, was obliged to deal with subjects other than what 'peculiarly describes their Undertaking', that, he said, 'was the main end of my Design'.[5]

Subsequent correspondence and entries in the Society's minute-books[6] show that Sprat was closely guided, and his work scrutinized by a wide range of persons—prominent Fellows and numerous committees set up by the Royal Society Council for that purpose. Sprat himself refers to this official surveillance:

. . . they had at first a *Register*, who was to take Notes of all that pass'd; which were afterwards to be reduc'd into their *Journals* and *Register Books*. This Task was first *perform'd* by Dr. *Croone*. But they since thought it more necessary, to appoint two *Secretaries*, who are to reply to all Addresses from abroad, and at home; and to publish whatever shall be agreed upon by the *Society*. These are at present, Dr. *Wilkins*, and Mr. *Oldenburg*, from

---

[3] The President, Viscount Brouncker, was an *ex officio* member of the Council.

[4] Sir Robert Moray and William Brereton (third Baron Brereton of Leighlin in 1664) each wrote to Christiaan Huygens giving him this news, Moray on 14 May 1663, and Brereton on 28 October 1663. The relevant passages from their letters are given below, pp. 140–1.

[5] Thomas Sprat, *History*, 'An Advertisement to the Reader'.

[6] Thomas Birch, an eighteenth-century Secretary of the Royal Society, edited and published the Society's minute-books up to December 1687, under the title *The History of the Royal Society* (London, 1756–7, 4 vols). This publication has served a very useful purpose in making available the general contents of the minute-books; but in editing the text Birch has often somewhat rephrased, and at times has even summarized, the original, with some loss of accuracy. So all references to the minute-books and to the letter-books (also usefully drawn on by Birch) have been made from the original manuscripts in the archives of the Royal Society. The minute-book of the general meetings of the Society is here referred to by its traditional title of 'Journal Book', and the minute-book of the meetings of the Council as the 'Council Book'.

whom I have not usurp'd this first imployment of that kind; for it is onely my hand that goes, the substance and direction came from one of them.[7]

The point here (and this has often been misunderstood) is that the Secretaries, in the persons of Wilkins and Oldenburg, derive their authority from the Society and act on its instructions. They, like Sprat, are answerable to it; and it is clear, as the evidence unfolds, that Sprat is subject to the orders of the Council itself.

In a letter to Robert Boyle dated 24 November 1664, Oldenburg says that he has read Sprat's manuscript of *The History of the Royal Society* and gives names of other members of the Council who have done so. He says:

> Mr. *Sprat* intends to begin next week to print the *History* of our Institution, which hath been perused by lord *Brounker*, Sir *R. Moray*, Dr. *Wilkins*, Mr. *Evelyn*, and others; but we are troubled, that you cannot have a sight of it, before publication. I see the author hath divided his discourse into three general heads . . . The Second consists of the narrative itself, and out of the registers and journals of the Society which the author hath been permitted to peruse, relateth the first occasion of their meetings, the encouragement and patronage which they received, their patent, their statutes, the whole order and scheme of their design, and the manner of their proceedings. . . . I must confess the stile is excellent, even, full, unaffected, but I know not, whether there be enough said of particulars, or, to speak more truly, whether there are performances enough for a Royal Society, that hath been at work so considerable a time.[8]

However, it was not published then, nor until, with substantial additions, it appeared as the complete work in the summer of 1667.[9]

It seems likely that Oldenburg's doubts about the amount of detail contained in the account were shared by others, for by order of the Council at its meeting of 21 December 1664, Dr.

---

[7] Thomas Sprat, *History*, p. 94.

[8] *The Works of the Honourable Robert Boyle*, ed. Thomas Birch, London, 1744, vol. V, p. 325.

[9] It was entered in the Stationers' Register on 25 July 1667, and was presented to the Royal Society at its meeting on 10 October 1667 (below, p. 15).

Wilkins, Dr. Goddard and Dr. Croone were to be 'a Committee to consider of the particulars to be inserted in the relation of the Society's Institution'.[10] This was followed by an order from the Council meeting of 11 January 1664/5:

> That Mr. Spratt be sent to by the Secretary to meet at Dr. Wilkins his house on Monday next, to consider of certain papers, to be inserted in the History of ye Society.[11]

At the Council meeting of 18 January 1664/5 the Committee appointed on 21 December reported that it had 'looked over a number of such papers', including contributions by various individuals. After these had been checked by the authors, they were to be handed to Sprat for inclusion, but before they were printed he was to 'present them to the perusal of the President'.[12] Further opinion on this was sought, for at its meeting of 16 May 1665 the Council set up another distinguished committee to consider the matter:

> Ordered, That the President, Sr Robert Moray, Sr William Petty, and Dr Wilkins be a Committee for reviewing Mr Sprat's Relation concerning the Institution and Designe of the Royal Society.[13]

At the Council meeting of 29 May another order was made:

> That Mr. Sprat be desired to take Notice in his Book of the Society, what is meant by their Council, when they grant an Imprimatur; and to draw up a draught concerning it, and offer it to the Council.[14]

It appears that at this point the Royal Society was considering publishing the book under its own imprimatur, which it had the right to do. It seems, however, that in the face of the considerable hostility towards the Society on academic and religious grounds,[15] it was considered prudent to seek an imprimatur outside its own walls. The book was published by the Royal Society's official printers, Martyn and Allestry, but carried the imprimatur of the Secretary of State, Sir William Morrice.

[10] Council Book, vol. I, p. 85.
[11] Ibid., p. 86. [12] Ibid., p. 87.
[13] Ibid., p. 92. [14] Ibid., p. 93.
[15] Academic hostility to the Royal Society is discussed at length below, Part One, Chapter 3. The Society's attitude to religion is discussed below, Part One, Chapter 6.

Joseph Glanvill, another Fellow, held back his own treatise on the Royal Society, so as not to forestall the *History*, and published it independently. Confirming that Sprat's is an authorized account, he gives the reason for his own publication:

> . . . because some *pious* men are afraid of an *Institution* they have heard but imperfectly of, and are *jealous* of what they have not had opportunities to understand, I have therefore given a *succinct* Account of the *Reason, Nature*, and *Designs* of *that Establishment*, for the information of such as have not met with their *Excellent HISTORY*.[16]

That, he says, is '*so full* and *so accurate* an Account of them and their *Designs*'[17] that it makes another account practically superfluous. Glanvill did, however, give further details about the work of particular Fellows, especially Boyle, though this information had already largely appeared in their own publications.

Glanvill, like Sprat, an Anglican cleric, brought out his book under the imprimatur of the Archbishop of Canterbury.[18] But this did nothing to appease the furious attacker of both books, the Royal Society's critic Henry Stubbe, who gives his own reasons for considering the *History* to be a product of the Royal Society as a body, as distinct from Glanvill's private publication:

> . . . that the R.S. did own it, any man knows that was in *London* at its publication: not to mention the Character which Mr. *Glanvill* and the *Transactor*[19] fix on it. Moreover, when the first *brute* of my designing to write against the R.S. did reach *London*, Sir *R[obert] M[oray]* writ to the Lady *E.P.* to inform them of my intentions; adding, That there was nothing in which the R.S. as

---

[16] Joseph Glanvill, *Plus Ultra: or the Progress and Advancement of Knowledge Since the Days of Aristotle*, London, 1668, Preface.

[17] Ibid., p. 83.

[18] Gilbert Sheldon, who was a Fellow of the Royal Society. Though not elected in the usual way, he appears on Sprat's list of Fellows in the *History*, p. 431; and like Clarendon (then Lord Chancellor), who appears for the first time as a Fellow there, Sheldon must have held an honorary Fellowship. Joseph Glanvill, *Plus Ultra*, 1668, Preface, also lists Sheldon as a Fellow.

[19] Henry Oldenburg, editor of *Philosophical Transactions* of the Royal Society. In the issue of July–September 1667 he had reviewed the *History* (below, p. 15).

a Body, could be concern'd, excepting this *History*: and if I would civilly represent unto them any defaults therein, they would take it kindly, and amend them. Hereupon I writ unto Him, as a Person whom I greatly honor, . . . complaining of the *Indignities* put upon my faculty by Mr. *Glanvill*, and their *History*, . . . and DEMANDED that the R.S. should disclaim *both of them by some authentick Declaration*, or I would not *desist*, whatsoever might befall me: But no repeated desires or Sollicitations of mine could prevail with *them* to *disclaim the History*: the other they were less concerned for, saying, He was a Private Person, and that the *sense of the R.S.* was not to be collected from the Writings of every *single Member*.[20]

By 21 June 1665 the Plague had become so alarming that the Royal Society decided to discontinue its meetings.[21] Sprat says that he was held up by this and the Fire which followed:

Thus far I was come in my intended *work*, when my *hand* was stop'd, and my *mind* disturb'd from writing, by the two greatest di[s]asters, that ever befel our *Nation*, the *fatal Infection*, which overspread the City of *London* in Sixty-five; and the *dreadful firing* of the City it self, in the year insuing. These two calamities may well be sufficient, to excuse the *delay* of publishing this *Book*:[22]

When Sprat took up his work again on the *History*, the Council resumed its supervision. On 4 January 1666/7 the Council ordered

that Mr. Hook do attend Dr. Wilkins, about reducing the Extracts of the Societies Journal books into a Method, for Mr. Spratt.[23]

At intervals throughout the next six months, until the actual publication, the Council of the Royal Society kept Sprat's progress under constant review, as the following extracts from the Council Minutes show:

28 March 1667
Dr Wilkins was desired to consider of the Instances that may be

---

[20] Henry Stubbe, *A Reply unto the Letter written to Mr. Henry Stubbe in Defense of the History of the Royal Society*, Oxford, 1671, pp. 19–20.
[21] Journal Book, vol. II, pp. 231 and 234.
[22] Thomas Sprat, *History*, p. 120.
[23] Council Book, vol. I, p. 120.

fit to be inserted in the History of the Society, and having done so, to present them to the Council.[24]

4 April 1667
It was also mentioned, that Mr Sprat desired to know, what he should do in the matter of inserting the Statutes into the History of the Society. It was thereupon thought good, that Dr. Wilkins should be desired, to peruse the said Statutes and so to abreviate them, as that the most material and least alterable particulars thereof might be inserted in the History.[25]

25 April 1667
Voted, That the Committee for the Additionals to the Society's Charter do meet on Monday next, about 6 of the Clock at the President's house, to consider of the Statutes of the Society to be inserted in their History.[26]

29 April 1667
Dr. Wilkins was desired to be mindfull of Selecting upon every Head of the Matters hitherto done by the Society, one or two instances to be offered to the Council for their approbation and then to be inserted into the History.
Ordered, that Mr. Hook do bring to Dr. Wilkins the several heads, he hath drawn up for that purpose.[27]

23 May 1667
It being moved again, that such Instances, as are to be inserted in the History of the Society might be resolved, upon, It was ordered, that it should be left to the President and Dr. Wilkins to agree upon such, as they should judge fit for that purpose.[28]

This is the last instruction about the book in the Royal Society's minute-books before it went to press. In the *Philosophical Transactions* of the Royal Society for July–September 1667, Oldenburg gave a very full and approving review of it.[29] The Journal Book records that at the meeting of 10 October 1667 Wilkins presented the book to the Royal Society, and

> Hearty Thanks were ordered to the author for his singular respect to the Society.[30]

[24] Council Book, Vol. I, p. 130.
[25] Ibid., p. 131.   [26] Ibid., p. 132.
[27] Ibid., p. 133.   [28] Ibid., p. 134.
[29] *Philosophical Transactions*, London, 1667, pp. 501–6.
[30] Journal Book, vol. III, p. 128.

B

The supervision of the Council ensured not only that the *History* was read, and corrected where necessary, by a considerable number of Fellows, but also, of great importance in this situation, that the Royal Society's policy of political and religious impartiality[31] was maintained, so that party interests were not allowed to intrude. Thus, although, after the Restoration, the Society had secured a Royal Charter, and had named the King its formal Founder and Patron,[32] it made no attempt in the *History* to disown its previous Parliamentarian associations during its first informal stage at Oxford.[33] Had expediency been the aim of the Society, it could have begun its story with its official inauguration in London in 1660.[34] But the *History*, declaring 'it is but just, that future times should hear the *names*, of its first *Promoters*',[35] recalled the Society's source at Oxford. Similarly, the *History* reflects the Society's impartiality in its fearless repudiation of the religious intolerance which then prevailed under the terms of the Clarendon Code.[36]

The Royal Society's control of the book did not end with its publication. At its meeting of 16 January 1667/8 the Society authorized a translation of the *History* into French;[37] and on the following 20 April the Council, intent on a translation into Latin, ordered that Oldenburg, in his capacity as Secretary, 'should be desired to speak to Mr. Martyn', the Society's official printer, 'and to let him know that the Council approved of' a suggested translator, and that it advised Martyn to arrange to pay the translator and print the book.[38] Apparently no agreement on this was reached, as another translator for an edition in Latin was proposed at a Council Meeting on 1 February 1668/9, and the Council was even willing to subsidize the printer.[39] Two years after its authorization of the French translation, the Royal Society issued a certificate to the translator confirming that the translation had been made on the order of the Society, and recorded this in the Journal Book on 3 March 1669/70. Meantime, only eight months after

---

[31] Below, pp. 150–8. [32] Below., p. 140.
[33] Thomas Sprat, *History*, pp. 52–4. [34] Below, pp. 110, 128, 131.
[35] Thomas Sprat, *History*, p. 53. The evidence for the correctness of Sprat's statement that the Royal Society originated at Oxford is summarized below, pp. 178–9.
[36] Below, pp. 150–1. [37] Journal Book, vol. III, p. 170.
[38] Council Book, vol. I, p. 161. [39] Ibid.

the *History* was published, the Council was already thinking in terms of a new edition, for on 13 April 1668 it ordered an item to be 'inserted in the next Edition of the Society's said History'.[40]

The Council's monopoly of the book is shown even in details. On 17 February 1667/8 the other Secretary, Wilkins, asked the Council's permission to take half a dozen copies of the *History* from the publisher 'to present to some persons, from whom he expects Contributions: And it was allowed him'.[41] The Royal Society, as such, also presented copies to eminent foreigners, among whom was the Italian, Prince Leopoldo de' Medici, brother of the Grand Duke Ferdinand II of Tuscany.

The Prince, patron and leader of the Florentine Accademia del Cimento, founded by him in 1657,[42] had first corresponded with the Society in May 1661. In response to a request from him the Society had set up a special committee, headed by the President, to correspond regularly, and had even obtained Charles II's formal consent to do this. On 8 May 1661

My Lord Brouncker, Mr. Boyle, Sir Kenelme Digby, Sir Robert Moray, Dr. Ent, The President in being, & Mr. Croone, [were] appointed [to be] a Comittee constantly to correspond with the Duke Leopoldus.

This Comittee to meet on Mundays att My Lord Brounckers Lodgings, & to make a speedy answer to the Duke's Letter.

Three of this Comittee at least to be a Quorum.[43]

and at the next meeting, on 15 May:

Sir Robert Moray having had occasion to acquaint His Majesty with the Duke of Florences Letter to the Society, had the Kings consent to return an answer.[44]

On 5 November 1667 the Royal Society presented the Prince with a copy of the recently published *History*, through the King's Resident in the Grand Duchy, Sir John Finch:[45]

[40] Council Book, vol. I, p. 160.   [41] Ibid., p. 154.

[42] The Cimento, which produced some important work in physics and mathematics, was dissolved in 1667 when Prince Leopoldo became a Cardinal.

[43] Journal Book, vol. I, p. 16.   [44] Ibid., p. 17.

[45] Sir John Finch had been a Fellow of the Royal Society since 20 May 1663, when he was nominated in a list of Fellows drawn up by order of the Council, under the terms of the Charter of 1663. He was the younger son of

Mr. Oldenburg read the Latin letter, he had drawn up, to be sent to Prince Leopold of Florence: which was approved of; and ordered to be sent to the said Prince in the name of the Society, subscribed by himself and adressed to Sir John Finch, accompanied also with an Exemplar of the History of the Society, as a Present to the same from them.[46]

The Prince acknowledged the gift through Sir John Finch, and his further thanks were conveyed, by his personal representatives, to the Society at their meeting of 17 December 1668. The Journal Book records:

> At this meeting were present two Italian Gentlemen; the one, the Marquesse Ricardi, the other Signor Alexandro Segni, both introduced by Count Ubaldino. They acquainted the Society of the singular respect, the Cardinal Leopoldo de Medicis had for them, and that he desired to have his Excuse made for not having himself returned his acknowledgements for the Book sent to him, (viz. The History of the R. Society) which he had been hindered to do, by his lately received dignity of Cardinal; but that since that time he had desired and already obtained the Pope's permission to correspond with this Society, which he now intended to make use of, to let them see the esteem he had of them and their Institution.
>
> The President thanked these Gentlemen for acquainting the Society with so favourable an inclination of his Eminency to them, and desired them that they would please to assure that Cardinal of the deep sense, the Society had of his favour to them, and that the Society would Study to entertain so noble and promising a correspondence with all reciprocal Services, that might be acceptable to his Eminency.[47]

Prince Leopoldo meantime had returned the compliment by sending the Royal Society a copy of the Cimento's *Saggi di Naturali Esperienze* which had also been published in 1667. This was formally received at the meeting of the Royal Society on 12 March 1667/8.[48]

The *History* is the only publication that ever received from

[46] Council Book, vol. I, p. 140.

[47] Journal Book, vol. IV, pp. 14–15.   [48] Ibid., vol. III, p. 188.

Sir Heneage Finch, Solicitor General, who had taken a prominent part in drawing up the Charters of 1662 and 1663, and was publicly thanked in Sprat's *History*, p. 143.

the Royal Society such supervision in its documentation; and this scrutiny was carried out by those who were chosen for their personal knowledge of the facts. It shows that Sprat was not speaking for himself nor for any other private person, but for the Royal Society as an institution, which considered this book to be its special concern, the first comprehensive and public account of its origin, policy and business.

2

A NEW SYSTEM

OF NATURAL PHILOSOPHY I

Francis Bacon

The early Royal Society is now regarded by historians merely
as a notable manifestation of the general climate of interest in
Natural Philosophy[1] which developed in the second half of the
seventeenth century, and, as such, pre-eminent only in the
degree of its fame and success. This was not the contemporary
view, and the Royal Society is revealed in a far more significant light as its story unfolds.

A number of societies with an interest of one kind or another
in natural phenomena had preceded it. In the sixteenth century there had been an Italian group round Giovanni Battista
della Porta, whose studies of natural phenomena were much
influenced by astrology, alchemy and the occult, practices
which the Royal Society as a body would have nothing to do
with. This group, founded in Naples in 1560, called itself
'Academia Secretorum Naturae', and its members 'Otiosi'.
From the beginning of the seventeenth century, intermittently,
there had been societies in France which were primarily discussion groups on philosophy, theology, literature and natural
phenomena. Marin Mersenne's 'Academia Parisiensis', founded

[1] Natural Philosophy was the study of natural phenomena in general, not
only what would now be called physics.

in 1635, was probably the most widely known of those in which scientific topics were prominent.[2] In Italy in the first three decades of the seventeenth century the studies of the Accademia dei Lincei, founded in 1603 by Federigo Cesi, Marchese di Monticelli, had perhaps been nearer to the work of the Royal Society. Members of this small group had carried out some experimental researches individually; Galileo had been a member. In England there had been clubs with an interest in 'the New Philosophy' or some aspect of it, preceding the first informal meetings of the Royal Society by a few years.[3]

But the Royal Society claimed to be an innovator without precedent in the history of science, and insisted on its uniqueness in no uncertain terms. When the Royal Charter was received by the Society in 1662, the President's official speech of thanks to the King emphasized this claim:

> this Society is already taken notice of and famous throughout all the learned parts of Europe: . . . the first foundation of the greatest Improvement of Learning and Arts, that they are capable of, and which hath never heretofore been attempted by any.[4]

In the *History* Sprat said:

> they . . . have overcome all oppositions, which are wont to arise, against the beginnings of great things . . . they have fram'd such an Assembly in six years, which was never yet brought about in six thousand.[5]

And again:

> They have contriv'd in their thoughts, and couragiously begun an *Attempt*, which all *Ages* had despair'd of.[6]

Not only did the Royal Society claim that what it stood for was unique; it also claimed that as an innovator its importance to posterity was incalculable:

> If now this *Enterprise* shall chance to fail . . ., the World will not only be frustrated of their present expectations, but will have just ground to despair of any future *Labors* . . . This will be the last

[2] Below, pp. 174-6.
[3] Below, Part Two, Chapters 1, 2 (pp. 185-6) and 3.
[4] Supplement to the Letter Book, vol. I, pp. 139-40.
[5] Thomas Sprat, *History*, p. 154. It was commonly thought that about 6000 years had elapsed since the Creation.
[6] Ibid., p. 318; and below, pp. 78-9.

great indeavor that will be made in this way, if this shall prove ineffectual: and so we shall not only be guilty of our own *Ignorance*, but of the *Errors* of all those that come after us.[7]

The question is, what was the nature of this unique and far-reaching contribution to science? The key to the answer is found in Sprat's *History*: Francis Bacon was the

one great Man, who had the true Imagination of the whole extent of this Enterprize, as it is now set on foot.[8]

The entire problem of the correlation between the Royal Society and Francis Bacon has been very much misunderstood and underestimated in the present century, mainly through failure to examine the contemporary situation. The Victorian image of Francis Bacon, distorted and inconsequential, continues to dominate historians; and the Royal Society's own exposition of its *raison d'être*, lost to mind if not to sight for at least two centuries,[9] continues to be ignored. Yet a true understanding of the Royal Society's debt to Bacon both delivers him from the Victorian charge of visionary vagueness and justifies the Society's claim.

Macaulay, in his much-quoted essay on Francis Bacon,[10] not only moulded the judgment of his own era, but prolonged his influence through Bacon's Victorian editors and translators Spedding and Ellis,[11] whose prefaces to Bacon's works still largely condition the approach to his text. Macaulay's chief error—and it was a fundamental error affecting his whole evaluation of Bacon's contribution to the development of science—was that he completely failed to understand Bacon's definition and exposition of induction, both in its scientific and historical contexts; therefore his explanation of it ended in a *non sequitur*.

What Macaulay did, in the first place, was to treat Bacon

---

[7] Thomas Sprat, *History*, p. 437.   [8] Ibid., p. 35.

[9] Above, Chapter 1; and below, Part One, Chapter 2.

[10] Lord Macaulay, *Critical and Historical Essays*, London, 1862, vol. 1 (reprinted from *The Edinburgh Review* of July 1837).

[11] *The Works of Francis Bacon*, ed. James Spedding, Robert Leslie Ellis and Douglas Heath, London, 1857–74, 14 vols. References to Bacon's works have been given from this edition as it is the only complete collection generally available. Where the original is in Latin, quotation has usually been made from the English translation, but the Latin text is provided in this edition for those who wish to consult it.

as though he were a scientist, which he was not, instead of as a philosopher, which he was; and, ignoring the whole of the first book of the *Novum Organum* (which was accorded remote admiration but no understanding), he went straight to the second book containing the 'instances'. Here, in order to illustrate a *process* of research, not the making of any particular new discovery, Bacon had shown the stages by which certain conclusions had been reached. Macaulay's curiously naïve comment on this was that Bacon's method, though correct, was useless, because it told us only what we already knew. What Macaulay really wanted was to see some actual and startling scientific discovery made in front of his very eyes; but this, as we shall presently see, when considering Bacon's concept of science, was not at all what Bacon had to offer. Reaching the end of his mental cul-de-sac, Macaulay said:

> We conceive that the inductive process, like many other processes, is not likely to be better performed merely because men know how they perform it. William Tell would not have been one whit more likely to cleave the apple if he had known that his arrow would describe a parabola under the influence of the attraction of the earth.[12]

The irony of Macaulay's dilemma, here, is that the *knowledge* that the arrow would describe a parabola under the influence of the earth's attraction was precisely what Bacon was intent on, for this implies the grasp of a physical law; and it was the discovery of laws that was at the heart of Bacon's concept of science, not proficiency in utilitarian skills, which, as he frequently pointed out, had always flourished among artisans:

> the mechanical arts . . ., as having in them some breath of life, are continually growing and becoming more perfect.[13]

Having missed the central point of Bacon's entire proposition, Macaulay, in his superficial reading of the first book of the *Novum Organum*—and indeed of the *De Augmentis Scientiarum*, which Bacon intended as the permanent framework of the *Novum Organum* in the exposition of his scientific theme at

[12] Lord Macaulay, *Critical and Historical Essays*, 1862, vol. 1, p. 404.
[13] Francis Bacon, *Instauratio Magna*, Praefatio: *Works*, vol. IV, p. 14. For the place of this composition in his scheme, see below, note 14.

large[14]—was led to another extraordinary error; for Macaulay, revealing his scanty acquaintance with the state of science in Bacon's time, supposed that Bacon

> went so far as to say, that, if his method of making discoveries were adopted, little would depend on the degree of force or acuteness of any intellect; that all minds would be reduced to one level . . .

concluding:

> The interval between a man of talents and a dunce is as wide as ever; and is never more clearly discernible than when they engage in researches which require the constant use of induction.[15]

It is very important that this absurd interpretation of Bacon's meaning, which is still much quoted against him, should be cleared up, for it implies a failure to recognize the real state of affairs which he sought to remedy. He was not referring to the relative abilities of researchers, which he knew perfectly well must vary (and on occasion said so),[16] talent here, as elsewhere being less common than mediocrity. In fact, Bacon was referring to 'the Idols[17] of the Theatre or of Systems,'[18] whereby a 'system' of Natural Philosophy according to the notions of this or that philosopher had beguiled and enslaved men's minds.

[14] The *De Augmentis Scientiarum*, which was a revised and much expanded version of *The Advancement of Learning* (1605), constituted the first part of Bacon's *Instauratio Magna* which was planned in six parts. The *De Augmentis Scientiarum*, however, was not published until 1623, three years after the second part, the *Novum Organum*. In order to explain his general aim briefly, and particularly to indicate the wider context of the *Novum Organum*, pending the publication of the *De Augmentis Scientiarum*, Bacon prefaced the *Novum Organum* by a general introduction (here referred to as '*Instauratio Magna*, Praefatio'), and by a plan of the work (here referred to as '*Instauratio Magna*, Distributio Operis'). In the same volume, following the two books of the *Novum Organum*, was the *Parasceve ad Historiam Naturalem et Experimentalem*' which, in effect, was a preface to the proposed third part, the 'Natural History'. See also below, p. 36 and note 55.

[15] Lord Macaulay, *Critical and Historical Essays*, vol. 1, p. 406.

[16] He said that the most demanding work 'may be done by some persons, though not by every one' (below, p. 53 and note 133), and in his *New Atlantis* the researchers range in their abilities from the competent to the exceptional.

[17] Bacon's word 'idola' means 'phantoms' or mental illusions (*Instauratio Magna*, Distributio Operis: *Works*, vol. IV, p. 27), not idols in the modern sense.

[18] Francis Bacon, *Novum Organum* I, Aph. LXII: *Works*, vol. IV, p. 63.

But 'the subtlety of nature' far outmatched 'the excellency and acuteness of individual wits',[19] and such 'systems', in their limitations and errors, were therefore bound to misrepresent the truth. Taking up this point, Bacon explained his metaphor as follows:

> there are Idols which have immigrated into men's minds from the various dogmas of philosophies, and also from wrong laws of demonstration. These I call Idols of the Theatre; because in my judgment all the received systems are but so many stage-plays, representing worlds of their own creation after an unreal and scenic fashion.[20]

The natural sciences should be sought for, he said,

> not arrogantly in the little cells of human wit, but with reverence in the greater world.[21]

These philosophical cults had lured men away from the study of nature itself, which in its workings gave the lie to this kind of mental ascendancy. This was the 'levelling'—imposed by the authority of scientific truth—to which Bacon was referring. The intellect would still play a part, and that—as he went on to explain—an important one, in the interpretation of data;[22] but it must always be subject to scientific fact itself, not to 'the strength and excellency of the wit', which invoked its own oracles.[23] It was in this context that he said:

> I contrive that the office of the sense shall be only to judge of the experiment, and that the experiment itself shall judge of the thing.[24]

The whole point about 'levelling' was so relevant to the state of science as it then was, and of such importance, that Bacon made it on numerous occasions. In one such passage in the *Novum Organum*, he said:

> the *Idols of the Theatre* are . . . received into the mind from the play-books of philosophical systems and the perverted rules of

[19] Francis Bacon, *Novum Organum* I, Aph. XXIV: *Works*, vol. IV, p. 51; and *Novum Organum*, Praefatio: *Works*, vol. IV, p. 41.
[20] Ibid., *Novum Organum* I, Aph. XLIV: *Works*, vol. IV, p. 55.
[21] Ibid., *Instauratio Magna*, Praefatio: *Works*, vol. IV, p. 21.
[22] Below, pp. 34 ff.
[23] Francis Bacon, *Instauratio Magna*, Praefatio: *Works*, vol. IV, p. 19.
[24] Ibid., Distributio Operis: *Works*, vol. IV, p. 26.

demonstration. To attempt refutations . . . would be merely inconsistent with what I have already said: for since we agree neither upon principles nor upon demonstrations there is no place for argument . . .

But the course I propose for the discovery of sciences[25] is such as leaves but little to the acuteness and strength of wits, but places all wits and understandings nearly on a level . . . But though particular confutations would be of no avail, yet touching the sects and general divisions of such systems I must say something; something also touching the external signs which show that they are unsound; and finally something touching the causes of such great infelicity and of such lasting and general agreement in error; that so the access to truth may be made less difficult, and the human understanding may the more willingly submit to its purgation and dismiss its idols.[26]

In his contemporary application of this criticism, Bacon was referring to 'Aristotelian' science, which was largely based on the works of Aristotle, and had been handed down almost unchanged from the medieval university teachers, the Schoolmen, from whom it had acquired an authoritarianism never claimed by Aristotle himself. Its approach to the teaching and study of science was the method of disputation, a system of logic expounded in Aristotle's *Organon*, by which certain premises were assumed, and a conclusion argued from them. Obviously, if the first assumption of a syllogism were incorrect or only partially correct, deductions from it could lead only to an unsatisfactory answer.

This approach was unsatisfactory also in its admixture of metaphysics, whose subject-matter and inquiries, Bacon maintained, were no legitimate part of science; in this realm of knowledge they were 'misplaced', and

this misplacing has caused a notable deficience . . . For the handling of final causes in physics [i.e. science] has driven away and overthrown the diligent inquiry of physical causes, and made men

---

[25] Although 'science' still carried the traditional meaning 'knowledge', and 'the sciences' included all the branches of academic learning, Bacon made it clear that in this whole context he was particularly concerned with 'the sciences which regard nature' (*Instauratio Magna*, Praefatio: *Works*, vol. IV, p. 20). See also below, p. 35 and note 54.

[26] Francis Bacon, *Novum Organum* I, Aph. LXI: *Works*, vol. IV, pp. 62–3.

to stay upon these specious and shadowy causes, without actively pressing the inquiry of those which are really and truly physical; to the great arrest and prejudice of science.[27]

Scientific inquiries therefore turned endlessly on themselves and were concerned with little beyond debating what had long been accepted on assumption:

> the sciences . . . stand almost at a stay, without receiving any augmentations worthy of the human race; insomuch that many times not only what was asserted once is asserted still, but what was a question once is a question still, and instead of being resolved by discussion is only fixed and fed; and all the tradition and succession of schools is still a succession of masters and scholars, not of inventors [i.e. discoverers] and those who bring to further perfection the things invented.[28]

This state of academic sterility had been a cause for repeated complaint by Bacon.[29] In the *Novum Organum* itself he pointed out that although there were those who dissented from the accepted practice, their protests and individual attempts to bring fresh life to these studies had been frustrated by the weight of the opposition:

> . . . in the customs and institutions of schools, academies, colleges, and similar bodies destined for the abode of learned men and the cultivation of learning, everything is found adverse to the progress of science. For the lectures and exercises there are so ordered, that to think or speculate on anything out of the common way can hardly occur to any man. And if one or two have the boldness to use any liberty of judgment, they must undertake the task all by themselves; they can have no advantage from the company of others. And if they can endure this also, they will find their industry and largeness of mind no slight hindrance to their fortune. For the studies of men in these places are confined and as it were imprisoned in the writings of certain authors, from whom if any man dissent he is straightway arraigned as a turbulent person and an innovator. . . . But arts and sciences should be like

---

[27] Francis Bacon, *De Augmentis Scientiarum* III. 4: *Works*, vol. IV, p. 363.
[28] Ibid., *Instauratio Magna*, Praefatio: *Works*, vol. IV, p. 14.
[29] Ibid., *Advancement of Learning* II, To the King: *Works*, vol. III, pp. 324–5; *De Augmentis Scientiarum* II, Ad Regem Suum: *Works*, vol. IV, pp. 286–8. See also below, pp. 187–8.

mines, where the noise of new works and further advances is heard on every side. But though the matter be so according to right reason, it is not so acted on in practice; and the points above mentioned in the administration and government of learning put a severe restraint upon the advancement of the sciences.[30]

Aristotle, said Bacon, had done a great disservice to Natural Philosophy by making it a slave to his system of logic.[31] It was in the light of this that Bacon's great work, published in 1620, urging the foundation of a new system of natural sciences was called *Novum Organum*, literally, 'the New *Organon*', which was to replace the old one.

The title-page of the *Instauratio Magna*, which Bacon placed at the front of the *Novum Organum*,[32] shows ships sailing through the Pillars of Hercules, which according to the ancient Greeks, marked the western boundary of the world. Bacon thus symbolized the *ne plus ultra*, or limit, of classical science. The function of the *Novum Organum* was 'to equip the intellect for passing beyond'.[33]

That an entire system of sciences, stultified and incapable of growth, still prevailed in the universities, which themselves dominated academic learning, is not generally realized.

'Aristotelian' astronomy was based on Artistotle's concept of the universe, with some variations and qualifications. The 'Aristotelian' system of the universe, briefly, and in its simplest form, was a series of revolving concentric spheres, like hollow glass balls, with the earth at rest at the centre. Each of the seven planets (including the sun) was carried round by a sphere, the moon being the nearest to the earth; round the planets went the sphere carrying the fixed stars. The celestial bodies were, as Bacon scornfully remarked, 'supposed to be fixed in their orbs like nails in a roof'.[34] Round the entire system went the

---

[30] Francis Bacon, *Novum Organum* I, Aph. XC: *Works*, vol. IV, pp. 89–90.

[31] Ibid., Aph. LIV, LXIII: *Works*, vol. IV, pp. 59, 64–5.

[32] *Instauratio Magna* (the Great Instauration) was the general title of the whole work (see above, p. 24, note 14), to which the *Novum Organum* was to be the key. Since the *Novum Organum*, the second part, was published earlier than the introductory part (the *De Augmentis Scientiarum*), Bacon placed the title-page of the whole series at the front of the *Novum Organum*, to which the illustration particularly relates.

[33] Ibid., *Instauratio Magna*, Distributio Operis: *Works*, vol. IV, p. 23. See also below, p. 61, note 169.

[34] Francis Bacon, *De Augmentis Scientiarum* III. 4: *Works*, vol. IV, p. 348.

primum mobile, which gave rise to the whole process. To 'save the appearances' a complicated arrangement of epicycles, eccentrics and equants had been devised by Ptolemy to qualify the main movements.

All matter below the moon was corruptible, the four 'elements' or 'essences' of which it was composed being, in descending order of merit, fire, air, water and earth. The elements were at rest only in their correct places, which they always tried to reach; therefore fire and air moved upwards, fire the more so, being more noble, while solid and liquid substances moved towards the centre of the earth, water being less base than earth and therefore slightly more buoyant. Each element had a 'quality' or state, in binary combination of hot, cold, wet, dry —thus fire was hot and dry, water cold and wet. All temporal matter was thought to exist in the form of various mixtures of elements, which explained irregularities in its behaviour; accordingly, fire, which contained a certain amount of earthiness, did not rise as far as it would otherwise have done. In the study and practice of medicine, in conjunction with the theory of 'qualities', were the four humours,[35] blood, choler (yellow bile), phlegm and melancholy (black bile). The physical and temperamental characteristics of each person were decided according to these categories.

Above the moon all matter was composed of a fifth 'element' or 'quintessence' which was incorruptible, and the movement of the celestial bodies was circular (an indication of perfection) and changeless. Thus natural and supernatural matter existed together in this conception of the universe, and all irregular movement, such as that of comets, was presumed to occur below the moon, in the region of natural corruption and change.

The heavenly bodies circling the earth exerted various astrological influences on it, including powerful ones on man himself, so there was no clearly marked line between astronomy and astrology, and the door was left open for the medieval pseudo-science alchemy, which still flourished among learned and unlearned alike.

Bacon was far from being the only one to see that such a concept of the natural order, even if considerably modified,

---

[35] Although preceding Aristotle, the Hippocratic theory of the four 'humours' or chief fluids of the body, was not a part of Aristotle's concept, but was incorporated in the Aristotelian philosophy by later writers.

presented grave obstacles to scientific progress. The so-called 'Ptolemaic' system, perhaps the most obviously disconcerting inheritance of the medieval Aristotelian concept of nature, was nevertheless contained in an intricate and deeply rooted structure of traditional academic philosophy and culture. The problem, therefore, did not simply turn on this or that theory, but on a general philosophy embodying a certain system of natural sciences. Historians of science have tended to overlook the importance of this kind of philosophical and psychological context, whose powerful general effect was to retard and repress intellectual initiative. In retrospect they have tended to simplify and therefore to falsify the real scientific position by isolating correct, or, more often, partially correct, perceptions made by individual investigators on some specific aspect of nature, and in the light of modern knowledge to give them undue emphasis. It is, perhaps, this selective way of dealing with scientific perceptions and discoveries which has given the impression that scientific knowledge up to the middle of the seventeenth century was more widespread and more advanced than in fact it was.

An example of this kind of problem is seen in the terms governing the Savilian Chair of Astronomy at Oxford University, at the time of its inauguration in 1619. The statute setting out the requirements for Astronomy (codified in 1636) stated that the Professor must lecture on Ptolemy's *Almagest* and mention 'in their places the innovations of Copernicus, Geber and other recent astronomers'.[36] This has sometimes been taken to indicate the virtual rejection of Aristotelianism, but that is not so.

The situation, in fact, betrays great perplexity in the minds of those concerned. The thirteen books of Ptolemy's *Almagest*, in which his mathematical system of the universe was expounded, were to remain the background for astronomical hypothesis. A further condition of the statute which belied a

[36] 'Astronomiæ Professor ad suum Munus sciat necessario pertinere interpretationem totius Mathematicæ Constructionis Ptolemæi, (Almagestum vocant,) adhibitis, suo loco, Copernici, Gebri et aliorum Recentium inventis . . .': *Statutes of the University of Oxford Codified in the Year 1636*, ed. John Griffiths, Oxford, 1888, p. 245. Geber (Jabir ben Aflah), an Arab who lived in Seville, had been very critical of the Ptolemaic system, and had pointed out various inconsistencies in it, but he had not proposed an alternative hypothesis. Geber died in 1140, so he could hardly be regarded as modern.

disinterested approach was that the Professor of Astronomy must lecture on 'the whole of divinatory Astrology', a condition which was confirmed when the statutes were codified in 1636.[37]

Both the founder of the Chair, Sir Henry Savile, and the first Professor himself, John Bainbridge, were still influenced in their thinking by an inheritance which had by no means been discarded. Earlier in 1619 Bainbridge had published a treatise on the appearance of a comet the year before, and, on the strength of this, Savile had immediately chosen him to be the first Savilian Professor of Astronomy. This work is entitled *An Astronomicall Description of the late Comet from the 18 Novemb. 1618 to the 16 December following. With certain Morall Prognosticks or Applications drawne from the Comets motion and irradiation amongst the celestiall Hieroglyphicks.*[38] In it he refers to Aristotle as 'that great and witty, but often mis-leading Peripateticke',[39] and shows some acquaintance with the work of 'that tresnoble Dane *Tycho Brahe*',[40] Kepler and Galileo, but the background of his thinking is still Aristotelian. Bainbridge is attracted by the heliocentric hypothesis of Aristarchus,[41] as a possible explanation of the comet's movement, but fears that this is dangerous ground, and that discussion of 'these mysteries' must in any

[37] 'Ad Astronomiæ Professorem similiter pertinebit, etiam interpretari et docere . . . totius in universum divinatricis Astrologiæ': *Statutes of the University of Oxford Codified in the Year 1636*, ed. John Griffiths, Oxford, 1888, p. 245.

[38] The first edition of this book, which was published in London, is dated 1618, and was entered in the Stationers' Register on 1 January 1618/19.

[39] John Bainbridge, *An Astronomicall Description of the late Comet*, London, 1618, p. 12.

[40] Ibid., p. 3. Tycho Brahe (1546–1601) made some valuable observations which were used by his successors (notably Kepler in his law concerning elliptical orbits) in their evidence for an heliocentric system, in opposition to the prevailing geocentric system; but Brahe himself was unaware that his own observations were consistent with elliptical orbits. For various reasons he did not accept the Copernican hypothesis, so he evolved a geocentric scheme in which the planets (with the exception of the moon) revolved round the sun, while the sun annually revolved round the earth, which was motionless at the centre: the moon also revolved round the earth, and the sphere of the fixed stars made a daily circuit round the whole.

[41] Ibid., p. 5. Aristarchus of Samos, a Greek who lived in the third century B.C., had put forward an heliocentric hypothesis, which was revived basically by Nicolaus Copernicus (1473–1543), and became famous as the 'Copernican hypothesis'. See below, p. 169 and note 28.

case be reserved for 'a more learned language'—presumably Latin.

He considers that astronomical observations have discredited the theory of solid orbs, and that the appearance of comets, evidently above the moon, is proof that the celestial regions are capable of change. But he does not for that reason automatically accept that the 'quintessence' belongs to the natural order. In attempting to answer his own question, 'What was the Comets materials', he offers as alternatives both a natural and a supernatural solution, a problem which he is not prepared to discuss:

> . . . whether this Comet and the like were caused by efficacie of nature (the ordinary power which God hath put into all his creatures) compacting the liquid aetheriall substance, or whether by the immediate power of the worlds Architect (*qui dixit, & facta sunt, mandauit, & creata sunt*: Spake and they were made, commanded and they were created) a new matter was presently created: I will not here curiously dispute; . . .[42]

In the second part of his treatise 'Morall Prognosticks or Applications of the late Comet or Blazing-Starre', Bainbridge considers at length its astrological significance as a presage of good or ill, and from his reading of the signs he is able to predict the following happy state of affairs:

> It is *Great Britaines* royall Court, which divine *Astraea* doth illustrate with her gracious and healthfull rayes, it is this fortunate Iland that is gouerned with her scales of iustice, and enriched with her spike of plentie. The worlds great Monarch hath crowned his Maiestie [James I] with the Imperiall Diademe of all the British Iles; and by this his Embassador [i.e. the comet] doth promise him a long and happie possession thereof, and to his posteritie for ever. As for his enemies, he hath and will cloath them with shame, but on him and his shall his crowne flourish in this life, and an immortal crowne of glory in the heavens.[43]

Considering that the subject of this 'divination' was the father of the future Charles I, one may feel that this method of exploring nature's secrets left much to be desired.

Another example of the retarding effect of Aristotelianism in

[42] John Bainbridge, *An Astronomicall Description of the late Comet*, London, 1618, p. 24.   [43] Ibid., p. 36.

the academic approach to science is seen in the statute governing the Sedleian Chair of Natural Philosophy, founded at
Oxford University in 1621 by Sir William Sedley. This statute,
also confirmed in 1636, required that the lectures should be
given entirely on specified works of Aristotle.[44]

Not only did Aristotelianism still condition the academic
approach to natural phenomena, but it constituted a fundamental obstruction to future development in that it provided
the only *system of sciences* that there was. As late as 1670, when
Aristotelianism was still being determinedly maintained in the
universities, Henry Stubbe, defending it against a supporter of
the Royal Society, put the case for those who, while admitting
it to be in some ways unsatisfactory, continued to uphold it—
there was no ready-made system to put in its place:

> Give therefore the *Aristotelians* leave to hold an *Hypothesis*, which
> is accommodated to the *polity* of our *Nation*, at least as *revocable*,
> till a better be *introduced*; and do not proceed in an exterminative
> way, till something else is ready to be *substituted*.[45]

Such people were often forced to the uncomfortable expedient
of having

> *One* Proposition *for* Sence,
> *And* th'other *for* Convenience.[46]

But more serious than this was the underlying threat that, to
avoid a philosophic vacuum, any potential new system might
be an adaptation of the old, and therefore stunted from the beginning. New discoveries, instead of at least acting as levers to
dislodge misconceptions piecemeal, were in danger, if accepted,
of becoming absorbed into the existing framework, effecting
only an isolated, and inevitably ambiguous, addition of knowledge, without significantly altering the approach as a whole.
Bacon was highly conscious of this predicament:

> It is idle to expect any great advancement in science from the
> superinducing and engrafting of new things upon old. We must

[44] 'Legat Prælector Naturalis Philosophiæ Aristotelis Physica, aut libros de
Cœlo et Mundo, aut de Meteoris, aut eiusdem parva Naturalia, aut libros de
Anima, necnon libros de Generatione et Corruptione': *Statutes of the University of Oxford Codified in the Year 1636*, ed. John Griffiths, Oxford, 1888, p. 36.
[45] Henry Stubbe, *The Plus Ultra Reduced to a Non Plus*, London, 1670, p. 14.
[46] Joseph Glanvill, *Plus Ultra, or the Progress and Advancement of Knowledge
Since the Days of Aristotle*, London, 1668, p. 68.

begin anew from the very foundations, unless we would revolve for ever in a circle with mean and contemptible progress.[47]

The situation was, therefore, that the natural sciences in their existing form were subservient to a particular intellectual concept in which disinterested research could find little place. Bacon held that this repressive control by one intellect, as it were, over others could be obviated only by the impartial and irrefutable evidence of experimental research. In short, the intellect was to be used in a different way—not the bare thing itself, whereby the aim was to out-argue another disputant within a fixed framework of assumptions, but the intellect informed or corrected by tangible contacts and aids, which hitherto had been almost entirely limited to the utilitarian practice of the artisan; and the aim was to be the discovery of the real working of nature:

> For the end which this science of mine proposes is the invention not of arguments but of arts; not of things in accordance with principles, but of principles themselves . . . And as the intention is different, so accordingly is the effect; the effect of the one being to overcome an opponent in argument, of the other to command nature in action.[48]

On the other hand, said Bacon, what was wrong with the skills and discoveries of utilitarian practice itself—such as those concerning navigation and the crafts of use to daily life—was the extremely limited range of the practitioner:

> . . . even in the great plenty of mechanical experiments, there is yet a great scarcity of those which are of most use for the information of the understanding. For the mechanic, not troubling himself with the investigation of truth, confines his attention to those things which bear upon his particular work, and will not either raise his mind or stretch out his hand for anything else.[49]

Bacon saw that it was mainly through this cleavage between the intellectual and the utilitarian that the sciences as such had become obsolete and sterile, and that a reconstruction of the system of sciences must be based on an alliance between these two spheres. By this he did not mean what he has sometimes

[47] Francis Bacon, *Novum Organum* I, Aph. XXXI: *Works*, vol. IV, p. 52.
[48] Ibid., *Instauratio Magna*, Distributio Operis: *Works*, vol. IV, p. 24.
[49] Ibid., *Novum Organum* I, Aph. XCIX: *Works*, vol. IV, p. 95.

been taken to mean, simply co-operation between persons—the thinking man and the practical man—though this had its place. It was to be a union of 'faculties' in one person, 'a true and lawful marriage between the empirical and the rational faculty'.[50] The practical skill and diligence which character-ized the approach of the artisan, freed from an attachment to immediate ends, must be carried into the realm of the intellect, itself freed from subservience to preconceived opinion. In this way the range of man's research might become the whole uni-verse, and the object of his investigation the *causes* of natural phenomena. To have discovered a cause in nature was to have perceived a law,[51] which in its turn would give rise to other discoveries and further laws.

According to Bacon's plan for 'the New Philosophy' a 'History of Nature' had to be compiled, constituting

the Phenomena of the Universe; that is to say, experience of every kind, and such a natural history as may serve for a founda-tion to build philosophy upon.[52]

In other words, the 'Natural History' was to consist of 'the primary material of philosophy and the stuff and subject mat-ter of true induction'.[53] By 'philosophy' he said, he meant 'the sciences',[54] that is, the branches or 'disciplines' into which academic knowledge as a whole was organized. The 'Natural History' then, was to be the factual material from which the new sciences were to be formed. But Bacon did not expect, as historians have supposed him to expect, that this factual mater-ial could finally be converted into laws in one all-embracing operation; on the contrary, he conceived the transformation as a continuous process. Bacon's plan for a scientific revolution has been considered unworkable largely because this important point has been missed; yet the Royal Society, under no such misapprehension, put the plan into action, and openly acknow-ledged the fact. So it would be well to examine the difficulty Bacon presents to the modern mind, particularly on this question.

[50] Francis Bacon, *Instauratio Magna*, Praefatio: *Works*, vol. IV, p. 19.
[51] Ibid., *Novum Organum* I, Aph. III: *Works*, vol. IV, p. 47.
[52] Ibid., *Instauratio Magna*, Distributio Operis: *Works*, vol. IV, p. 28.
[53] Ibid., *Parasceve ad Historiam Naturalem et Experimentalem*: *Works*, vol. IV, p. 254; and *De Augmentis Scientiarum* II. 3: *Works*, vol. IV, p. 298.
[54] Ibid., *De Augmentis Scientiarum* 11. 1: *Works*, vol. IV, p. 293. See also above, p. 26, note 25.

The most serious obstacle is that Bacon's terms are often highly individual, and must always be related to his definitions and explanations, especially when he gives a brief summary of a major aspect of his system; and in general it must be borne in mind that Bacon is essentially a philosopher, using the idiom of philosophy even when he is dealing with concepts of science. On the most important of all the practical issues, the compiling of the vast 'Natural History', he is supposed capable of wanting to amass an infinite quantity of undigested material which was somehow to be reduced to scientific order at a later stage. This misunderstanding will now be considered.

Bacon's plans and percepts, when set out in their simplest forms, do have an appearance of architectural rigidity, but these are merely charts to show the skeletal structure; they are not meant to show the living organism in growth and action. His 'Plan of the Work' is in six stages,[55] and the reader who isolates this ground-plan from the rest may receive the impression that a simple (and impossible) metamorphosis was expected. Such a reader may gain a similar impression from Bacon's summary of the stages in the development of science, as he envisaged it. This summary was represented as a 'pyramid'[56] whose base consisted of the 'Natural History' referred to above (that is, of the *facts* of nature itself). The next stratum was 'Physic', which, he said, 'inquires and handles the Material and Efficient Causes' (that is, formulates *laws* of natural phenomena), and was to be the first or lower of the two strata comprising 'the Interpretation of Nature', which was the work of the intellect.[57] The stratum above 'Physic' was 'Metaphysic' which did not carry the traditional connotation, and Bacon gave warning of this:

> I desire men to observe that I use the word *metaphysic* in a different sense from that which is commonly received. And here it

55 Francis Bacon, *Instauratio Magna*, Distributio Operis: *Works*, vol. IV, pp. 22–33.
56 Ibid., *De Augmentis Scientiarum* III. 4: *Works*, vol. IV, pp. 361–2.
57 Ibid., *Works*, vol. IV, p. 346. A sub-title of the *Novum Organum* is 'True Directions concerning the Interpretation of Nature'. Bacon planned a second volume which would continue to guide the work when it reached an advanced stage, 'being', he said, 'nothing more than an application of the second part [of the existing *Novum Organum*] in detail and at large' (*Instauratio Magna*, Distributio Operis: *Works*, vol. IV, p. 31).

may be convenient to explain my general purpose touching the use of terms . . .[58]

'Metaphysic' was the same in kind as 'Physic', though taken to a much more advanced stage—that is, it was concerned not just with evolving laws, but with 'the investigation of Forms' or 'Formal Causes', by which he meant the formulation of 'fundamental and universal laws'.[59] This stratum reached to the final stage, the apex of the pyramid, which Bacon considered to be beyond man's scope:

> As for the cone and vertical point ("the work which God worketh from the beginning to the end", namely, the summary law of nature) it may fairly be doubted whether man's inquiry can attain to it.[60]

But Bacon never regarded the growth of science as a rigid exercise in which practice and intellect were employed at separate stages. He was here speaking in philosophical terms: the 'Natural History', as it developed, was 'to supply the understanding with information for the building up of philosophy [i.e. sciences]'[61]—that is, the intellect was gradually to be informed and prepared for the stage when it was ready to come into its own. This was when scientific facts could be translated into laws, whose enunciation would indicate the emerging structure of the new system. Bacon made what at first sight appears to be a line of demarcation here, because he considered that this was the point at which the compiler of the 'Natural History' entered the realm of philosophy; for this is the point where particular facts or 'individuals' are superseded by generalizations:

> The sense, which is the door of the intellect, is affected by individuals only.[62]

but philosophy

> discards individuals; neither does it deal with the impressions immediately received from them, but with abstract notions de-

[58] Francis Bacon, De Augmentis Scientiarum III. 4: Works, vol. IV, p. 344.
[59] Ibid., Novum Organum II, Aph. V, IX: Works, vol. IV, pp. 123, 126; also De Augmentis Scientiarum III. 4: Works, vol. IV, p. 346.
[60] Ibid., Works, vol. IV, p. 362. Bacon's reference is to Ecclesiastes III. 11.
[61] Ibid., Novum Organum I, Aph. XCVIII: Works, vol. IV, p. 94.
[62] Ibid., De Augmentis Scientiarum II. 1: Works, vol. IV, pp. 292–3.

rived from these impressions; in the composition and division whereof according to the law of nature and fact its business lies. And this is the office and work of Reason.[63]

In other words Natural Philosophy takes the raw material of natural phenomena and

lays it up in the understanding altered and digested.[64]

In fact, Bacon was indicating a general direction or order in an infinitely complex movement, rather than making artificial stratal divisions. Obviously the first stage had to be the collection and selection of material, and the establishment of particular facts before deductions could be made from them. Particular facts had to precede minor laws, and minor laws had to precede major laws. In short:

I propose to establish progressive stages of certainty . . . starting directly from the simple sensuous perception.[65]

In practice Bacon visualized this progression as a continuous and expanding process of discovery. This approach, he said,

derives axioms from the senses and particulars, rising by a gradual and unbroken ascent, so that it arrives at the most general axioms last of all.[66]

and again:

But then, and then only, may we hope well of the sciences, when in a just scale of ascent, and by successive steps not interrupted or broken, we rise from particulars to lesser axioms; and then to middle axioms, one above the other; and last of all to the most general.[67]

And in practice there was no discernible stage at which the intellect first came in:

For the lowest axioms differ but slightly from bare experience . . .[68]

Nor did the process end with laws; it was to be a continually ascending and descending scale in which laws, once discovered,

[63] Francis Bacon, *De Augmentis Scientiarum* II. 1: *Works*, vol. IV, p. 292.
[64] Ibid., *Novum Organum* I, Aph. XCV: *Works*, vol. IV, p. 93.
[65] Ibid., *Novum Organum*, Praefatio: *Works*, vol. IV, p. 40.
[66] Ibid., *Novum Organum* I, Aph. XIX: *Works*, vol. IV, p. 50.
[67] Ibid., Aph. CIV: *Works*, vol. IV, p. 97.   [68] Ibid.

were directed downwards to further experiment and fresh facts:

> from the new light of axioms, which having been educed from those particulars by a certain method and rule, shall in their turn point out the way again to new particulars, greater things may be looked for. For our road does not lie on a level, but ascends and descends; first ascending to axioms, then descending to works.[69]

In this building-up process an hypothesis became a law only when it had been proved in practice by producing new information which was itself experimentally verifiable.[70] Bacon was well aware that an erroneous or incomplete hypothesis might fit the data,[71] but further experiments would help to corroborate or invalidate it; and, conversely, inaccurate particulars would be revealed by the application of the law:

> mistakes in experimenting, unless they abound everywhere, will be presently detected and corrected by the truth of axioms.[72]

At the same time the alert intellect never wasted accidental opportunities, even mistakes, for a mistake might prove quite as profitable as a particular success;[73] and in the whole process of discovery Bacon stressed the role of negative evidence, holding it to be an invaluable factor in the framing of positive laws.[74]

First and last he condemned the impatient experimenter who was anxious for 'results', and was willing to come to premature conclusions. The experimenter, he said, must always be tentative in his thinking, and, even when he came to a conclusion, should record the means by which he had reached it, so that any possible mistake or omission could the more easily be seen

---

[69] Francis Bacon, *Norum Organum* I, Aph. CIII: *Works*, vol. IV, p. 96.

[70] Ibid., Aph. XXIV–XXV: *Works*, vol. IV, p. 51. See also *Valerius Terminus, Of the Interpretation of Nature* 12: *Works*, vol. III, p. 242.

[71] He frequently made this point in its application to astronomy—'many theories of the heavens may be supposed, which agree well enough with the phenomena and yet differ with each other' (*Novum Organum* I, Aph. CXVI: *Works*, vol. IV, p. 104).

[72] Ibid., *Parasceve ad Historiam Naturalem et Experimentalem* VIII: *Works*, vol. IV, p. 260; also *Novum Organum* I, Aph. CXVIII: *Works*, vol. IV, p. 105.

[73] Ibid., *De Augmentis Scientiarum*, V. 2: *Works*, vol. IV, p. 421.

[74] Ibid., *Novum Organum* I, Aph. XLVI: *Works*, vol. IV, p. 56; also *Parasceve ad Historiam Naturalem et Experimentalem* IX: *Works*, vol. IV, pp. 261–2.

and corrected by others.[75] In this context Bacon's own resistance to the Copernican hypothesis is not only reasonable, but scientifically impeccable. The great exponent of 'the New Philosophy' refused to accept what is often regarded as the symbol of scientific emancipation because the factual evidence was insufficient. Bacon said that the theories of Ptolemy, Copernicus and Tycho Brahe were all interpretations which fitted the appearances, and that other theories might well be proposed which would also serve this purpose. But, said Bacon, before any particular theory could be regarded as more than an hypothesis, much more should be known about the physical nature of the whole universe,[76] for

> astronomy presents only the exterior of the heavenly bodies . . . beautiful indeed and skilfully arranged into systems; but the interior (namely the physical reasons) is wanting, out of which (with the help of astronomical hypothesis) a theory might be devised which would not merely satisfy the phenomena (of which kind many might with a little ingenuity be contrived), but which would set forth the substance, motion, and influence of the heavenly bodies as they really are.[77]

It is now known that the Copernican hypothesis, even when qualified by Kepler's theory of elliptical orbits, was not entirely correct in its limited exposition of the universe. That the sun was immovable while the earth revolved round it, was not then capable of conclusive proof, as indeed it never can be, since the sun is not in fact immovable but only appears so in relation to the solar system. Bacon was aware that the complete answer must depend on many exact and comprehensive observations and calculations—'For it is works we are in pursuit of, not speculations; and practical working comes of the due combination of physics [i.e. science] and mathematics'.[78]

Another criticism of Bacon which has often been made is that

---

[75] Francis Bacon, *Parasceve ad Historiam Naturalem et Experimentalem*, IX: *Works*, vol. IV, p. 261: also *Historia Naturalis et Experimentalis*, Norma Historiæ Præsentis: *Works*, vol. V, p. 136.

[76] Ibid., *Descriptio Globi Intellectualis*: *Works*, vol. V, pp. 510 ff. See also below, p. 46, note 101.

[77] Ibid., *De Augmentis Scientiarum* III. 4: *Works*, vol. IV, p. 348.

[78] Ibid., *Parasceve ad Historiam Naturalem et Experimentalem*, VII: *Works*, vol. IV, p. 259. Bacon's far-reaching approach to the problem is discussed below, p. 46.

he conceived the processes of scientific discovery to be practically automatic, and overlooked the importance of selection in
arriving at conclusions. On the contrary, he was well aware
that selection, and indeed intuition, must play an important
part, but since intellectual initiative was the factor which had
so much got out of hand in the past, he felt obliged to give constant warning against its uninhibited use, and saw no need to
emphasize its presence. The intellect must in fact be 'weighted'
by all the requirements of scientific proof, and not be allowed
to follow its natural inclination to fly off to premature conclusions:

> The understanding must not therefore be supplied with wings,
> but rather hung with weights, to keep it from leaping and fly-
> ing.[79]

With this qualification always in mind the scientist not only
selected, but made 'imperfect axioms' or 'provisional rules',[80]
that is, hypotheses, to help himself towards the formulation of
laws: he

> establishes provisionally certain degrees of assurance, for use and
> relief until the mind shall arrive at a knowledge of causes in which
> it can rest.[81]

The selective faculty is seen at large in Bacon's tentative
organization of the proposed 'Natural History'. It must be
remembered that at this stage, according to Bacon's concept,
no actual natural sciences existed; he therefore made a 'Catalogue of Particular Histories'[82] which would have to be compiled. The Catalogue was intended rather as an indication of
major fields of study than as a definitive boundary for scientific
research. It touches vast areas of natural phenomena, and is
remarkable for its range and penetration. The hundred and
fifty 'Histories' are concerned with 'Concretes' or 'Bodies', that
is, matter in a physical sense. In addition, Bacon urged the

---

[79] Francis Bacon, *Novum Organum* I, Aph. CIV: *Works*, vol. IV, p. 97.

[80] Ibid., *Historia Naturalis et Experimentalis*, Norma Historiæ Præsentis:
Works, vol. V, p. 136.

[81] Ibid., *Instauratio Magna*, Distributio Operis: *Works*, vol. IV, p. 32.

[82] The Catalogue was appended to *Parasceve ad Historiam Naturalem et
Experimentalem* when it was published (with the *Novum Organum*) in 1620
(*Works*, vol. IV, pp. 265–71).

study of such important manifestations as heat, motion, light, weight and density.[83]

Almost all the 'Histories' are subjects which belong to what are now the natural sciences proper and contiguous sciences, involving the physical sciences, the biological sciences, medicine, mathematics and psychology, and including many subdivisions such as cosmography, meteorology, oceanography, mineralogy, physical geography, geology, botany, the chemistry of plants, zoology, anthropology, ethnology, anatomy, physiology, genetics, embryology, gynaecology, dietetics, geneology, pathology, therapeutics, pharmacology, surgery, optics and other specialized branches of medical science.

The last thirty 'Histories' are mainly concerned with useful arts, crafts and technical skills such as agriculture, printing and navigation 'and of the crafts and arts thereto belonging'. In a general notice to the reader, prominently placed at the end of the Catalogue, Bacon pointed out that areas of research often overlap, that 'many of the experiments must come under more titles than one', and went on to reinforce his distinction between natural sciences, on the one hand, and technical and technological skills on the other. Where the subject of study had a context both in the sciences themselves and in these 'mechanical arts'—he gave as an example the study of plants and that of the art of gardening—research on it should be done in relation to the appropriate science; for this would help to build up sciences themselves, which was of immeasurably greater importance than merely improving crafts or industries (though, as he had said before, those would benefit ultimately, and to a much greater extent):

> It may not be amiss to observe that, whereas many of the experiments must come under more titles than one (as the History of Plants and the History of the Art of Gardening have many things in common), it will be more convenient to investigate them with reference to Arts, and to arrange them with reference to Bodies. For I care little about the mechanical arts themselves; only about those things which they contribute to the equipment of philosophy

---

[83] Francis Bacon, *Historia Naturalis et Experimentalis*, Norma Historiæ Præsentis: *Works*, vol. V, p. 135; also *Instauratio Magna*, Distributio Operis: *Works*, vol. IV, p. 29; and *Novum Organum* I, Aph. CXIX: *Works*, vol. IV, p. 106.

[i.e. sciences]. But these things will be better regulated as the case arises.[84]

At all stages the ability to ask the significant question was of the utmost importance, for 'a faculty of wise interrogating is half a knowledge'.[85] With this in mind, Bacon went on to show the selective faculty in action. Expressing his belief that

> The place where a thing is to be looked for may be marked, and as it were indexed.[86]

he chose centres of research or 'topics' within the indicated fields of study or 'Particular Histories':

> In each Title, after an Introduction or Preface, Particular Topics or Articles of Inquiry are immediately proposed, as well to give light in the present, as to stimulate further inquiry. For questions are at our command, though facts are not.[87]

These 'interrogatories' were not only intellectual questions, but questions put in the form of proposed experiments—'I give Injunctions touching new experiments contrived, as far as can be at present foreseen, to meet the special object of inquiry'.[88] Such 'injunctions' constituted a deliberately selected line of research: they 'form a kind of Designed History',[89] an essential part of the approach. 'For', he asked, 'what other course is open to us on first entering on our path?'[90]

Far from underestimating the importance of selection, Bacon knew that the faculty of recognition or diagnosis was an essential part of inductive research, whether in science proper or in the application of its principles to other fields. He saw this faculty, not just as an ingredient in the making of particular discoveries, but as a prime factor in the creation of sciences; for the new sciences he envisaged were not to be static accumulations of facts.[91] Their function was to organize discovery in such

[84] Francis Bacon, *Parasceve ad Historiam Naturalem et Experimentalem*, Catalogus Historiarum Particularum: *Works*, vol. IV, p. 271.

[85] Ibid., *De Augmentis Scientiarum* V. 3: *Works*, vol. IV, p. 423.

[86] Ibid., *Works*, vol. IV, p. 422.

[87] Ibid., *Historia Naturalis et Experimentalis*, Norma Historiæ Præsentis: *Works*, vol. V, p. 135.

[88] Ibid., *Works*, vol. V, p. 136.

[89] Ibid.   [90] Ibid.

[91] Incidentally, the place where Bacon's contribution to science has, misguidedly, sometimes been sought, is his *Sylva Sylvarum*. This, published post-

a way as continually to create new opportunities for discovery; and the chief means of doing this was progressively to advance the centres of inquiry or focal points of research:

> I for my part receive particular Topics (that is places of invention [i.e. of discovery] and inquiry appropriated to particular subjects and sciences) as things of prime use. They are a kind of mixtures of logic with the proper matter of each science. For he must be a trifler and a man of narrow mind who thinks that the perfect art of invention of knowledge can be devised and propounded all at once; and that then it needs only to be set at work. Let men be assured that the solid and true arts of invention grow and increase as inventions themselves increase; so that when a man first enters into the pursuit of any knowledge, he may have some useful precepts of invention; but when he has made further advances in that knowledge, he may and ought to devise new precepts of invention, to lead him the better to that which lies beyond.[92]

Not only would the scientist thus move forward, but he would correspondingly increase his ability to gauge future possibilities, for 'in sciences every step forward on the journey gives a nearer view of that which is to come'.[93] He concludes:

> In the meantime I again repeat my former advice; namely, that men ought so to vary their particular topics, as, after any great advance has been made in the inquiry, to set out another and again another topic, if they desire to climb the heights of the

---

[92] Francis Bacon, *De Augmentis Scientiarum* V. 3: *Works*, vol. IV, p. 424.
[93] Ibid.

---

humously in 1627 by his chaplain and friend, William Rawley, is different in kind from the parts of the *Historia Naturalis* already published or proposed. The *Sylva Sylvarum* is a miscellaneous collection (containing some smaller collections as well as separate items) of experiments, queries and suggestions concerning natural phenomena. Among the thousand entries are many derived from books, including the classics, as well as from life. Bacon himself said of this miscellany that 'men will think many of the experiments contained in this collection to be vulgar and trivial, mean and sordid, curious and fruitless' and that 'it may seem an indigested heap of particulars'; and, indeed, separated from its context in the *Novum Organum*, it may well give such an impression. What Bacon meant to show was that the alert mind, in its normal encounters with all kinds of unexceptional natural phenomena and notions about them, might find worthwhile subjects for study.

sciences . . . For we can command our questions, though we cannot command the nature of things.[94]

Bacon was able to take up only a few of his suggested 'Histories', and even these inquiries, at this stage, were not so much in order to find the answers as to put the questions which might eventually lead to the answers. The first of these 'Histories', published in his lifetime, was 'The History of the Winds'[95] which contained many questions and suggestions for further inquiry on the origin, nature and effects of movements in the atmosphere. This really constituted the beginning of meteorology as a science, as distinct from local studies which were not related to the wider context and remote causes. At the end of this 'Interrogation' Bacon said:

Such then are the articles of inquiry. Some of them, I am well aware, it is beyond the power of our present experience to answer. But as in civil trials a good lawyer knows how to put questions suitable to the case, but knows not what the witnesses can answer; so it is with us in Natural History. Let posterity look to the rest.[96]

The next 'History', also published by Bacon himself, was 'The History of Life and Death',[97] whose central consideration was the process of gradual decay in the living body (apart from specific disease) as it approached old age; of the contributory factors, including heredity; and of possibilities for the mitigation of the condition, and repair of expended organs.

The 'History' which was probably meant to follow this, 'The History of Dense and Rare or the Contraction and Expansion of Matter in Space' was not published until 1658.[98] Bacon had meant it to be published after 'The History of the Winds',[99] but apparently it was not ready. He considered this subject to

---

94 Francis Bacon, De Augmentis Scientiarum V. 3: Works, vol. VI, p. 427.
95 Ibid., Historia Naturalis et Experimentalis ad Condendam Philosophiam: sive Phaenomena Universi, 'Historia Ventorum' (1622): Works, vol. V, pp. 137–200.
96 Ibid., Works, vol. V, p. 145.
97 Ibid., 'Historia Vitæ et Mortis' (1623): Works, vol. V, pp. 213–335.
98 Ibid., 'Historia Densi et Rari' (1658): Works, vol. V, pp. 337–400.
99 He had placed it second to 'The History of the Winds' on his preliminary list of six 'Histories' which he meant to consider first (Historia Naturalis et Experimentalis: Works, vol. V, p. 129).

be one of great difficulty, but of the highest importance to science, and that the work on it would be 'amply compensated by the vast and universal utility of the inquiry'. Pressing the point further, he said:

> Seeing therefore that it is a thing of all others the most fundamental and universal, we must gird ourselves up to deal with it; for indeed without it all philosophy [i.e. science] is utterly discinct and disorderly.[100]

Another 'History', which, though written as early as about 1612, remained unpublished in Bacon's lifetime, was 'The History of Celestial Bodies'.[101] This is interesting in its evidence of Bacon's tentative, though far-reaching and penetrating mode of thought. In these 'Inductive Topics, or Articles of Interrogation concerning the heavens'[102] Bacon refused to be sidetracked by the raging controversy on the Ptolemaic and Copernican systems, asking not, 'Which system?' but, characteristically, 'Is there a system, if there be, what is the centre of it?' and going on to raise such questions as 'the substance of the stars, *whether they are solid or flamy*, and the ether or interstellar spaces in the heaven, *whether they consist of body or vacuum*'; he was also concerned with the 'depth' or extent of the universe, and considered the likelihood of 'very many impressions, concussions, reciprocations, and fluctuations in the heaven', producing 'condensations and rarefactions of bodies, which may procure and prepare the way to generations and alterations'— leading to the question 'whether stars are in long revolutions of ages created and dissipated?'. In the context of such questions, and in the light of his own tentative answers, Bacon affirmed his standpoint—that he was convinced of his general direction while lacking the factual knowledge to pronounce on particular problems:

> These then are the things I see, standing as I do on the threshold of natural history and philosophy [i.e. science]; . . . Nevertheless

[100] Francis Bacon, *Historia Naturalis et Experimentalis*, 'Historia Densi et Rari', Aditus: *Works*, vol. V, p. 340.

[101] This is in Chapters V–VII of *Descriptio Globi Intellectualis* (*Works*, vol. V, pp. 510–44) to which Bacon appended *Thema Cœli* (below, note 103). These two compositions, which are really the parts of one work, were published in 1653, and were therefore available to the embryo Royal Society in its preparatory stage at Oxford, though not, unless in manuscript, before the inception of this club in about 1648.

[102] Ibid., Chapter V: *Works*, vol. V, p. 513.

1. Francis Bacon (Baron Verulam, Viscount St. Albans). Detail from the portrait by Paul van Somer. *From the Gorhambury Collection, by permission of the Earl of Verulam.*

FRANCISCI
DE VERULAMIO,
Summi Angliæ
CANCELLARII,
Instauratio
magna.

Multi pertransibunt & augebitur scientia.

LONDINI
Apud Joannem Billium,
Typographum
Regium.

Anno 1620

2. Title-page of Francis Bacon's *Instauratio Magna*, placed at the front of his *Novum Organum* (1620), showing ships sailing through the Pillars of Hercules, the symbolic limit of classical science. *By courtesy of the Bodleian Library, Oxford.*

I repeat once more that I do not mean to bind myself to these; for in them as in other things I am certain of my way, but not certain of my position.[103]

Bacon himself possessed the faculty of diagnosis in a very high degree, as he demonstrated throughout his works. One particularly relevant example, since it occurs in his own exposition of scientific selection, is the astounding hypothesis on the nature of heat. Having made a preliminary, though systematic, examination of the subject, with the long-term aim of discovering its 'Form' or 'Law with its clauses',[104] he offered the following:

> From a survey of the instances, all and each, the nature of which Heat is a particular case appears to be Motion. . . . Heat itself, its essence and quiddity, is Motion and nothing else.[105]

Bacon had defined the scientific method, but he was not at all under the impression that genuine experimental research in itself was new. When discussing contributory obstacles to the growth of science he referred to experimental work which had, up to a point, combined theory and practice, but expressed his belief that spasmodic or solitary efforts, even outstanding ones, could not solve the problem. The fault here, he said, was that the experiments, and even the discoveries when made, were far less productive than they might have been, because they were isolated, neither gaining from, nor illuminating discoveries in other aspects of science.[106] Even the work of Galileo, whom Bacon much admired, did not escape this criticism. He referred to Galileo's 'memorable efforts' with the telescope, but regretted that this work and that of other 'learned men' was not more extensive.[107]

Far from wishing to belittle such contributions to the advancement of science, Bacon's aim was to build up an organized body of inductive knowledge in which all scientific discovery would find its true context, and be most effectively developed. For this reason he insisted that the 'Natural History', whose function it was 'to give light to the discovery of causes and

[103] Francis Bacon, *Thema Cœli*: *Works*, vol. V, pp. 545–59.
[104] *Ibid.*, *Novum Organum* II, Aph. II: *Works*, vol. IV, p. 120.
[105] *Ibid.*, Aph. XX: *Works*, vol. IV, p. 150.
[106] *Ibid.*, *Novum Organum* I, Aph. LXXXVIII: *Works*, vol. IV, pp. 86–7.
[107] *Ibid.*, *Novum Organum* II, Aph. XXXIX: *Works*, vol. IV, pp. 193–4; and *Descriptio Globi Intellectualis*: *Works*, vol. V, pp. 512–13.

supply a suckling philosophy with its first food',[108] must take into its scope the entire range of natural phenomena, not merely some aspects, studied and developed in isolation:

> In the history which I require and design, special care is to be taken that it be of wide range and made to the measure of the universe . . . For that fashion of taking few things into account, and pronouncing with reference to a few things, has been the ruin of everything.[109]

And if individual practical discoveries could notably benefit mankind, how much more important it was, he said, to discover the means by which the process of discovery itself could be set in action:

> Again, if men have thought so much of some one particular discovery as to regard him as more than man who has been able by some benefit to make the whole human race his debtor, how much higher a thing to discover that by means of which all things else shall be discovered . . .[110]

It has often been supposed by superficial readers of Bacon's carefully weighed and closely packed exposition, set out in the first book of the *Novum Organum* and summarized in the *De Augmentis Scientiarum*, that he expected an overwhelming change to come about in the course of a few years, bringing with it a rich harvest of material benefits. This was not at all what he expected, nor even hoped. He was speaking relatively, and simply meant, as he had already indicated at length in his exposition, that in comparison with the thousands of years of man's history, in which only a few discoveries of major importance had been made, and those mainly by chance, the new system would immeasurably speed up scientific discovery.[111]

Bacon's approach was a long-term one, and he repeatedly warned against snatching at premature results of a purely utilitarian kind, in preference to pursuing the course of inquiry

---

[108] Francis Bacon, *Instauratio Magna*, Distributio Operis: *Works*, vol. IV, p. 29.
[109] Ibid., *Parasceve ad Historiam Naturalem et Experimentalem*, IV: *Works*, pp. 255–6.
[110] Ibid., *Novum Organum* I, Aph. CXXIX: *Works*, vol. IV, p. 115.
[111] Ibid., Aph. CIX: *Works*, vol. IV, pp. 99–100; also *Parasceve ad Historiam Naturalem et Experimentalem*: *Works*, vol. IV, p. 252.

farther, with the promise of greater intellectual enlightenment. He used various images to emphasize this: he had no intention, he said, of mowing the moss, or of reaping the green corn; he also drew the analogy of Atalanta's race, in which a golden apple thrown in her path distracted her from the true goal, losing her the race and the much greater prize.[112] Experiments of 'light' were more important than experiments of 'fruit' in building up new, developing sciences:

> But then only will there be good ground of hope for the further advance of knowledge, when there shall be received and gathered together into natural history a variety of experiments, which are of no use in themselves, but simply serve to discover causes and axioms; which I call *"Experimenta lucifera"*, experiments of *light*, to distinguish them from those which I call *"fructifera"*, experiments of *fruit*.
>
> Now experiments of this kind have one admirable property and condition; they never miss or fail. For since they are applied, not for the purpose of producing any particular effect, but only of discovering the natural cause of some effect, they answer the end equally well whichever way they turn out; for they settle the question.[113]

Such knowledge, he said, was like 'the seeds of things' which were 'of much latent virtue, and yet of no use except in their development . . . useless indeed for the present, but promising infinite utility hereafter'.[114] So important was this factor in his system that he repeated his admonition several times:

> Upon this point therefore above all I must say again what I have said already,—that at first and for a time I am seeking for experiments of light, not for experiments of fruit.[115]

Such knowledge, he said, would bring with it, in a comparatively short time, not just a few discoveries, but a mastery over nature hitherto undreamed of.

Bacon's goal was 'these twin objects, human Knowledge and

[112] Francis Bacon, *Instauratio Magna*, Distributio Operis: *Works*, vol. IV, p. 29; and *Novum Organum* I, Aph. LXX, CXVII, vol. IV, pp. 71, 105.
[113] Ibid., Aph. XCIX: *Works*, vol. IV, p. 95.
[114] Ibid., Aph. CXXI: *Works*, vol. IV, pp. 107–8.
[115] Ibid., p. 107.

human Power', which 'do really meet in one'.[116] Pure knowledge, or scientific truth was of first importance:

> For I am building in the human understanding a true model of the world, such as it is in fact, not such as a man's own reason would have it to be; a thing which cannot be done without a very diligent dissection and anatomy of the world.[117]

But products and practical results were the irrefutable evidence of that truth:

> For fruits and works are as it were the sponsors and sureties for the truth of philosophies.[118]

And Bacon arrived at his inevitable conclusion:

> Truth therefore and utility are here the very same things: and works themselves are of greater value as pledges of truth than as contributing to the comforts of life.[119]

Yet the practical benefit of mankind was the proper application of mature scientific knowledge, said Bacon, an issue whose implications concerned morality and religion as well as philosophy.[120]

Not only was 'the New Philosophy' to take the entire universe as its parish, but it was to cross the academic frontiers whose rigid limits had hitherto divided Natural Philosophy from contiguous departments of knowledge. Describing Natural Philosophy as properly 'the great mother' of the arts and sciences, Bacon considered that it should inform and nourish philosophical truth in all its branches, and deplored that some sciences had been 'parted from their roots'.[121] In referring to the role of science as the nourisher of other branches of learning, he not only mentioned existing categories which would benefit, such as astronomy, optics and medicine; he also indicated new sciences in the realm of 'human philosophy',[122] in, for

[116] Francis Bacon, *Instauratio Magna*, Distributio Operis: *Works*, vol. IV, p. 32.
[117] Ibid., *Novum Organum* I, Aph. CXXIV: *Works*, vol. IV, p. 110.
[118] Ibid., Aph. LXXIII: *Works*, vol. IV, p. 73.
[119] Ibid., Aph. CXXIV: *Works*, vol. IV, p. 110.
[120] Ibid., *Instauratio Magna*, Praefatio: *Works*, vol. IV, pp. 20–1. See also below, pp. 143 ff.
[121] Ibid., *Novum Organum* I, Aph. LXXIX, LXXX, CVII: *Works*, vol. IV, pp. 78–9, 98.
[122] Ibid., Aph. LXXX, CXXVII: *Works*, vol. IV, pp. 78–9, 112.

example, moral and political philosophy. In moral philosophy he recommended the study of what he called 'the Georgics of the mind',[123] that is, the practical study of man as a psychological and social being.

At the same time, he said, there should be no artificial division between any of the branches of knowledge themselves, for the arrangement of knowledge into arts and sciences was merely a convenient way of organizing what was in fact related; thus the boundaries of particular sciences should be 'lines to mark and distinguish', not 'sections to divide and separate'.[124]

Bacon's great concept of a new system of Natural Philosophy became renowned throughout the western world as 'the New Philosophy', for it was designed to supersede 'the old philosophy', and it would be well to consider what this means. It has often been thought that what Bacon advocated in place of Aristotelianism was experiment, that what he put in antithesis were, on the one hand, random knowledge (plus speculation), and, on the other hand, inductive experiment; but that is not so. What in fact he put in antithesis were, on the one hand, random knowledge *and experiment*, and, on the other hand, *sciences*. What he advocated was not merely inductive experiment (though that was an essential factor), but new, live *sciences* for old, dead *sciences*:

> the works already known are due to chance and experiment rather than to sciences; for the sciences we now possess are merely systems for the nice ordering and setting forth of things already invented [i.e. discovered]; not methods of invention or directions for new works.[125]

and:

> As the sciences which we now have do not help us in finding out new works, so neither does the logic which we now have help us in finding out new sciences.[126]

It may therefore be seen that such terms as 'the experimental method' and even 'the inductive method' are not very meaningful as labels of his concept. It was the whole context in which

---

[123] Francis Bacon, *De Augmentis Scientiarum* VII. 3: *Works*, vol. V, p. 29.
[124] Ibid., IV. 1: *Works*, vol. IV, p. 373.
[125] Ibid., *Novum Organum* I, Aph. VIII: *Works*, vol. IV, p. 48.
[126] Ibid., Aph. XI: *Works*, vol. IV, p. 48.

induction was to be used that constituted Bacon's great contribution. His proposal was not, of itself, concerned with any
particular method, nor with any particular theory; his aim
was both less specific and immeasurably more profound than
that—the creation, from the foundations, of a completely new
system of sciences, an organized body of related inductive
knowedge capable of continuous, unlimited development; for

> the empire of man over things depends wholly on the arts and the
> sciences.[127]

Sciences were the collective measure of man's knowledge of
nature, and, therefore, unless they were dead wood (as the
Aristotelian natural sciences were), infinitely greater in their
potential than any particular discovery, however important,
or than any individual experimenter, however brilliant. Moreover, particular theories, however persuasive, might be erroneous, but the cumulative evidence of inductive sciences would
sooner or later act as a corrective. In short, 'a true and active
philosophy'[128] (that is, living sciences) was the way, and the
only way, of ensuring the accuracy, effective expansion, organization and continuity of scientific knowledge.

This is the real significance of Bacon's plan. And the magnitude of what he proposed cannot be too much emphasized; for
this, missed even by some of his own admirers during the following century, has been entirely overlooked by modern historians of that crucial period. The point was missed then, as
now, by some, because preoccupation with the details obscured
the immensity of the whole design; a design which in its tremen-
dous range and penetration was almost too large to grasp, or,
when set in action, to attribute to the vision of one man. The
Royal Society knew otherwise.

Bacon's idea of a new system of Natural Philosophy was not
only an intellectual concept; he brought a powerful practical
imagination to bear on its problems. It must be a corporate
undertaking: the work must be divided, though not isolated,
and then combined. His insistence on a corporate approach was
not only a practical measure for covering the ground more
thoroughly and more quickly; it was also based on the know-

---

[127] Francis Bacon, *Novum Organum* I, Aph. CXXIX: *Works*, vol. IV, p. 114.
[128] Ibid., *Parasceve ad Historiam Naturalem et Experimentalem*: *Works*, vol. IV. p. 252.

ledge that the greatest obstacle to the accomplishment of a long
and difficult task may be psychological. Individuals, particularly
the most discerning, seeing the vastness of what lay ahead,
might become paralysed by despair.[129] Mutual encouragement was likely to mitigate this tendency and ensure continuous
efforts.

It was to be the work of successive generations.[130] Just as
there was to be no ill-conceived snatching at immediate utilitarian discoveries, neither were the sciences themselves to become
permanently organized at an immature stage.

The obvious question of financial support was to be answered
by putting the cost on public funds (as in the *New Atlantis*) or
on some public person or large institution, for this was 'a great
. . . a royal work, and of much labour and expense'.[131] But the
independence of the work was to be maintained even if it were
state-financed, as in the kingdom of New Atlantis:

> And this we do also: we have consultations, which of the inven-
> tions and experiences which we have discovered shall be published,
> and which not: and take all an oath of secrecy, for the concealing
> of those which we think fit to keep secret: though some of those
> we do reveal sometimes to the state, and some not.[132]

Bacon summarized these points of practical policy in his *De
Augmentis Scientiarum*:

> I take it that all those things are to be held possible and perform-
> able, which may be done by some persons, though not by every
> one; and which may be done by many together, though not by
> one alone; and which may be done in the succession of ages,
> though not in one man's life; and lastly, which may be done by
> public designation and expense, though not by private means and
> endeavour.[133]

---

[129] Francis Bacon, *Novum Organum* I, Aph. XCII, CXIII: *Works*, vol. IV,
pp. 90–1, 102.

[130] Ibid., Aph. CXIII: *Works*, vol. IV, p. 102.

[131] Ibid., Aph. CXI: *Works*, vol. IV, p. 101. (See also below, p. 150 and
note 29.)

[132] Ibid., *New Atlantis*: *Works*, vol. III, p. 165. This research was not state-
controlled, as stated by Christopher Hill, *Intellectual Origins of the English
Revolution*, Oxford, 1965, p. 74.

[133] Ibid., *De Augmentis Scientiarum* II, Ad Regem Suum: *Works*, vol. IV, p.
291. (Bacon had previously said this in *The Advancement of Learning II*,
To the King: *Works*, vol. III, pp. 328–9.)

In his rejection of the barren verbosity and contentious hair-splitting of the Aristotelians, Bacon recommended that the new scientist should avoid controversy, and should express himself in simple, direct, even stark, language.

> And for all that concerns ornaments of speech, similitudes, treasury of eloquence, and such like emptinesses, let it be utterly dismissed. Also let all those things which are admitted be themselves set down briefly and concisely, so that they may be nothing less than words. For no man who is collecting and storing up materials for ship-building or the like, thinks of arranging them elegantly, as in a shop, and displaying them so as to please the eye; all his care is that they be sound and good, and that they be so arranged as to take up as little room as possible in the warehouse. And this is exactly what should be done here.[134]

and again:

> we (who as faithful secretaries do but enter and set down the laws themselves of nature and nothing else) are content with brevity, and almost compelled to it by the condition of things.[135]

Thus this use of language was a functional necessity, and was to be regarded strictly as a technical expedient. Bacon, a great stylist himself, was not suggesting that the language of science should supersede, or even encroach on, the cultural language, for science was concerned with the raw material of knowledge, not with its embellishment:

> But it is always to be remembered that this which we are now about is only a granary and storehouse of matters, not meant to be pleasant to stay or live in.[136]

Turning from the approach as a whole to the work itself, Bacon explained his own position. He was a guide rather than a performer, and he wanted to make it quite clear that even as a guide he was not a secret dictator. He laid down no particular methods for performing experiments, for 'the art of discovery may advance as discoveries advance';[137] if scientists aimed at 'the

[134] Francis Bacon, *Parasceve ad Historiam Naturalem et Experimentalem*, III: *Works*, vol. IV, pp. 254–5.
[135] Ibid., X: *Works*, vol. IV, p. 262.
[136] Ibid., III: *Works*, vol. IV, p. 255.
[137] Ibid., *Novum Organum* I, Aph. CXXX: *Works*, vol. IV, p. 115.

formation of true axioms' they would 'find out for themselves the methods in which the history[138] should be composed. For the end rules the method'.[139] Nor was it his aim to produce any specific discovery. Even his preliminary collection of data was only an indication of what might be done, not a basis for actual scientific deductions:

> And as I do not seek to found a school, so neither do I hold out offers or promises of particular works. It may be thought indeed, that I who make such frequent mention of works and refer everything to that end, should produce some myself by way of earnest. But my course and method, as I have often clearly stated and would wish to state again, is this,—not to extract works from works or experiments from experiments (as an empiric), but from works and experiments to extract causes and axioms, and again from these causes and axioms new works and experiments . . . And . . . I candidly confess that the natural history which I now have, whether collected from books or from my own investigations, is neither sufficiently copious nor verified with sufficient accuracy to serve the purposes of legitimate interpretation.[140]

But if he omitted to provide many of the answers, Bacon brought a new awareness of problems.

While insisting that the scientist was powerless to contravene the laws of nature—

> For man is but the servant and interpreter of nature: . . . For the chain of causes cannot by any force be loosed or broken, nor can nature be commanded except by being obeyed.[141]

—he realized that deliberate intervention in its course might well reveal important new facts and potentials. Therefore nature should not only be studied 'free and at large (when she is left to her own course . . .)', but should be studied even more when 'under constraint', when 'by art and the hand of man she is forced out of her natural state and squeezed and moulded'.[142]

---

[138] The 'Natural History', that is, the compilation of scientific data.
[139] Francis Bacon, *Parasceve ad Historiam Naturalem et Experimentalem* II: *Works*, vol. IV, p. 254.
[140] Ibid., *Novum Organum* I, Aph. CXVII: *Works*, vol. IV, pp. 104–5.
[141] Ibid., *Instauratio Magna*, Distributio Operis: *Works*, vol. IV, p. 32; and *Novum Organum* I, Aph. III: *Works*, vol. IV, p. 47.
[142] Ibid., *Instauratio Magna*, Distributio Operis: *Works*, vol. IV, p. 29.

This implies not only new phenomena, but processes and substances which did not exist in nature, and the discovery of unsuspected and unforeseeable laws:

> For in things artificial nature takes orders from man, and works under his authority: without man, such things would never have been made. But by the help and ministry of man a new face of bodies, another universe or theatre of things, comes into view.[143]

In a list appended to the first edition of the *New Atlantis*, entitled 'Magnalia Naturæ, præcipue quoad usus humanos' (the mighty works of nature in their particular application to the benefit of man), Bacon included 'Making of new species . . . Drawing of new foods out of substances not now in use . . . Making new threads for apparel; and new stuffs; such as paper, glass, etc. . . . Artificial minerals and cements'.[144]

Bacon drew attention to the fact that hitherto little account had been taken of those phenomena which lay outside the direct perception of the senses:

> Hence it is that speculation commonly ceases where sight ceases; insomuch that of things invisible there is little or no observation. Hence all the working of the spirits inclosed in tangible bodies lies hid and unobserved of men. So also all the more subtle changes of form in the parts of coarser substances (which they commonly call alteration, though it is in truth local motion through exceedingly small spaces) is in like manner unobserved. And yet unless these two things just mentioned be searched out and brought to light, nothing great can be achieved in nature, as far as the production of works is concerned. So again the essential nature of our common air, and of all bodies less dense than air (which are very many), is almost unknown.[145]

In his insistence on the importance of mathematics in science,[146] Bacon called for a far greater degree of precision in recording results:

[143] Francis Bacon, *Parasceve ad Historiam Naturalem et Experimentalem*, I: *Works*, vol. IV, p. 253.

[144] Ibid., *New Atlantis* [appendix]: *Works*, vol. III, pp. 167–8.

[145] Ibid., *Novum Organum* I, Aph. L: *Works*, vol. IV, p. 58.

[146] Bacon's attitude to mathematics is another issue on which Macaulay's misleading influence still persists. Bacon continues to be accused of denying the importance of Pure Mathematics, but that is not so. He considered its future development to be essential, and saw it as vital to the expansion of

Nothing duly investigated, nothing verified, nothing counted, weighed, or measured, is to be found in natural history: and what in observation is loose and vague, is in information deceptive and treacherous . . .[147]

And inquiries into nature have the best results when they begin with physics [i.e. science] and end in mathematics. Again, let no one be afraid of high numbers or minute fractions. For in dealing with numbers it is as easy to set down or conceive a thousand as one, or the thousandth part of an integer as an integer itself.[148]

He realized that an important instrument in the development of science was its means of expression in mathematical or notational language. In arithmetic more 'formulas for the abridgment of computation . . . especially with regard to progressions'[149] must be sought and used, and algebra must be 'perfected'.[150] In recording data a large number of particulars could be 'drawn up and marshalled' by arranging them in tables,[151] whether as 'an enumeration' or 'as a series'.[152] These tables would do more than provide a convenient way of organizing details; they would, he said, help the mind to understand and digest the information contained in them.[153] Tabulation helped, too, in prognostication, and 'prognostics' were valuable

> not only on account of the use of predictions, but because they lead the way to causes [i.e. indicate laws]. For prognostics show either the preparations of things before they are produced into action, or their commencements before they are perceptible to the sense.[154]

[147] Francis Bacon, *Novum Organum* I, Aph. XCVIII: *Works*, vol. IV, p. 94.
[148] Ibid., *Novum Organum* II, Aph. VIII: *Works*, vol. IV, p. 126.
[149] Ibid., *De Augmentis Scientiarum* III. 6: *Works*, vol. IV, pp. 370–1.
[150] Ibid., *Works*, vol. IV, p. 371.
[151] Ibid., *Novum Organum* I, Aph. CII: *Works*, vol. IV, p. 96.
[152] Ibid., *Historia Naturalis et Experimentalis*, Norma Historiæ: *Works*, vol. V, p. 135.
[153] Ibid., *Novum Organum* I, Aph. CII: *Works*, vol. IV, p. 96.
[154] Ibid., *Historia Naturalis et Experimentalis*, 'Historia Ventorum': *Works*, vol. V, p. 145.

Applied Mathematics. His point here was simply that Pure Mathematics, whose method was the same as that of traditional Logic, had in the past 'exercised domination' over science as such, by imposing its own method, precisely as Aristotelian Logic had done. Pure Mathematics was still to be a science in its own right, but it must never again be allowed to 'domineer over' the methods of the inductive sciences. See *De Augmentis Scientiarum* III. 6: *Works*, vol. IV, p. 370; and ibid., III. 4: *Works*, vol. IV, p. 348.

Bacon foresaw great developments in Applied Mathematics, including new branches of the subject:

> In Mixed Mathematics . . . I predict that hereafter there will be more kinds of them, if men be not idle. For as Physic [i.e. science] advances farther and farther every day and develops new axioms, it will receive fresh assistance from Mathematic in many things, and so the parts of Mixed Mathematics will be more numerous.[155]

In his whole approach he stressed the importance of studying the normal first and knowing it thoroughly before considering deviations from it, an admonition that was very much needed, considering the almost obsessional preoccupation with monstrosities and abnormalities, which prevailed. Similarly, he said that the unexceptional should be the continuous study of the experimenter:

> There will be met with also in my history and experiments many things which are trivial and commonly known; many which are mean and low; . . . And . . . for those things which seem common; let men bear in mind that hitherto they have been accustomed to do no more than refer and adapt the causes of things which rarely happen to such as happen frequently; while of those which happen frequently they never ask the cause, but take them as they are for granted. And therefore they do not investigate the causes of weight, of the rotation of heavenly bodies, of heat, cold, light, hardness, softness, rarity, density, liquidity, solidity, animation, inanimation, similarity, dissimilarity, organisation, and the like; but admitting these as self-evident and obvious, they dispute and decide on other things of less frequent and familiar occurrence . . .
>
> And for things that are mean or even filthy,—things which (as Pliny says) must be introduced with an apology,—such things, no less than the most splendid and costly, must be admitted into natural history. Nor is natural history polluted thereby; for the sun enters the sewer no less than the palace, yet takes no pollution.[156]

The relationships which existed in the categories of natural objects should be studied. The unit should be the species, not just single examples:

[155] Francis Bacon, *De Augmentis Scientiarum* III. 6: *Works*, vol. IV, p. 371.
[156] Ibid., *Novum Organum* I, Aph. CXIX–CXX: *Works*, vol. IV, p. 106.

... it cannot too often be recommended and enjoined, that men's diligence in investigating and amassing natural history be henceforward entirely changed, and turned into the direction opposite to that now in use. For hitherto men have used great and indeed over-curious diligence in observing the variety of things, and explaining the exact specific differences of animals, herbs, and fossils; most of which are rather sports of nature than of any serious use towards science. Such things indeed serve to delight, and sometimes even give help in practice; but for getting insight into nature they are of little service or none. Men's labour therefore should be turned to the investigation and observation of the resemblances and analogies of things, as well in wholes as in parts. For these it is that detect the unity of nature, and lay a foundation for the constitution of sciences.[157]

He continually pointed out that research should not merely be concerned with static instances nor with particular stages, but with processes in action, what he called 'the motions of nature in their gradual progress'.[158] He gave some examples:

For instance, if we are inquiring into the vegetation of plants, we must begin from the very sowing of the seed, and observe (as we may easily do, by taking out day after day the seeds that have lain in the ground two days, three days, four days, and so on, and carefully examining them) how and when the seed begins to puff and swell, and to be as it were filled with spirit; secondly, how it begins to burst the skin and put forth fibres, at the same time raising itself slightly upwards, unless the ground be very stiff; also, how it puts forth its fibres, some for the root downwards, and some for the stem upwards, and sometimes also creeping sideways, if it there finds the ground more open and yielding; with many other things of the kind. In the same way we should examine the hatching of eggs, in which we might easily observe the whole process of vivification and organisation, and see what parts proceed from the yolk, and what from the white of the egg, and so forth ...

The same too should be attempted with inanimate substances; as I have done myself in investigating the expansion of liquids by fire.[159]

---

[157] Francis Bacon, *Novum Organum* II, Aph. XXVIII: *Works*, vol. IV, pp. 166–7.
[158] Ibid., Aph. XLI: *Works*, vol. IV, p. 201.
[159] Ibid., *Works*, vol. IV, pp. 201–2.

Similarly, the structure of the living body, rather than dissections alone, should be examined, and the processes and functions of the body both in health and disease should be studied.[160]

He urged the study of what he called 'the latent Process':

> . . . not certain measures or signs or successive steps of process in bodies, which can be seen; but a process perfectly continuous, which for the most part escapes the sense.[161]

Some examples which he gave are 'the process of development in the generation of animals, from coition to birth' and 'the whole course and continued action of nutrition, from the first reception of the food to its complete assimilation'.[162]

Another of the 'inner chambers' of nature yet to be entered was the study of the internal structures of organic and inorganic matter. Among the examples Bacon suggested in this field of research were 'in plants and animals' such subjects as 'the root, the leaf, the flower, flesh, blood, and bones'; and in minerals such subjects as iron and stone.[163]

Bacon made no attempt to inaugurate particular sciences, believing that they must evolve gradually as knowledge progressed. He had provided the machine,[164] as he put it, which would take the experimenter 'to the very brink of operation'.[165] From that point he trusted in man's innate intelligence, 'the native and genuine force of the mind',[166] for it was his intention to 'hand over to men their fortunes, now their understanding is emancipated and come as it were of age'.[167] Nevertheless, in his Catalogue of suggested areas and centres for study, and indeed

---

[160] Francis Bacon, *De Augmentis Scientiarum* IV. 2: *Works*, vol. IV, p. 386, and the 'Catalogue of Particular Histories' (above, p. 41), where many physiological processes are mentioned as subjects for study.

[161] Ibid., *Novum Organum* II, Aph. VI: *Works*, vol. IV, p. 124.

[162] Ibid., Aph. V: *Works*, vol. IV, p. 123.

[163] Ibid., Aph. VII: *Works*, vol. IV, p. 125.

[164] Ibid., *Instauratio Magna*, Epistola Dedicatoria: *Works*, vol. IV, p. 12.

[165] Ibid., Distributio Operis: *Works*, vol. IV, pp. 24–5.

[166] Ibid., *Novum Organum* I, Aph. CXXX: *Works*, vol. IV, p. 115.

[167] Ibid., *Novum Organum* II, Aph. LII: *Works*, vol. IV, p. 247. In a fragment which is very similar to his 'Norma Historiæ Præsentis' in *Historia Naturalis et Experimentalis* (published in 1622), and was first published by Thomas Tenison in *Baconiana* in 1679, Bacon expresses the same intention: '. . . it is enough for me if I do my part in setting the thing on foot' (*Abecedarium Naturæ: Works*, vol. V, p. 211).

throughout his works concerning science, his general perceptions and his details were often capable of turning the mind to whole new fields of investigation. At the same time, he could, on occasion, make wrong assumptions—such as thinking that warm water froze more quickly than cold,[168] under the same conditions, a kind of error which was such a give-away of the guesswork scientist that his followers would really have had no excuse for swallowing him whole.

This paradoxical situation is the key to the Royal Society's debt to Bacon. Not as an exemplar of science, but as a philosopher, his insight provided the impulse for a remarkable movement, which was to put into practice the beginning of a deliberately planned scientific revolution.

Bacon had examined the problem, particularly in his *Novum Organum*, and suggested the remedy: the reconstruction of the natural sciences. If the *Novum Organum* is seen as a kind of ground-plan, the pegging-out of major considerations, his *New Atlantis*, in the literary form of a utopia, is a simplified model of a pioneer society in action. Just as the *Novum Organum* was literally 'the New *Organon*', intended to equip the new scientists to pass beyond the limits of classical science, so the island of New Atlantis symbolized (and at the same time transformed) the legendary Atlantis of the ancient Greeks, which was supposed to lie beyond the Pillars of Hercules.[169] The ultimate goal of Bacon's scientific society was to discover the laws of the working of all physical phenomena, for the proper use and benefit of humanity:

> The End of our Foundation is the knowledge of Causes, and secret motions of things; and the enlarging of the bounds of Human Empire, to the effecting of all things possible.[170]

Bacon was not confident that his vision of new sciences would be generally accepted. He thought it possible that future ages might pass the judgment on him 'that I did no great things, but simply made less account of things that were accounted

---

[168] Francis Bacon, *Novum Organum* II, Aph. L: *Works*, vol. IV, p. 238.
[169] Ibid., *Novum Organum* I, Aph. CXXII: *Works*, vol. IV, pp. 108–9; and *New Atlantis*: *Works*, vol. III, pp. 141–3. (See above, p. 28 and note 33. Plato's account of Atlantis is in the *Timaeus* and the *Critias*; see also below, pp. 225–6.)
[170] Ibid., *New Atlantis*: *Works*, vol. III, p. 156.

great'.[171] This in no way affected his own confidence, for he concluded the passage:

> In the meanwhile, as I have already said, there is no hope except in a new birth of science; that is, in raising it regularly up from experience and building it afresh; which no one (I think) will say has yet been done or thought of.[172]

171 Francis Bacon, *Novum Organum* I, Aph. XCVII: *Works*, vol. IV, p. 94.
172 Ibid.

3

A NEW SYSTEM

OF NATURAL PHILOSOPHY II

The Royal Society

Twenty years after Bacon's death in 1626, the position had still
not changed significantly. He had sounded the trumpet call to
action, as he himself described it,[1] but lack of determined leadership among adherents of 'the New Philosophy', much confusion,
and above all, sustained resistance from the academic body
as a whole, had preserved the stalemate. Bacon had seen that
the chief reason for the blockage was academic paralysis; and
the major source of this was the universities, the nerve-centres
of academic learning. The external history of the Royal
Society is very much concerned with the struggle against the
universities, which continued far longer than is generally
realized, until well into the eighteenth century.

The Royal Society, following Bacon, declared that a new
'*Systeme* of *Natural Philosophy*' must be built up,[2] and vigorously
initiated the process. That the movement originated within
the University of Oxford is not very surprising. The universities were fundamentally involved, and reform here, at the seat
of the trouble, was the obvious thing to those who understood
the problem. As the *History* states, many individual members of

[1] Francis Bacon, *De Augmentis Scientiarum* IV. 1: *Works*, vol. IV, pp. 372–3.
[2] Thomas Sprat, *History*, pp. 327–8; and below, pp. 76 ff.

the University and others 'of Philosophical Minds' who frequented it, 'had begun a *free way* of reasoning' at that time.[3] This was a valuable potential, but, of itself, unorganized as it was, and lacking focus or direction, unlikely, as subsequent events show, to dislodge the existing system, and still less likely to replace it by another. The founders of the Oxford experimental science club,[4] led by John Wilkins, were essentially university men, concerned about the state of the natural sciences. With Wilkins's appointment to a university office in 1648, as Warden of Wadham College, the necessary leadership for constructive, concerted action was provided. This small group of men had decided that the old order must change. In deliberately setting the process in motion they knew the immensity of what they were attempting. They knew that there would be powerful resistance even within their own walls, but convinced that their action was eminently reasonable, they hoped that reason would speak for itself.

Both inside and outside the universities there were many who failed to grasp the group's intention, or were simply hostile to change as such. Their cry was that the centuries-old teaching of Aristotle was being discredited and cast off wholesale, that the universities (especially Oxford University) were being undermined. These allegations, begun during the period of the Oxford club, and continuing for many years after the Royal Society's formal incorporation, were repeatedly denied.

In the sense that this group uncontentiously sought, by sheer practical evidence, to displace the existing system of natural sciences, of course its opponents were justified in their fears, though not in supposing that it was intent on altering systems of traditional learning which did not concern science.

In 1651 the work of the group, only recently begun, and impeded by many practical difficulties, was still in an embryo state. Its leaders, knowing that academically they were in hostile country, were conducting themselves with caution and tact, for nothing was to be gained by antagonizing the main body of their own university or of academic opinion elsewhere. So when, in that year, Thomas Hobbes, in his *Leviathan*, attacked the whole range of Aristotelian learning in the universities, the club did not welcome his efforts. In a witty rejoinder[5] Seth

[3] Thomas Sprat, *History*, p. 53.
[4] See below, Chapter 4.   [5] Below, pp. 65–6 and note 12.

Ward, a member of the club and Professor of Astronomy,[6] reproached Hobbes for his 'fuming spleene', and said that his real motive was 'the desire that Aristotelity may be changed into Hobbeity, & instead of the Stagyrite,[7] the world may adore the great Malmsburian[8] Phylosopher'.

In 1654 John Webster attacked the Aristotelian natural sciences at much greater length, dedicating his pamphlet[9] to John Lambert, Major General of the Army, and at that time the most powerful man in England after Cromwell himself. Webster addressed himself to 'all that truly love the Advancement of Learning in the Universities of Cambridge and Oxford, or elsewhere'.

In his criticisms of the prevailing domination of Aristotelianism in the academic system of natural sciences, Webster professed to follow Bacon, and indeed pressed for a new system which seemed to embody Bacon's approach to science. But Webster's understanding of Bacon was aberrant, and he wanted to combine 'the New Philosophy' with alchemical, astrological and occult ideas and practices, derived from medieval and contemporary writers. Webster's attack on the existing system of Natural Philosophy, however, gave John Wilkins an opportunity to explain his standpoint, and in an open letter addressed to Seth Ward he made a tactful statement of the general approach of those who shared his views.[10] Wilkins first paid tribute to Aristotle's immense contribution to learning, but implicitly concurred with the charge of Aristotelian domination in the natural sciences by stating that those who disagreed with that system had liberty to do so:

> And although we do very much honour *Aristotle* for his profound judgment and universall learning, yet are we so farre from being tyed by his opinions, that persons of all conditions amongst us take liberty to discent from him, and to declare against him, according as any contrary evidence doth ingage them, being ready to follow the banner of truth by whomsoever it shall be lifted up.[11]

Wilkins's introductory letter was followed by a much longer reciprocal letter, forming the body of the pamphlet, by Seth

---

[6] Below, p. 104.   [7] Aristotle: from his birthplace, Stagira.
[8] Thomas Hobbes was born at Malmesbury, Wiltshire.
[9] John Webster, *Academiarum Examen or the Examination of Academies*, London, 1654.
[10] *Vindiciae Academiarum*, Oxford, 1654.   [11] Ibid., p. 2.

Ward, who, at Wilkins's request, had taken up Webster's points in detail.[12] On the subject of astronomy, his own particular responsibility, Ward answered with some asperity that the teaching at Oxford was not Aristotelian, that students of any proficiency accepted

> the *Copernican System*, (as it was left by him, or as improved by *Kepler, Bullialdus*, our own Professor [i.e. Seth Ward himself], and others of the Ellipticall way) either as an opinion, or at leastwise, as the most intelligible and most convenient Hypothesis.[13]

and that astrology was not being taught there. He agreed that in the universities

> . . . instead of verball Exercises we should set upon experiments and observations, that we should lay aside our Disputations, Declamations, and Publick Lectures, and betake ourselves to Agriculture, Mechanicks, Chymistry, and the like.

and that

> It cannot be denied that this is the way, and the only way to perfect Naturall Philosophy and Medicine.[14]

---

[12] The pamphlet was published anonymously, but some obvious clues were meant to leave the informed reader in no doubt of its authorship. Anthony Wood was a contemporary who correctly identified this writer as John Wilkins. Each of the two writers had provided a lightly disguised 'signature' consisting of the final letters of his two names: thus John Wilkins was N.S. and Seth Ward H.D. Wood at first thought that N.S. stood for John Wallis, but he corrected this (in his own copy of the pamphlet, now in the Bodleian Library, catalogue no. Wood B.24 (10)). In his *Athenae Oxonienses*, Oxford, 1691–2, vol. II, 628, Wood said of the pamphlet: 'Before this book is an Epistle written to the author by one who subscribes himself *N.S.* i.e. *John Wilkins* of *Wadh. Coll*, being the two last letters of both his names'.

Wilkins had also referred to Thomas Hobbes's attack on the universities in his *Leviathan*, and Seth Ward took up this as well, briefly, in an 'Appendix' (pp. 51–61); see above, pp. 64–5. Ward later devoted a whole book to refuting Hobbes's theories (*In Thomae Hobbii Philosophiam Exercitatio Epistolica*, Oxford, 1656), which he also addressed to Wilkins: 'Ad Amplissimum Eruditissimumque Virum D. Iohannem Wilkinsium S.T.D. Collegii Wadhamensis Gardianum'.

[13] *Vindiciae Academiarum*, Oxford, 1654, p. 29.

[14] Ibid., p. 49. Seth Ward, himself a mathematician, resented Bacon's reference to 'the daintiness and pride of mathematicians, who will needs have this science almost domineer over Physic [i.e. science]' (*De Augmentis Scientiarum* III. 6: *Works*, vol. IV, p. 370; and above, p. 56 note 146). He accused Bacon, quite unfairly, of ignoring the importance of mathematics

In the course of his discussion he mentioned their experimental science club, as evidence that these principles were being put into action.[15] During 1658-9 the Oxford club moved out of its university background to London when the various fortunes of most of its leading members made it more convenient to meet there. With the departure from Oxford of this enlightening and ameliorating influence, it appears that Aristotelianism closed in again. In 1666, when the Plague disrupted the meetings of the Royal Society, and many of the Fellows temporarily moved to Oxford, Oldenburg wrote to Boyle on 5 October from London:

> Methinks you are so many fellows of the Society, that you can make more than a quorum, but that you want the president. I rejoice to find by yours, that you intend to make so good use of that opportunity as you did; and I hope, since you are so many, and so considerable ones of our body, you will make it a part of your business, so to insinuate the designs of the Royal Society into the Oxonians, that they may relish them as much, as most of them have been reported to disgust them, and give them cause to prefer that solidity of knowledge, the said Society aims at, before scholastical intentions.[16]

Joseph Glanvill, even before he became a Fellow of the Royal Society, was one of those who had been greatly concerned about the paralysing effects of the Aristotelian approach to science, and had been vociferous about it. In *The Vanity of Dogmatizing*, published in 1661, while discussing the whole problem, he said:

> The *Aristotelian Hypotheses* give a very dry and *jejune* account of Nature's *Phænomena*. For as to its more *mysterious* reserves, *Peripatetick* enquiry hath left them unattempted; and the most forward notional Dictators sit down here in a contented ignorance: and as if nothing more were knowable then is already discover'd, they put stop to all endeavours of their Solution. *Qualities*, that were *Occult* to *Aristotle*, must be so to us; and we must not *Philosophize*

---

[15] *Vindiciae Academiarum*, pp. 35-6; and below, p. 113.
[16] Robert Boyle, *Works*, ed. Thomas Birch, 1744, vol. V, pp. 337-8.

(*Vindiciae Academiarum*, p. 25), a complaint which was not sustained by the Royal Society itself. (For Bacon's statements on the importance of mathematics, see above, pp. 56-8.)

beyond *Sympathy and Antipathy*: . . . Nor is the *Aristotelian Philosophy* guilty of this sloth and Philosophick penury, only in remoter abstrusities: but in solving the most ordinary causalities, it is as defective and unsatisfying. Even the most common productions are here resolv'd into *Celestial influences, Elemental combinations, active* and *passive* principles, and such *generalities*; while the particular manner of them is as hidden as *sympathies*. And if we follow *manifest qualities* beyond the empty signification of their Names; we shall find them as *occult*, as those which are professedly *so*. That heavy Bodies descend by *gravity* . . . and again, that *Gravity* is a *quality* whereby an heavy body descends, is an impertinent *Circle*, and teacheth nothing.

. . . What a *Romance* is the story of those impossible *concamerations, Intersections, Involutions* and feign'd *Rotations* of *solid Orbs?* All substituted to salve the credit of a broken ill-contrived *Systeme*. . . . That the *Galaxy* is a *Meteor*, was the account of *Aristotle*: But the *Telescope* hath autoptically confuted it: . . . and a *Comet* is no more ground for *Astrological presages* then a *flaming* Chimney.[17]

He gave many examples of error and inconsistency in the system, concluding:

The *Aristotelian Philosophy* is inept for New discoveries; and therefore of no accommodation to the *use* of *life* . . . I do not think, that all Science is *Tautology*: The last Ages have shewn us, what *Antiquity* never saw; no, not in a *Dream*.[18]

[17] Joseph Glanvill, *The Vanity of Dogmatizing*, London, 1661, pp. 169-75. (In the *History*, pp. 364-5, Sprat speaks very strongly against the practice of astrological divination. He says:

It is indeed a disgrace to the Reason, and honor of mankind, that every fanatical *Humorist* should presume to interpret all the *secret Ordinances of Heven*; and to expound the Times, and Seasons, and Fates of Empires, though he be never so ignorant of the common *Works of Nature*, that lye under his Feet. There can be nothing more injurious than this, to mens public or private peace . . . For this *melancholy*, this *frightful*, this *Astrological* humor disarms mens hearts, it breaks their courage; it confounds their Councils, it makes them help to bring such [predicted] calamities on themselves: First they fancy, that such ill accidents must come to pass: And so they render themselves fit subjects to be wrought upon, and very often become the *instruments*, to bring those effects about, which they fondly imagined were inevitably threatn'd from Heven.

In its attitude to astrology the Royal Society followed Bacon in the *Novum Organum* I, Aph. XLVI.)

[18] Ibid., pp. 178, 188.

A revised version of this work, entitled *Scepsis Scientifica*, was dedicated to the Royal Society and published in 1665. The Society was pleased to find itself 'so well understood, at last by some',[19] and Glanvill was made a Fellow.[20] His *Plus Ultra*, published in 1668, just after Sprat's *History*, is mainly an expansion of this theme, with the Royal Society as the unprecedented champion of the breakthrough. Upholding the Society, Glanvill had a grim crack 'against a Disputing Man, who is afraid to believe his Eyes against Aristotle'. Such a man reminded him, said Glanvill,

> . . . of the *good Woman*, who when her Husband urged in an occasion of difference, 'I saw it, and shall I not *believe my own Eyes*?' Replied briskly, 'Will you believe your own Eyes before your own dear Wife?' And it seems *this Gentleman* thinks it unreasonable we should *believe ours* before his *own dear Aristotle*.[21]

In the *History* Sprat explains at length that this stranglehold on science is the main obstacle to progress, and that its removal and replacement by a new '*Systeme* of *Natural Philosophy*' is an essential condition for satisfactory growth.[22] At the same time he emphasizes that the Royal Society has no intention of sweeping away all the wisdom of the ancients; the universities need not be anxious. In this, and in all other ways, Sprat says he will 'represent this *Model*, to be inoffensive', and in doing so will 'secure all the Ancient *Proprietors* in their *Rights*: A work as necessary to be done, in raysing a *new Philosophy* as we see it is in building a *new London*'.[23] The Society's only interest is in a new system of natural sciences; he reiterates:

> And it is in this alone, that I can allow, there will be any alteration made, by this reformation of *Knowledge*.[24]

[19] Oldenburg to Boyle, London, 10 December 1664: Robert Boyle, *Works*, ed. Thomas Birch, 1744, vol. V, p. 328.
[20] At the general meeting on 7 December 1664 the book was presented to the Royal Society by Lord Brereton, who then proposed Glanvill as a Fellow. He was elected and admitted at the next meeting, on 14 December.
[21] Joseph Glanvill, *Plus Ultra, or the Progress of Knowledge Since the Days of Aristotle*, 1668, pp. 65–6.
[22] Below, pp. 76 ff.
[23] Thomas Sprat, *History*, p. 323. He was writing soon after the Fire of London.
[24] Ibid., p. 327.

Sprat's assurance was repeated by Glanvill in his *Plus Ultra*, where he gave many 'Celebrated Names' of Fellows, which he thought might 'serve to remove' the 'groundless suspicion which some have entertained, *viz.* That the *Universities* are undermined by this new *Philosophick Society*'.[25]

But these efforts to dispel misunderstanding and hostility were not well received. On 9 July 1669 at a ceremony which could scarcely have been more public—the formal opening of the new Sheldonian Theatre at Oxford University, 'with the greatest splendor & formalitie that might be, & therefore drew a world of strangers & other Companie to the University from all parts of the Nation'—the Public Orator of the University, according to John Evelyn, took occasion to make 'some malicious & undecent reflections on the *Royal Society* as underminers of the University, which was very foolish and untrue'.[26]

Other contemporary accounts of this episode confirm the intensity of antagonism towards the Royal Society as a body. John Wallis, writing from Oxford on 17 July to Robert Boyle, said:

> Dr. *South*, as university orator, made a long oration. The first part of which consisted of satyrical invectives against *Cromwell*, fanaticks, the Royal Society, and new philosophy; the next, of ecomiasticks, in praise of the archbishop, the theatre, the vice-chancellor, the architect, and the painter; the last, execrations against fanaticks, conventicles, comprehension, and new philosophy, damning them *ad infernos, ad gehennam.*[27]

Ironically, 'the archbishop' and 'the architect' were both Fellows of the Royal Society—Gilbert Sheldon, Archbishop of Canterbury,[28] the donor of the building, and Christopher Wren, the architect. Anthony Wood also recorded his impressions:

> . . . the Vicechancellor spake to the Orator, that in the University's name he make a public recognition of the benefits they had re-

[25] Joseph Glanvill, *Plus Ultra, or the Progress of Knowledge Since the Days of Aristotle*, 1668, Preface.
[26] *The Diary of John Evelyn*, ed. E. S. De Beer, Oxford, 1955, vol. III, pp. 531-2.
[27] Robert Boyle, *Works*, ed. Thomas Birch, 1744, vol. V, p. 514.
[28] Above, p. 13, note 18.

ceived. Upon which he proceeded to celebrate the Benefaction in a copious Oration; which being ended with great applause (notwithstanding displeasing to many for divers passages therein reflecting on the Royal Society) . . .[29]

The text of Robert South's oration now appears to be lost, but Isaac D'Israeli, writing in 1814, quotes from it, saying:

The ever-witty South, in his Oration at Oxford, made this poignant reflexion on the Royal Society:—"Mirantur nihil nisi pulices, pediculos, et seipsos"—They can admire nothing except fleas, lice, and themselves![30]

At Cambridge University the reaction was much the same. When Peter du Moulin tried to publish a book of verse there, poems in praise of the Royal Society were banned. Writing to Boyle (to whom the book was dedicated) on 28 December 1668, Du Moulin said:

One of the prime licensers of the book, Dr. *Gunning*, would not suffer the heroicks in commendation of the Royal Society to be printed with their fellows. It grieves me to see a feud between that noble Society and the Universities, to which Mr. *Glanvill*'s books have much contributed. Your great credit, prudence, and moderation, may stop that growing evil, if any thing in the world can.[31]

John Evelyn, who knew more than Du Moulin about the reason for the Royal Society's unpopularity with the universities, did not consider Glanvill's efforts to defend the Society in any way to blame. Writing to Glanvill on 24 June 1668, to acknowledge a copy of *Plus Ultra*, conveyed to him through Oldenburg, Evelyn had said:

I do not conceive why the Royall Society should any more concern themselves for the empty and malicious cavells of these

[29] Anthony Wood, *The History and Antiquities of the University of Oxford*, 1792–6, vol. II, p. 801.

[30] Isaac D'Israeli, *Quarrels of Authors*, London, 1814, vol. II, p. 21. This quip recalls a similar one made by James Harrington ten years before, when the Royal Society was still in its preparatory stage at Oxford (below, p. 116).

[31] Robert Boyle, *Works*, ed. Thomas Birch, 1744, vol. V, p. 594. Peter du Moulin (1601–84) had been a tutor in the Boyle family. Peter Gunning (1613–84) was then Master of St. John's College, Cambridge, and Regius Professor of Divinity.

delators, after what you have say'd; but let the moon-dogs bark on, 'till their throats are drie; the Society every day emerges, and her good Genius will raise up one or other to judge & defend her; whilst there is nothing which dos more confirme me in the nobleness of the designe, than this spirit of contradiction which the devil (who hates all discoveries of these false & praestigious ways that have hitherto obtain'd) dos incite to stirr up men against it.[32]

Commenting on this cleavage between the universities and the Royal Society, George Thomson, a Doctor of Medicine of Leyden University, writing in 1671, said of the Royal Society:

Neither are the two *Universities* like to be impaired in their splendor by this most satisfactory way of inquiring into the Cause of Natural things, unless they endeavour to keep us still hoodwink'd, & by *Paralogisms, subtil Arguments, deceitful Sophistry* to dispute us out of Truth, perswading us out of our Senses.[33]

Anthony Wood, writing in about 1671, also remarked on the situation, indicating that the Royal Society would have liked to underline its initiative in the sciences by conferring degrees:

The Universitie [i.e. Oxford] look upon it as obnoxious—they desire to confer degrees—the Universitie sticke against [this].[34]

Thomas Hobbes was another of those outside the Royal Society who recognized that it had taken over the traditional leadership of the universities in the natural sciences. In 1679 he remarked that the Royal Society's semi-official journal, *The Philosophical Transactions*, had superseded traditional academic textbooks in the study of natural phenomena:

[32] *The Diary and Correspondence of John Evelyn*, ed. William Bray, London, 1906, vol. III, p. 357.
[33] George Thomson, Μισοχυμιας 'Ελεγχος; *or, a Check given to the insolent Garrulity of Henry Stubbe*, London, 1671, pp. 44–5.
[34] Bodleian Library MS. Tanner 102, fol. 117 (and Anthony Wood, *Life and Times*, ed. Andrew Clark, Oxford, 1891–, vol. III, p. 354). On this slip of paper Wood adds: 'Stubs writes against them' (the Royal Society). Henry Stubbe's first attack on the Royal Society was *Legends no Histories*, London, 1670, which Anthony Wood said came out in October 1669 (writing at the bottom of the title-page in his own copy, now Bodleian Library W.140(1)). On two other slips of paper (ff. 116 and 118) Wood also refers to Stubbe's pamphlets against the Royal Society, mentioning *Legends no Histories* and others published in 1670 and 1671.

And as for Natural Philosophy, is it not remov'd from *Oxford* and *Cambridge* to *Gresham-College* in London, and to be learn'd out of their *Gazets*?[35]

Drawing attention to this comment, John Aubrey gives a gloss on Hobbes, emphasizing that the new leader is not Gresham College itself, but the Royal Society, which held its meetings there:

> . . . he had a high Esteeme for the Royall Societie, (having sayd that Naturall Philosophy was removed from the Universities to Gresham-Colledge) [meaning the Royall Societie that meetes there] . . .[36]

Academic opposition died far more slowly than is generally realized. In 1690 John Locke, who had been a Fellow of the Royal Society since 1668, published *An Essay Concerning Humane Understanding*, dedicating it to his friend Thomas Herbert, Earl of Pembroke, then President of the Royal Society. In the *Essay* Locke had a good deal to say against 'the Art of Disputing' as a means of studying science, and commented on the reluctance with which it was being abandoned:

> The Commonwealth of Learning, is not at this time without Master-Builders, whose mighty Designs in advancing the Sciences, will leave lasting Monuments to the Admiration of Posterity; But every one must not hope to be a *Boyle*, or a *Sydenham*; and in an Age that produces such Masters, as the Great *Huygenius*, and the incomparable Mr. *Newton*, with some others of that Strain; 'tis Ambition enough to be employed as an Under-Labourer in clearing the Ground a little, and removing some of the Rubbish, that lies in the way to Knowledge; which certainly had been very much more advanced in the World, if the Endeavours of ingenious and industrious Men had not been much cumbred with the learned but frivolus use of uncouth, affected, or unintelligible Terms, introduced into the Sciences, and there made an Art of. . . . Vague and insignificant Forms of Speech, and Abuse of Language, have so long passed for Mysteries of Science: And hard

---

[35] Thomas Hobbes, *Behemoth; or an Epitome of the Civil Wars of England, from 1640, to 1660*, London, 1679, p. 155.
[36] Bodleian Library MS. Aubrey 9, fol. 54 (and John Aubrey, *Brief Lives*, ed. Andrew Clark, London, 1898, pp. 371–2). These are Aubrey's own square brackets.

and misapply'd Words, with little or no meaning, have, by Prescription, such a Right to be mistaken for deep Learning and heighth of Speculation, that it will not be easie to persuade either those who speak, or those who hear them, that they are but the Cover of Ignorance, and hindrance of true Knowledge.[37]

This was censured by senior members of Oxford University, who in 1703 attempted to suppress the book. In April 1704 Locke's friend James Tyrrell wrote to him:

. . . in the beginning of November last there was a meeting of the Heads of Houses then in town; it was there proposed by Dr. Mill[38] and seconded by Dr. Maunder[39] that there was a great decay of logical exercises in the University which could not be attributed to anything so much as the new philosophy which was too much read, in particular your book and Le Clerc's;[40] philosophy against which it was proposed that a programma should [be] published, forbidding all tutors to read them with their pupils. This was like at first to have passed till it was opposed by some others present, and particularly Dr. Dunster[41] who not only said he thought the making the programma would do more harm than good, first by making so much noise abroad, as if the University were about to forbid the reading of all philosophy since that of Aristotle; next that he thought that instead of the end proposed, it would make young men more desirous to buy and read those books . . . Then at another meeting their resolution upon the whole was that upon Dr. Edwards[42] proposal they agreed that instead of a programma, all heads of houses should give the tutors instructions not to read those books to their pupils and to prevent them doing it by themselves as much as lay in their power.[43]

---

[37] John Locke, *An Essay Concerning Humane Understanding*, London, 1690, The Epistle to the Reader.

[38] Principal of St. Edmund Hall.

[39] Master of Balliol.

[40] Jean Le Clerc (1657–1736). Tyrrell had previously written to Locke that some Heads of Houses wanted tutors 'neither to read your *Essay* nor Le Clerc's *Physics* nor *Logic* to their pupils, since those works had much discouraged the noble art of disputation': Maurice Cranston, *John Locke*, London, 1957, p. 467.

[41] Warden of Wadham.

[42] Vice-Chancellor of the University and Principal of Jesus College.

[43] Maurice Cranston, *John Locke*, London, 1957, p. 467.

Tyrrell ended by saying that he believed they had 'thought fit to drop it', as it was evidently not being put into practice in some colleges that he knew of.

The long story of the stubborness of the universities' resistance to the early Royal Society underlines the Society's tenacity in keeping to its course, and illuminates its vital role in the development of modern science.

The internal history of the early Royal Society is the story of the *Novum Organum* in action for the first time. Echoing Sprat's tribute in the *History* to Francis Bacon as the intellectual source of the Royal Society,[44] Abraham Cowley, in verse a good deal less felicitous than Sprat's prose, says:

> *Bacon*, like *Moses*, led us forth at last,
> The barren Wilderness he past,
> Did on the very Border stand
> Of the blest promis'd Land,
> And from the Mountains Top of his Exalted Wit,
> Saw it himself, and shew'd us it.[45]

Turning to the general implications of this, Sprat says of 'the True Philosophy' that it

> must be first of all begun, on a scrupulous, and severe examination of particulars: from them, there may be some general Rules, with great caution drawn: But it must not rest there, nor is that the most difficult part of its course: It must advance those Principles, to the finding out of new effects, through all the varieties of Matter: and so both the courses must proceed orderly together; from experimenting, to Demonstrating, and from demonstrating to Experimenting again.[46]

He pays generous tribute to the experimenters who, as individuals, have pursued this path in making some particular discoveries. To them 'there is as much honor to be payd, as can be due to any one single humane Wit: But', he is obliged to add:

> they must pardon us, if we still prefer the joynt force of many men.[47]

The ultimate goal of the Royal Society, he says, is 'to overcome the mysteries of all the Works of Nature',[48] and the

---

[44] Above, p. 22.   [45] Thomas Sprat, *History*, Dedicatory ode, stanza V.
[46] Ibid., p. 31.   [47] Ibid., pp. 38–9.   [48] Ibid., p. 64.

application of this knowledge is 'for the Benefit of humane life'.[49] Again, acknowledging relationship between the various aspects of science, he says:

> And this is the highest pitch of *humane reason*; to follow all the links of this chain, till all their secrets are open to our minds; and their works advanc'd, or imitated by our hands.[50]

Therefore the Royal Society's search has no physical limits. It is

> . . . towards the setling of an universal, constant, and impartial survey of the whole *Creation*.[51]

Oldenburg, writing to John Winthrop, Governor of Connecticut, just after the publication of Sprat's *History*, reiterates this:

> Sʳ, you will please to remember that we have taken to taske the whole Universe, and that we were obliged to doe so by the nature of our Dessein.[52]

Following Bacon, Sprat maintains that, to put their intention into practice, experiments alone are not enough. The whole *'Systeme of Natural Philosophy'* or *'Physics'*, by which was meant all the sciences of natural phenomena, must be 'cut away':

> But yet the change will be so advantageous, that I have no reason to dissemble it. I grant indeed that the greatest part of the former Body of *Physics*, may hereby chance to fall to the ground. But to what sum will the dammage amount? What can we lose, but only some few *definitions*, and idle *questions*, and empty *disputations*? Of which I may say as one did of *Metaphors, Poterimus vivere sine illis*. Perhaps there will be no more use of Twenty, or Thirty obscure Terms, such as *Matter*, and *Form*, *Privation*, *Entelichia*, and the like. But to supply their want, an[53] infinit variety of *Inventions, Motions*, and *Operations*, will succeed in the place of words . . . instead of Idle talking, and wandring, under its fruitless shadows; as the *Peripatetics* did in their first institution, and their Successors have done ever since.[54]

[49] Thomas Sprat, *History*, p. 2.   [50] Ibid., pp. 110–11.   [51] Ibid., p. 124.
[52] The letter is dated 13 October 1667 (*Proceedings of the Massachusetts Historical Society, 1878*, Boston, 1879, p. 230).
[53] By a misprint 'an' appears as 'and', but is corrected in the errata at the end of the *History*.
[54] Thomas Sprat, *History*, p. 327.

Confirming that their intention is to build up new sciences, Sprat points out that England is geographically well placed as a centre of information:

This their care of an *Universal Intelligence*, is befriended by *Nature* its self, in the situation of *England*: . . . those that border upon the *Seas*, are most properly seated, to bring home matter for *new Sciences* . . .[55]

and that London would be the most convenient headquarters 'for a perpetual habitation, wherein the Universal Philosophy might settle it self'.[56]

The work was to be one of continual development:

They have try'd, to put it into a condition of perpetual increasing; by settling an inviolable correspondence between the hand, and the brain. They have studi'd, to make it, not onely an Enterprise of one season, or of some lucky opportunity; but a business of time; a steddy, a lasting, a popular, an uninterrupted Work. They have attempted, to free it from the Artifice, and Humors, and Passions of Sects; to render it an Instrument, whereby Mankind may obtain a Dominion over *Things*, and not onely over one anothers *Judgements*. And lastly, they have begun to establish these Reformations in Philosophy, not so much, by any solemnity of Laws, or ostentation of Ceremonies; as by solid Practice, and examples: not, by a glorious pomp of Words; but by the silent, effectual, and unanswerable Arguments of real Productions.[57]

Even in its early days, critics were already asking what the Royal Society had done, what new discoveries it had made. Sprat, writing when it had survived the first difficulties and oppositions 'which are wont to arise, against the beginnings of great things',[58] tells them, but not without considerable rebuke:

This certainly alone were enough to free them from all imputation of idleness, that they have fram'd such an Assembly in six years, which was never yet brought about in six thousand. Besides this the world is to consider, that if any that think, the whole compass of their work might have come to a sudden issue: they seem neither to understand the intentions of the *Royal Society*,

[55] Thomas Sprat, *History*, p. 86. [56] Ibid., pp. 86–7.
[57] Ibid., p. 62. [58] Ibid., p. 154.

nor the extent of their task. It was never their aim, to make a violent dispatch. They know that precipitancy in such matters, was the fault of the Antients: And they have no mind, to fall into the same error, which they indeavour to correct. They began at first on so large a Bottom, that it is impossible, the whole Frame should be suddenly compleated. 'Tis true, they that have nothing else to do, but to express, and adorn conclusions of Knowledge already made, may bring their Arts to an end, as soon as they please. But they who follow the slow, and intricate method of Nature, cannot have the seasons of their productions, so much in their own power . . . If we should require them, immediately to reduce all their labours, to publick, and conspicuous use, by this dangerous speed, we should draw them off from many of the best Foundations of Knowledge. Many of their noblest discoveries, and such as will hereafter prove most serviceable, cannot instantly be made to turn to profit.[59]

and again:

It is strange that we are not able to inculcate into the minds of many men, the necessity of that *distinction* of my Lord *Bacons*, that there ought to be *Experiments* of *Light*, as well as of *Fruit* . . . If they will persist in contemning all *Experiments*, except those which bring with them immediate *gain*, and a present *harvest*: they may as well cavil at the Providence of God, that he has not made all the seasons of the year, to be times of *mowing*, *reaping*, and *vintage*.[60]

Sprat returns to this point in his summing-up at the end of the Second Part of the History, in which he has discussed the purpose, policy and achievements of the Royal Society:

They have contriv'd in their thoughts, and couragiously begun an *Attempt*, which all *Ages* had despair'd of. It is therefore fit that they alone, and not others, who refuse to partake of their burden, should be Judges by what steps, and what pace, they ought to proceed.

Such men are then to be intreated not to interrupt their *Labors* with impertinent rebukes; they are to remember, that the *Subject* of their *Studies* is as large as the *Univers*: and that in so vast an *Enterprise*, many intervals and disappointments must be recon'd upon. Though they do not behold that the *Society* has already

[59] Thomas Sprat, *History*, pp. 154–5 (and above, p. 77).   [60] Ibid., p. 245.

3. John Wilkins, founder of the Oxford experimental science club in about 1648, while Warden of Wadham College, Oxford. *By courtesy of Wadham College, Oxford.*

4. Frontispiece of the Royal Society's presentation copy of Sprat's *History of the Royal Society* (1667). On the left is the President (Viscount Brouncker); centre, a bust of the formal Patron and Founder, Charles II, being crowned with a laurel wreath by Fame, and surmounted by the coat-of-arms granted by him to the Society; and right, Francis Bacon, the Royal Society's inspirational source. Below the engraving is written in John Wilkins's hand: 'Presented to the R. Society from the Author by the hands of Dr John Wilkins, Octob. 10. 1667.' *By courtesy of the Royal Society.*

fill'd the world with *perfect Sciences*; yet they are to be inform'd, that the nature of their *Work* requir'd that they should first begin with *immethodical Collections* and *indigested Experiments*, before they go on to finish and compose them into *Arts*.[61]

As Christopher Wren said in the very early years of the Royal Society:

> in many Things we must be content to plant Crab stocks for Posterity to graft on.[62]

The first point about their recognition of Bacon as their guide is, then, their conscious grasp of the problem and their comprehensive, long-term approach.

Sprat explains how they have set about putting the venture into action, following Bacon's belief that mind and hand should work together and that the approach should be corporate, the labours first to be distributed and then combined. By this means says Sprat, the errors to which solitary work might succumb were less likely to occur, there would be the benefits of communication of discovery, not only in the immediate context, but in other branches of science, and the continuity of the work would be ensured:

> . . . the Task was divided amongst them, by one of these two ways. First, it was sometimes referr'd to some *particular men*, to make choice of what *Subject* they pleased, and to follow their own humour in the *Trial*; . . .
>
> Or else secondly, the *Society*, it self made the distribution, and deputed whom it thought fit for the prosecution of such, or such Experiments. And this they did, either by allotting the *same Work* to *several* men, separated from one another; or else by *joyning* them into *Committees* (if we may use that word in a Philosophical sence, . . .) By this *union* of *eyes*, and *hands* there do these *advantages* arise. Thereby there will be a full *comprehension* of the object in *all* its appearances; and so there will be a mutual communication of the light of one *Science* to another: whereas *single labours* can be but as a prospect taken upon one side. And also by this fixing of several mens thoughts upon one thing, there will be an excellent

[61] Thomas Sprat, *History*, pp. 318–19.
[62] From an address to the Royal Society in its first years, probably 1664 (*Parentalia*, ed. Stephen Wren, London, 1750, p. 221). His reference is to the crab-apple tree, the simple, original 'stock' on which more highly evolved strains of apple may be grafted.

D

cure for that *defect* . . . to do wonderful things in the *beginning*;
but shortly after, to be overborn by the multitude, and weight of
their own thoughts; then to yield, and cool by little and little;
. . . For this, the best provision must be, to join many men together; . . .[63]

In this way 'a continual race of *Experimenters*'[64] would be
established.

It was their basic principle that wherever possible, all experiments should be carried out by their own members under
careful scrutiny, otherwise individual discoveries made by
others might pass insufficiently verified into the general body
of knowledge:

. . . I shall lay it down, as their *Fundamental Law*, that whenever
they could possibly get to *handle* the subject, the *Experiment* was
still perform'd by some of the *Members* themselves. The want of this
exactness, has very much diminish'd the credit of former *Naturalists*.[65]

Their approach was flexible; there was no prescribed way of
conducting experimental work. They undertook

not to prescribe to themselves, any certain *Art of Experimenting*,
within which to circumscribe their thoughts: But rather to keep
themselves free, and change their course, according to the different circumstances, that occur to them in their operations; and
the several alterations of the Bodies, on which they work. The true
Experimenting has this one thing inseparable from it, never to be a
fix'd and *settled Art*, and never to be *limited* by constant Rules.[66]

The work of compiling the research was not to fall on the
experimenters alone, but was to be undertaken 'by the *joint
labours* of the whole *Society*'.[67] There was work for '*Minds* of all
sizes . . . from the most ordinary capacities, to the highest and
most searching *Wits*'.[68]

The Royal Society was fully conscious of its responsibility
in the pioneer work which was essential in the creation of new
sciences. It therefore declared its determination to show the
utmost caution in stating conclusions, and to record its findings

---

[63] Thomas Sprat, *History*, pp. 84–5.   [64] Ibid., p. 430.
[65] Ibid., p. 83.   [66] Ibid., p. 89.
[67] Ibid., p. 97.   [68] Ibid., p. 435.

in such a way that succeeding ages might the more easily detect
and correct mistakes:

> To this fault of *Sceptical doubting*, the *Royal Society* may perhaps be
> suspected, to be a little too much inclin'd: because they always
> professed, to be so backward from *setling* of *Principles*, or *fixing*
> upon *Doctrines*. But if we fairly consider their intentions, we shall
> soon acquit them. Though they are not yet very daring, in estab-
> lishing conclusions; yet they lay no injunctions upon their suc-
> cessors not to do the same, when they shall have got a sufficient
> store for such work. It is their study, that the way to attain a
> *solid speculation*, should every day be more and more persued: which
> is to be done, by a long forbearing of *speculation* at first, till the
> matters be ripe for it; and not, by madly rushing upon it in the
> very beginning . . . Whatever they have resolv'd upon; they have
> not reported, as *unalterable Demonstrations*, but as *present appearances*:
> delivering down to future Ages, with the good success of the
> Experiment, the *manner* of their progress, the *Instruments*, and the
> several differences of the *matter*, which they have apply'd: so that,
> with their mistake, they give them also the means of finding it out.
> To this I shall add, that they have never affirm'd any thing, con-
> cerning the cause, till the trial was past: whereas, to do it before,
> is a most venomous thing in the making of *Sciences*: for whoever
> has fix'd on his *Cause*, before he has experimented; can hardly
> avoid fitting his *Experiment*, and his Observations, to his own *Cause*,
> which he had before imagin'd; rather than the *Cause* to the truth
> of the Experiment it self.[69]

It was not their primary aim either to prove or disprove
particular theories, but to produce a substantial body of evidence, which, continually growing, would be of untold value
to those who followed:

> The *Society* has reduc'd its principal observations, into one *com-*
> *mon-stock;* and laid them up in publique *Registers*, to be nakedly
> transmitted to the next Generation of Men; and so from them to
> their Successors. And as their purpose was, to heap up a mixt
> Mass of *Experiments*, without digesting them into any perfect
> model: so to this end, they confin'd themselves to no order of
> subjects; and whatever they have recorded, they have done it, not
> as compleat Schemes of opinions, but as bare, unfurnish'd His-
> tories.[70]

---

[69] Thomas Sprat, *History*, pp. 106–8.   [70] Ibid., p. 115.

The Society was extremely conscious of the temptation to organize the new sciences permanently at an immature stage, a disastrous limitation of the system which was being replaced. The immediate aim was therefore no more than to prepare a foundation on which posterity could build:

> For it is certain, that a too sudden striving to reduce the *Sciences*, in their beginnings, into Method, and Shape, and Beauty; has very much retarded their increase . . .
>
> By their fair, and equal, and submissive way of *Registring* nothing, but *Histories*, and *Relations*; they have left room for others, that shall succeed, to *change*, to *augment*, to *approve*, to *contradict* them, at their discretion. By this, they have given *posterity* a far greater power of judging them; than ever they took over those, that went before them.[71]

Besides its cautious and tentative attitude, Sprat emphasizes another general precept derived by the Royal Society from Bacon—the study of the normal and the unexceptional:

> Their other care has been, to regard the *least*, and the *plainest* things, and those that may appear at *first* the most *inconsiderable*; as well as the *greatest Curiosities*. This was visibly neglected by the *Antients* . . . If they could gather together some extraordinary Qualities of *Stones*, or *Minerals*, some Rarities of the *Age*, the *food*, the *colour*, the *shapes* of *Beasts*, or some *vertues* of *Fountains*, or *Rivers*: they thought, they had perform'd the chiefest part of *Natural Historians*. But this course is subject to much corruption. It is not the true following of *Nature*; For that still goes on in a steddy Rode . . . It stops the severe progress of *Inquiry*: Infecting the mind, and making it averse from the true *Natural Philosophy*:[72]

The Royal Society, while firmly believing in its destiny, was under no illusions. Sprat refers to its 'painful digging, and toiling in *Nature*'.[73] The wonder is, that, working without even elementary instruments of modern accuracy, and confronted on all sides by hostility—academic, religious and political— they were able to keep their eye on the object and achieve what they did. Sprat gives both a general indication of the work they have covered and many instances. To give all the details, he

[71] Thomas Sprat, *History*, p. 116.
[72] Ibid., p. 90.   [73] Ibid., p. 94.

says, would be impossible, but he first indicates the direction
they are taking:

> It would now be needless to set down all the steps of their pro-
> gress . . .; how they observ'd all the varieties of *Generations*, and
> *corruptions*, natural, and artificial; all the increasings and lessen-
> ings; agreements, and oppositions of things; how, having found
> out a *cause*, they have apply'd it to many other *effects*: and the
> *effects* to different *causes*; how they were wont to change the In-
> struments and places, and quantities of matter, according to
> occasions: and all the other subtilties, and windings of Trial,
> which are almost infinite to express.[74]

Since their ultimate goal is so distant, not to be realized in
their generation, they must always bear in mind that laws discovered are not to be sterile, but productive of works, otherwise
the undertaking would become a vast academic exercise, without application to human life. They deplore

> the rendring of Causes barren: that when they have been found
> out, they have been suffer'd to lye idle; and have been onely us'd,
> to increase thoughts, and not works. This negligence is of all
> others the most dangerous: It is a *Shipwrack* in the end of the
> *voiage*, and thence the more to be pitied: It is a corruption, that
> both hinders additions, and eats out the knowledge that has been
> already obtain'd.[75]

It was right that they should have regard for the present, as
well as the future, and turn to account some of their immediate
discoveries:

> . . . they have taken care, to satisfie the *hopes* of the *present times*;
> which else might justly languish, and grow cold about this enter-
> prise: if they once saw, that nothing would be ripe in their days;
> but that all was to come up *hereafter*, for the advantage of those,
> that are yet unborn. They consulted the good of *Future* times; but
> have not neglected their *own*; . . .[76]

The Journal Book of the Royal Society, which records the
minutes of their general meetings, the Council Minute Book
and *The Philosophical Transactions*[77] contain accounts of much

[74] Thomas Sprat, *History*, p. 89.
[75] Ibid., p. 109.   [76] Ibid., pp. 109–10.
[77] First published in 1665 by Henry Oldenburg.

experimental work done by the Society. But in so wide a spread, the whole design cannot be seen in each particular. The function of the *History* is to give coherence to the mass of details by relating them to underlying principles. This is obviously necessary where many kinds of work are going on at once, and where, at times, what is being done, of itself, might seem almost meaningless. Moreover, it would be useless to deny that, in its details, the work, or deductions from it, were sometimes unprofitable or irrelevant.

The Royal Society in practice did not embody Bacon's concept in a consistently pure form. As Sprat said (and as Bacon had foreseen), since this was an institution made up of individuals, there were in it 'minds of all sizes'. Some of these minds lacked the capacity for a real grasp of the principles involved, while earnestly endeavouring to add to man's useful knowledge. Contributions at this level, mainly concerned with utilitarian improvements and contrivances, and recipes for making cider, and the like, cannot be said to indicate a distinction between the Royal Society and other societies. Neither did the indulgence of a taste for sensational and highly coloured accounts of 'rarities' and monstrosities which were sometimes 'brought in' at the meetings, nor the occasional absurdity like 'the scheme of a cart with legs instead of wheels' or 'spectacles for seeing in the dark', reflect the serious purpose of the Society. Even Boyle was not immune from occasional aberrations. A few sentences of lively, incautious conversation, faithfully recorded in the minutes of a general meeting, echo ironically in modern ears:

> Mr. Boyle mentioned, that he had been informed, that the much drinking of Coffe[e] did breed the Palsy.
> The Bishop of Exeter [SethWard] seconded him, and said, that himself had found it dispose to paralytical effects; . . .
> Mr. Graunt affirmed, that he knew two Gentlemen, great Drinkers of Coffe[e], very paralytical.
> Dr. Whistler suggested, that it might be enquired, whether the same persons did take much Tobacco.[78]

Yet, notwithstanding some unedifying and occasionally simply silly excursions, the element which may be called the leaven in the lump, the element which constituted a genuine and important distinction of function, prevailed. And that this

78 Journal Book, vol. II, p. 179 (Meeting of 18 January 1664/5).

was so owes much to the guiding hands of the leaders, who expressed and maintained the essentials of Royal Society policy through its Council.

It had always been the practice of the Society, as the need arose, to nominate small, informal committees from among its number to consider or advise on particular courses of experiment, or inventions; but following the effective Charter of 1663, and the setting in action of the Council,[79] more formal and extensive measures were taken to organize and relate the work. At its meeting of 7 December 1663 the Council ordered

> that Dr. Merret, Dr. Whistler, and Mr. Hoskins, doe peruse the Books of the Society, wherein the Experiments and other Philosophical matters, treated of at their Meetings, are recorded; together with their Journal Books; and consider, which do relate to and depend upon one another; as also, wherein they may be defective, and how further to be prosecuted.[80]

On 27 January 1663/4 the Council ordered

> that the President move this day the Society to appoint a Committee of Physitians, that are Fellows of the Society, constantly to consider, what is necessary to be prosecuted in Anatomy and Chirurgery [i.e. surgery].[81]

On 23 March 1663/4 the Council ordered that committees should be set up for the general improvement of science. By the next Council meeting, a week later, the plan for the committees was complete: 'a draught of Eight Committees . . . was read, and ordered to be offered to the Society at their meeting this afternoon, for their approbation'.[82] At this meeting it was also ordered that the Council should give directions on the choice and preparation of the experiments to be carried out by the Society as such.

These committees were drawn up on a scale never before attempted, and represented a major feat of organization. The eight projects were as follows:

> 1. Mechanical. To consider of and improve all Mechanical Inventions; 2. Astronomical and Optical; 3. Anatomical; 4. Chymical; 5. Georgical [agricultural]; 6. For Histories of Trades

---

[79] See below, pp. 137–40.
[80] Council Book, vol. I, pp. 41–2.
[81] Ibid., p. 52.
[82] Ibid., pp. 60–1.

[accounts of crafts]; 7. For Collecting all the Phænomena of Nature hitherto observed, and all Experiments made and recorded; 8. For Correspondence.[83]

The Council was well represented on all the committees, which included some distinguished foreign Fellows, notably the Dutch scientist Christiaan Huygens and the German astronomer Johannes Hevelius.

The first committee had sixty-nine members, among whom appeared such well-known names as John Wilkins, Robert Boyle, Christopher Wren, Seth Ward (then Bishop of Exeter), Sir William Petty, John Wallis, Viscount Brouncker (the President), Robert Hooke (the Curator), Sir Robert Moray, Sir Paul Neile and Christiaan Huygens.

The other committees were smaller and of various sizes, but throughout the scheme care was taken that each contained leading members who were also serving on at least one other committee, so that no part of the work should become isolated. Thus, of leading members who were at that time also members of the Council, Wilkins was on five out of the eight committees, Boyle on seven, Sir Robert Moray on five, Christopher Wren on three, Seth Ward on two, and Jonathan Goddard on four.

In 1666 the arrangements for experimental work carried out at actual meetings of the Royal Society came under fire from Sir Robert Moray, who considered that the importance of relating experiment in its stages and in its aspects was not being sufficiently demonstrated. At the Council Meeting of 4 December he therefore proposed

> that the Council would take into consideration, how the Experiments at the publick Meetings of the Society might be best carried on; whether by a continued Series of Experiments, taking in collateral ones, as they are offered, or by going on in that promiscuous way that has obtain'd hitherto.[84]

About two years later (on 1 February 1668/9) the Council resolved to set up committees to meet regularly to direct this work,[85] and the proposal was put to the general meeting of the Society on the following 11 February by the President (Viscount Brouncker) himself. Some famous names were again

---

[83] Journal Book, vol. II, pp. 61–5.
[84] Council Book, vol. I, pp. 116–17.   [85] Ibid., p. 175.

among those 'named for that purpose'—'the Bishops of Sarum
and Chester' (Seth Ward and John Wilkins), Robert Boyle,
Sir Robert Moray, Sir George Ent, Christopher Wren, John
Locke, Jonathan Goddard and the Curator, Robert Hooke.
They were to 'make use of the Operator for trying Experi-
ments', and 'Every Member of the Society was to have the
Liberty of being present . . . and to assist in promoting the
work'.[86]

Sprat devotes many pages to the work done in the first few
years of the Royal Society's existence. The Society's achievement is all the more remarkable when seen against the practical difficulties which beset it: constant financial struggle,
vicissitudes due to the lack of permanent, independent accommodation, and disturbance of the work by the Plague, followed by the Fire of London.[87] Sprat summarizes 'in short
compass those parts of the visible World, about which they have
chiefly bestow'd their *pains*',[88] and for convenience groups the
researches loosely under eleven general subject-headings.

This summary[89] will be recounted here at length, for it con-
veys not only something of the range and achievement of the
experimenters, but a sense of the work as a whole in the making,
which has been overlooked by those historians of science who
have been intent on following the course of particular discoveries. Some of these experiments, even to the casual eye, are
indeed seen to be of great potential importance—such as those
on the nature and properties of the air, and on heat and temperature; on animal and human respiration, and on the trans-
fusion of blood. Yet the continued belief in the spontaneous
generation of insects[90] is a reminder of the prevailing state of
biological knowledge at the time. In that context the experiment 'of a Spiders not being inchanted by a Circle of *Unicorns-
horn*, or *Irish Earth*, laid round about it',[91] is, if over-cautious,
not entirely absurd; and 'of Flesh not breeding Worms, when
secur'd from Fly-blowings'[92] proclaims a minor triumph. Of far
greater significance, though, than any specific piece of research,

[86] Journal Book, vol. IV, pp. 29–30.
[87] Below, Chapter 5.   [88] Thomas Sprat, *History*, p. 215.
[89] Ibid., pp. 215–27.   [90] See below, p. 90.
[91] See below, p. 90. ('Unicorn's horn' was a name applied to rhinoceros
horn and to the 'horn' or projecting tooth of the narwhal.)
[92] Below, p. 91.

even of a high order, is the consciousness, clearly brought out in the summary, of science as a body of related knowledge, as opposed to isolated pockets of experiment. Already there is considerable 'communication of the light of one *Science* to another',[93] the study of combustion, for example, overlapping with the work on metals and minerals, and with the work on the nature and properties of air, which itself has common ground with the investigations on plant growth, and on the physiological study of respiration; and so on.

The catalogue of research begins with the list of experiments on combustion:[94]

> Of this sort, they have made *Experiments*, to find the lasting of the burning of a Candle, Lamp or Coals, in a Cubic foot of common, rarify'd, and *condens'd* [i.e. compressed] *Air*: to exhibit the sudden extinction of Candles, Lamps, and lighted Coals, when they are put into *satiated Air*: . . . to shew that the greatest and most lasting heat, without a supply of fresh *Air*, is unable to burn Wood, Sulphur, and most other combustible matters: to find the comparative heat of all kinds of *Fires*, and *Flames* of several Materials, as of Sulphur, Camphire, Spirit of Wine [i.e. alcohol], Oyl, Wood, Coal, Seacoal, Iron: to find out at what degree of heat, Lead, Tin, Silver, Brass, Copper, Gold will melt.
>
> Experiments . . . discerning the strength of several kinds of Gunpowder . . . : of bending Springs by the help of Gunpowder: . . . . of the Recoyling of Guns.[95]

Other experiments were made 'of Candles, and Coals, extinguish'd by the damps of a deep Well', and 'of reducing Copper to a very combustible substance'.

They made many experiments 'in order to find out the nature, properties, and uses of *Air*.[96] Such as these'—and Sprat lists scores of them, including:

> *Experiments* for determining the height of the *Atmosphere*, for finding the pressure of the *Atmosphere*: on the tops of Mountains, on the surface of the earth, and at the bottoms of very deep Pits, and Mines, by the help of *Quick-silver*, and other contrivances: for

---

93 Thomas Sprat, *History*, p. 85. (See above, p. 79.)
94 Ibid., pp. 215–17.
95 A record of the experiments on the recoiling of guns is given on pp. 233–9, among the detailed examples of the work.
96 Ibid., pp. 217–19.

finding the pressure of the *Atmosphere*, both in the same place, and places very far removed.

Experiments to determine the possible bounds of expansion, and condensation [i.e. contraction] of the *Air*, by heat and cold, by exhausting and compressing: to determine the strength of *Air* under the several degrees of *rarefaction*, and *condensation* [i.e. compression]: of the force of condens'd [i.e. compressed] *Air* in Wind-Guns: to state the comparative gravity [i.e. relative density] of the *Air* to other fluid, and solid Bodies: . . .

Experiments of the Propagation of Sounds, through common, rarify'd, and condens'd [i.e. compressed] *Air*: of . . . its capacity to penetrate some Bodies, and not others: . . . of the use of *Air* in breathing.

The experiments on respiration included attempts to maintain breathing artificially in animals by the use of bellows,[97] and to revive asphyxiated animals by the same means. Other experiments were made

to try how long a man can live, by expiring, and inspiring again the same *Air*: to try whether the *Air* so respir'd, might not by several means be purify'd, or renew'd: to prove that it is not the heat, nor the cold of this respired *Air*, that choaks.

They tested 'the respiring of *Animals*, in *Air* much rarify'd, and the fatal effects': and recorded 'the quantity of fresh *Air* requisite for the life of a respiring *Animal*, for a certain space of time'. They made air 'unfit for respiration, by satiating it, by suffering Candles, or Coals to burn in it, till they extinguish themselves', and 'of including living *Animals*, and kindled Coals, and Candles, in a large Glass, to observe which of them will be first extinguish'd'; other experiments were on 'the not growing of Seeds for want of *Air*'. They also made tests on 'the resistance of the *Air* to bodies mov'd through it' and to test 'the velocity, and strength of several *Winds*'.

Another important part of their work was to find out 'the substance, and properties of *Water*'.[98] This included experiments on 'the Comparative Gravity [i.e. relative density] of *Salt Water*, and *fresh*, and of several *Medicinal Springs*'; experiments concerning weight—when substances were dissolved in water, or when objects were placed in it; 'of the pressure of the

[97] An account of this work is given by Sprat on p. 232.
[98] Ibid., pp. 219–21.

Water at several depths under its surface', and of changes of temperature at various depths of the sea. Water was tested as a conductor of sound, and for its resistance to 'Bodies mov'd on its surface' and to 'Bodies mov'd through its substance'. Experiments were made on 'the expansion, and condensation [i.e. contraction] of *Water* by heat and cold'. Attempts were made to compress water; its tendency to rise 'in small *Tubes*' was recorded, and its 'being able to penetrate through those Pores, where *Air* will not'. They performed experiments 'of the passing of *Water* through the coats of a Mans stomach: . . . of *Hydrostaticks* . . .: of raising *Water* above its Standard [i.e. level] by sucking:' and many others.

Research was done on metals and minerals,[99] including some very careful and accurate investigations which showed the increase in weight on what was in fact the oxidation of metals;[100] experiments were carried out to test the breaking-point of metals by stretching them with weights, and to test the expansion and contraction of glass; the distillation of coal was a subject of investigation; the extraction of metals from their ores, another; experiments on magnetism were concerned with exploring the field round the magnet.

Many experiments on plant growth were performed,[101] including the growth of plants 'in several kinds of Water; as *River-water, Rain-water, Distill'd-water, May-dew*': and 'of hindring the growth of Seed Corn in the Earth, by extracting the Air: and furthering their growth, by admitting it'. Other experimental work was done on grafting.

Under '*Experiments Medicinal, and Anatomical*'[102] a wide range is indicated:

> as of cutting out the Spleen of a Dog: of the effects of Vipers biting Dogs: of a Camæleon, and its dissection: of preserving *Animals* in Spirit of Wine, Oyl of Turpentine, and other Liquors: of injecting various Liquors, and other Substances, into the veins of several creatures.
>
> *Experiments* of destroying *Mites* by several Fumes: of the equivocal Generation of *Insects*:[103] . . . of making Insects with Cheese, and Sack: . . . of a Spiders not being inchanted by a Circle of *Unicorns-horn*, or *Irish Earth*, laid round about it.[104]

[99] Thomas Sprat, *History*, pp. 221–2. [100] Ibid., pp. 228–9.
[101] Ibid., pp. 222–3. [102] Ibid., p. 223.
[103] See above, p. 87. [104] Above, p. 87.

Experiments . . . with *Florentine* Poyson, and several *Antidotes* against it: of making Flesh grow on, after it has been once cut off: . . . of the reviving of *Animals* strangled, by blowing into their *Lungs*: of Flesh not breeding Worms, when secur'd from Fly-blowings:[105] of the suffocation of *Animals* upon piercing the *Thorax*: . . . of transfusing the blood of one *Animal* into ano ther.

Another course of research was on heat and temperature:[106]

as of freezing: of cold, and heat: of freezing Water freed from Air: of the time, and manner of the contraction in freezing luke-warm Water: of the temperature of several places, by seal'd *Thermometers*; as of several Countries; of the bottoms of deep Mines, Wells, Vaults, on the tops of Hills, at the bottom of the Sea.

Experiments of the contraction of Oyl of *Vitriol*, and divers other Oyls by *freezing*: . . . of shewing Ice to be capable of various degrees of cold, greater than is requisite to keep it Ice: of producing cold by the dissolution of several Salts: . . . of a membranous substance separable from the blood by *freezing*: . . . of making a Standard of Cold by *freezing* distill'd-water [i.e. fixing freezing-point on a thermometer].

Other experiments were to study

Rarity, Density, Gravity [i.e. weight], *Pressure, Levity, Fluidity, Firmness, Congruity, &c.*[107] as of the Nature of *Gravity*: of the cohæsion of two Flat Marbles [i.e. adhesion by air-pressure]: of compressing the Air with *Mercury* to find its spring: of the weights of Bodies, solid and fluid: . . .

and included:

Experiments for examining, whether the gravity of Bodies alter, according as they are carried a good way above, or below the surface of the Earth: . . .

Investigations were made on light,[108] including the refraction of light on passing through water, ice, glass, etc., and on sound:[109]

of Ecchos and reflected *sounds*: of Musical *sounds*, and *Harmonies*: . . . of making a *deaf*, and *dumb* man to speak.

105 Above, p. 87.   106 Thomas Sprat, *History*, p. 224.
107 Ibid., pp. 224-5.   108 Ibid., p. 225.   109 Ibid.

Experiments under the heading 'Motion'[110] included:

of the velocity of the descent of several Bodies of divers fashions through several Liquors: of determining the velocity of Bodies falling through the Air; try'd by many wayes: of the *swift motion* of sounds: . . . of the strength of falling Bodies, according to the several Heights, from which they fall: . . .

Experiments of the swiftness of a Bullet shot with extraordinary Powder: of the best Figure [i.e. shape] of the weight of a *Pendulum* for *Motion*: of the *Motion* of Pendulous Bodies of various figures: to determine the length of *Pendulums*: to find the velocity of the vibrations of a sounding string: to find the velocity of *motion*, propagated by a very long extended Wire: for explaining the inflection of a streight motion into a circular, by a supervening attractive power towards the Center, in order to the explaining of the *motion* of the Planets.

Experiments of the circular and complicated *motion* of *Pendulums*, to explain the *Hypothesis* of the Moons moving about the Earth: of comparing the *Motions* of a circular *Pendulum*, with the *motion* of a streight one: of the propagation of *motion* from one Body to another: . . . of communicating of the strength of Powder for the bending of Springs; . . .

The last group is '*Experiments Chymical, Mechanical, Optical*'.[111] At this point much of the work had already appeared under at least one previous heading, and the mechanical instruments and devices which Fellows 'have either *invented*, or *advanc'd*, for the ease, strength, and direction of their *senses*, in the motions of *Nature*, and *Art*', are listed at length elsewhere;[112] so the examples given in this section are really only an indication of the variety of this wide field.

Sprat goes on to list observations of natural phenomena which, of course, overlap some of the deliberately contrived experimental work.[113]

To their *Experiments* I will subjoin their *Observations*, which differ but in name from the other, the same fidelity, and truth being regarded in collecting them both.

He refers to observations on stars, comets, planets,[114] lightning,

---

[110] Thomas Sprat, *History*, pp. 225–6.   [111] Ibid., pp. 226–7.
[112] Ibid., pp. 246–51.   [113] Ibid., pp. 241–3.
[114] Particular contributions on the moon and the satellites of Jupiter are given by Sprat on pp. 180–9.

atmospheric pressure and its relation to weather conditions,[115] and briefly mentions many others, including:

> on *Mines*, and *Minerals*: on the Concretions of *Wood*, *Plants*, *Shells* and several *Animal* Substances: on the effects of Earthquakes, Fiery Eruptions, and Inundations: on Lakes, Mountains, Damps, subterraneous Fires: on Tides, Currents, and the Depth of the Sea.

Various botanical and zoological studies have been made, such as 'the Anatomy of *Trees*' and the 'Anatomy of *Fishes*', as well as some observations on agricultural practice and problems, such as disease in corn, with suggestions for improvement. In addition Sprat gives a long list of the 'Discourses and Theories'[116] based on their researches, which Fellows had published or read as papers before the Royal Society. This list contains some notable contributions to science, among them Boyle's publications up to this date, including his historic researches on the properties of air, and Willis's brilliant work on the nervous system and the brain.[117] Sprat takes this opportunity to reiterate Bacon's precept on the use of hypothesis:

> In this Collection of their *Discourses*, and *Treatises*, my Reader beholding so many to pass under the name of Hypotheses, may perhaps imagine that this consists not so well with their Method, and with the main purpose of their *Studies*, which I have often repeated to be chiefly bent upon the *Operative*, rather than the *Theoretical Philosophy*. But I hope he will be satisfied, if he shall remember, that I have already remov'd this doubt, by affirming, that whatever *Principles*, and *Speculations* they now raise from things, they do not rely upon them as the absolute end, but only use them as a means of farther *Knowledge*. This way the most speculative *Notions*, and *Theorems* that can be drawn from matter, may conduce to much profit.[118]

Bacon had advocated new sciences, not as an end, but as a means. The Royal Society, putting his vision into practice, consciously began to lay the foundations of new sciences. Its policy

---

[115] A treatise 'Method for making a History of the Weather' is given by Sprat, *History*, pp. 173-8, together with a table 'At one View representing to the Eye the Observations of the Weather for a Month' on p. 179.
[116] Ibid., pp. 254-6.
[117] Below, p. 120.   [118] Thomas Sprat, *History*, p. 257.

was a deliberate and concerted attack on the whole known frontier of natural phenomena.

Its general approach did not consist in any prescribed methods, but, following Bacon's recommendations, constituted a combination of factors, all of importance, and inseparable from one another. This was that the work should be carried out by means of methodical, sustained and comprehensive practical experiment, by men working as a group, as opposed to purely academic, spasmodic or isolated investigations.

Sprat's exposition of the role of the new society is the only comprehensive contemporary account, but his statements are confirmed by independent sources. One is Henry Power, who, with Sir Justinian Isham, became one of the first elected Fellows under the new Charter of 1663. His *Experimental Philosophy*, substantially written by 1 August 1661, was printed, though not published, in 1663.[119] In it he gives details of many observations made with the microscope, and other experiments carried out by him inductively, before he was a Fellow. He comments:

> But these, and a hundred more Experiments of this nature are every day excogitated and tried by our Noble Society of *Gresham-Colledge*,[120] which in a little time will be improved into far nobler Consequences and Theories, than can possibly be done by the single Endevours of any person whatsoever.[121]

Addressing his final chapter to '*the generous* VIRTUOSI, *and Lovers of Experimental Philosophy*', he says:

> You are the enlarged and Elastical Souls of the world, who, removing all former rubbish, and prejudicial resistances, do make way for the Springy Intellect to flye out into its desired Expansion. When I seriously contemplate the freedom of your Spirits, the excellency of your Principles, the vast reach of your Designs, to unriddle all Nature; methinks, you have done more than men already, and may well be placed in a rank Specifically different from the rest of groveling Humanity.

[119] The Preface is dated 1 August 1661, and the date of printing is given on the title pages of the three books in the volume; the publication date, 1664, appears on the general title page of the whole book.
[120] Not Gresham College itself, but the Royal Society which met there. See below, Part Two, Chapter 2.
[121] Henry Power, *Experimental Philosophy*, p. 149.

And this is the Age wherein all mens Souls are in a kind of fermentation and the spirit of Wisdom and Learning begins to mount and free it self from those drossie and terrene Impediments wherewith it hath been so long clogg'd, and from the insipid phlegm and *Caput Mortuum* of useless Notions, in which it hath endured so violent and long a fixation.

This is the Age wherein (me-thinks) Philosophy comes in with a Spring-tide; and the Peripateticks may as well hope to stop the Current of the Tide, or (with *Xerxes*) to fetter the Ocean, as hinder the overflowing of free Philosophy: Me-thinks, I see how all the old Rubbish must be thrown away, and the rotten Buildings be overthrown, and carried away with so powerful an Inundation.

These are the days that must lay a new Foundation of a more magnificent Philosophy, never to be overthrown: that will Empirically and Sensibly canvass the *Phænomena* of Nature, deducing the Causes of things from such Originals in Nature, as we observe are producible by Art, and the infallible demonstration of Mechanicks: and certainly, this is the way, and no other, to build a true and permanent Philosophy: . . .[122]

Power's Fellowship was proposed by John Wilkins on 24 June 1663, and he was elected and admitted at the next meeting of the Royal Society, on 1 July. His book was published in the following year by John Martyn and James Allestry, the official publishers to the Royal Society.

Joseph Glanvill's summing-up, in his *Plus Ultra*, of the Royal Society's intention is also worth quoting at some length. He says that up to Bacon's time the science that

obtained in the *Schools*, was but a *combination* of *general Theories* and *Notions*, that were concluded *rashly*, without *due information* from *particulars*, and spun out into unprofitable *niceties*, that tend to *nothing* but *Dispute* and *Talk*, and were never like to advance any *Works* for the *benefit* and *use* of men.

This being consider'd, the *deep* and *judicious Verulam* made the *complaint*, represented the *defects* and unprofitableness of the *Notional* way, proposed *another* to *reform* and inlarge *Knowledge* by *Observation* and *Experiment*, to *examine* and *record Particulars*, and so to rise by degrees of *Induction* to *general Propositions*, and from *them* to take *direction* for *new Inquiries*, and *more Discoveries*, and other *Axioms*; that our Notions may have a *Foundation* upon which

[122] Henry Power, *Experimental Philosophy*, pp. 191–2.

a *solid Philosophy* may be built, that may be *firm*, *tite*, and close *knit*, and suted to the *Phænomena* of things: So that *Nature* being *known*, it may be *master'd*, *managed*, and *used* in the Services of humane Life.

He goes on:

> This was a *mighty Design* . . . But to the carrying it on, It was necessary there should be many *Heads* and many *Hands*, and *Those* formed into an *Assembly*, that might *intercommunicate* their *Tryals* and *Observations*, that might joyntly *work*, and joyntly *consider*; that so the *improvable* and *luciferous Phænomena*, that lie scatter'd up and down in the *vast Champaign* of *Nature*, might be *aggregated* and brought into a *common* store. This the *Great* Man *desired*, and form'd a *SOCIETY* of *Experimenters* in a *Romantick Model*, but could do no more; His time was not ripe for such Performances.
>
> *These* things therefore were consider'd also by the later *Virtuosi*, who several of them *combined* together, and set themselves on work upon this *grand* Design; in which they have been so happy, as to obtain the *Royal Countenance* and *Establishment* . . .[123]

Glanvill refers to misconceptions about the Society's purpose, and states its ambition, following Bacon, of rebuilding science from the foundations:

> . . . the main *intendment* of this *Society* is to erect a well-grounded *Natural History*.[124]

Like Sprat he rebukes those who ask 'the *captious Question*'— 'What have they done?'

> those . . . do not comprehend the *vastness* of the Work of this *Assembly*, or have some *phantastical Imaginations* of it. They consider not the *Design* is laid as *low* as the *profoundest Depths* of Nature, and reacheth as *high* as the *uppermost Story* of the *Universe*; That it extends to all the *Varieties* of the *great World*, and aims at the benefit of *universal Mankind*. For could they expect that such *mighty Projects* as *these* should *ripen* in a *moment*? Can a *Cedar* shoot up out of the *Earth* like a *blade* of *Grass*?[125]

He says that the work 'must proceed *slowly*, by degrees almost *insensible*', and that in 'so *immense* an Undertaking . . . wherein

[123] Joseph Glanvill, *Plus Ultra*, 1668, pp. 86–8.
[124] Ibid., p. 89.   [125] Ibid., pp. 90–1.

all the generations of Men are concerned' one age can do only a limited amount. The work of his own age 'can be little *more* than to remove the *Rubbish*, lay in *Materials*, and *put* things in *order* for the *Building* . . . We must *seek* and *gather*, *observe* and *examine*, and *lay up* in *Bank* for the Ages that come after'.[126]

Further confirmation of the Royal Society's purpose and policy comes from an anonymous writer, who is defending the Society against Stubbe's attacks on the *History*, and through it on the Society itself. The pamphlet, *A Brief Vindication of the Royal Society*,[127] is evidently by a Fellow, since he speaks as one of them, and is extremely knowledgeable about the Society's affairs. This, too, is produced by one of the Royal Society's official publishers, John Martyn. The writer's intention is, he says, 'in a short Vindication to represent the true End and Work of that Institution'.[128] In one passage he says:

And since they are perswaded with the Excellent Lord *Verulam*, and many other judicious Moderns, that hitherto all sorts of Naturalists have been too hasty in establishing Systems of Natural Philosophy, before they had laid a solid and comprehensive Foundation to build upon; they have esteemed it a laudable and useful Undertaking to endeavour, that all industrious and sagacious Inquirers of Nature every where may conjoyn their Researches, studies, and labours, . . . in order to the composing a faithful History of Nature and Art, that may contain a competent stock of Observations and Experiments, frequently and carefully made by Intelligent and Cautious men, which may serve for a Magazeen of Materials, of which hereafter, by duly considering the whole, and comparing all the parts together, may be raised (if possible) such a Systeme of natural Philosophy, as may give a rational Accompt of the Appearances and Effects of Nature, and enable men to infer from confronted Causes and Effects such consequences, as may conduct to the greater benefit and ampler accommodations of Humane life.[129]

Following Bacon's fundamental belief that the intellectual and the practical must be combined, the Royal Society

---

[126] Joseph Glanvill, *Plus Ultra*, p. 91.
[127] *A Brief Vindication of the Royal Society: from the late Invectives and Misrepresentations of Mr. Henry Stubbe, By a Well-wisher to that Noble Foundation*, London, 1670.
[128] Ibid., p. 2.   [129] Ibid., pp. 3–4.

admitted to its ranks 'all extraordinary men, though but of ordinary Trades [i.e. crafts]'.[130] This means that no one of talent was debarred on social grounds. It does not mean that the Royal Society was largely composed of artisans. On the contrary, the Society acted on Bacon's warning that the artisan was usually intent on his own immediate ends, otherwise the whole aim of the Society would have been defeated. Explaining this, Sprat says:

> The *Tradesmen* themselves, having had their hands directed from their Youth in the same *Methods of Working*, cannot when they pleas so easily alter their custom, and turn themselves into new Rodes of Practice. Besides this they chiefly labor for present livelyhood, and therefore cannot defer their *Expectations* so long, as is commonly requisit for the ripening of any *new Contrivance*. But especially having long handled their *Instruments* in the same fashion, and regarded their *Materials*, with the same thoughts, they are not apt to be surpriz'd much with them, nor to have any extraordinary *Fancies*, or *Raptures* about them.
>
> These are the usual defects of the *Artificers* themselves: Whereas the men of freer lives, have all the contrary advantages . . . They come to try those *operations*, in which they are not very exact, and so will be more frequently subject to commit errors in their proceeding: which very faults, and wandrings will often guid them into new *light*, and new *Conceptions*.[131]

The professional man, particularly the academic, was also inclined towards an habitual mode of thought, said Sprat, and though there were 'very many men of *particular Professions*', in the Society, he indicated his satisfaction that the great majority were men of uncommitted mind, who at the same time had sufficient leisure to devote to serious research: 'yet the farr greater Number are *Gentlemen*, free and unconfin'd'.[132]

Some historians, in the mistaken belief that the scientific revolution in the second half of the seventeenth century was brought about mainly by the practice of artisans, have seen the Royal Society's resolve to renounce 'the luxury and redundance of *speech*'[133] and 'to return back to the primitive purity, and shortness, when men deliver'd so many *things*, almost in an equal number of *words*',[134] as 'the triumph of the standards of

[130] Thomas Sprat, *History*, p. 67.   [131] Ibid., pp. 391–2.
[132] Ibid., pp. 66–9.   [133] Ibid., p. 111.   [134] Ibid., p. 113.

the common man over those of his social superiors'.[135] But here again the source was Bacon himself, and the choice, as he had pointed out, was one of functional necessity. It was not concerned with social attitudes at all. The rejection of 'volubility of *Tongue*'[136] was the rejection of the disputing method of the Aristotelians, the language of 'Wits, or Scholars'[137] in favour of 'Mathematical plainness'.[138] In its functional directness this kind of language resembled that of the practical man—the artisan, the countryman, the merchant[139]—which the Royal Society not surprisingly preferred to the 'amplifications, digressions, and swellings of style'[140] of the pedant.

Sprat rejects equally the sophisticated language of academy, commonwealth and court as unsuitable for the purpose of science. Academic language was verbose and satiated with outworn terms;[141] the language of the commonwealth was too rhetorical, seeking to sway opinions by plausibility;[142] that of courts too ornamental and poetical.[143] The mode the Royal Society adopted was that recommended by Bacon; it was not a literary form, and the Royal Society knew this. In the *History* Sprat says that experimental philosophy will not impair 'the usual *Arts*, whereby we are taught the Purity, and Elegance of *Languages* . . . the same words, and the same waies of Expression will remain'.[144] The only effect on the language, he said, would be an addition to its vocabulary and imagery.[145]

Though the English language may have derived something more from the idiom of science than Sprat predicted, it is not from this source that modern English has taken its character.[146] The prose form which did emerge triumphantly during the second half of the seventeenth century, the style of which Dryden was the great exponent, was not characterized by scientific starkness. Its outstanding quality was not plainness but flexibility: another, and quite distinct, reaction against a previous form—against the weighted splendour of Renaissance prose.

[135] Christopher Hill, *Intellectual Origins of the English Revolution*, Oxford, 1965, p. 130.

[136] Thomas Sprat, *History*, p. 112.   [137] Ibid., p. 113.

[138] Ibid.   [139] Ibid.   [140] Ibid.

[141] Ibid., pp. 15–19.   [142] Ibid., p. 19.   [143] Ibid.

[144] Ibid., p. 324.   [145] Ibid., pp. 413, 415–17.

[146] Christopher Hill assumes that the literary form which emerged at about the same time, derived from the technical idiom of science. (*Intellectual Origins of the English Revolution*, Oxford, 1965, p. 130.)

That new style was the one through which the main-stream of modern English prose was to flow, the style to which Samuel Johnson paid tribute for its clarity, vigour, variety, lightness of touch, ease and grace.[147] Not only was there no fusion into a single form of the language of science and the literary idiom, but the divergence between the two continued to such a degree that they are now often regarded as expressions of two cultures. Sprat himself in the Royal Society's *History* did not employ the style which he recommended to scientists, for the obvious reason that he was writing history, not science.

Bacon's only general recommendation which the Society did not adopt was that the institution should run on public funds. This was not because public money was unwelcome, but because it was not forthcoming; and the originators of the Royal Society held that it was better to make a small start than no start at all.[148]

To Bacon's vision of a new system of Natural Philosophy the Royal Society had given a local habitation and a name. For the first time in history an entire system of science had been inaugurated, whose concept did not embody the fatal seeds of its own ultimate sterility. This was because it depended on no particular theory nor on any individual experimenter, but on the facts of nature itself. It was from these, gradually accumulating in a growing body of related knowledge, that the embryo structure of new sciences had already begun to emerge.

On the immeasurable difference between individual researches, however brilliant, and such sciences, there can be no need to dwell. But while, presumably, agreeing on this point, historians cling to the assumption that this momentous innovation was 'in the air', and came about without any conscious policy or concerted effort. Such a view takes no account of the prevailing petrifaction of the system of natural sciences throughout Europe, and not less in England than elsewhere. Bacon had correctly diagnosed the nature of the disorder as essentially intellectual—one of concept rather than of performance—and this judgment was confirmed in the protracted hostility of the universities towards the Royal Society, which alone put Bacon's vision into action.

[147] Samuel Johnson, *Lives of the English Poets*, ed. George Birkbeck Hill, Oxford, 1905, vol. 1, p. 418 (on John Dryden).
[148] Below, pp. 129-30.

4

THE OXFORD EXPERIMENTAL
SCIENCE CLUB

It is the conscious grasp of the whole problem which sets Bacon apart from his contemporaries, and it is the conscious embodiment of his vision which distinguishes the Royal Society from all earlier societies interested in natural phenomena.

It was just over twenty years after Bacon's death that the insight, leadership and energy necessary to put his plan into action first appeared, with the Oxford experimental science club.

In Sprat's account of the origin of the Royal Society, he explains that it had three phases: 'the *preparation, growth* and *compleat Constitution* of the *Royal Society*'. These 'three Periods of Time', he says, comprise, in the first stage, 'the *first occasions* of this Model'—that is, the meetings at Oxford from about 1648–59 and afterwards for a time in London, until (on 28 November 1660)[1] 'they began to make it a form'd, and *Regular Assembly*'; in the second stage, their efforts 'till they receiv'd the publick assistance of *Royal Authority*'; and in the third stage, 'what they *have done*, since they were made a *Royal Corporation*'.[2]

---

[1] Below, pp. 110, 131.
[2] Thomas Sprat, *History*, p. 52.

Speaking of the preparatory stage at Oxford, Sprat says:

> It may seem perhaps, that . . . I go too far back, and treat of things, that may appear to be of too private, and Domestick concernment, to be spoken in this publick way.[3]

Yet the Royal Society wanted its story told from the beginning, so that posterity might know the originators:

> But if this *Enterprise*, which is now so well establish'd, shall be hereafter advantageous to Mankind (as I make no scruple to foretel, that it will) it is but just, that future times should hear the *names*, of its first *Promoters*: That they may be able to render particular thanks to them, who first conceiv'd it in their minds, and practis'd some little draught of it long ago.[4]

Sprat describes the circumstances in which the new club was conceived. In the person of John Wilkins and in the dissatisfaction which he and other members of the University felt with the prevailing system of natural sciences, it appears that the man and the moment had come together:

> It was therefore, some space after the end of the Civil Wars at *Oxford*, in *Dr. Wilkins* his Lodgings, in *Wadham College*, which was then the place of Resort for Vertuous, and Learned Men, that the first meetings were made, which laid the foundation of all this that follow'd. The *University* had, at that time, many Members of its own, who had begun a *free way* of reasoning; and was also frequented by some *Gentlemen*, of Philosophical Minds, whom the misfortunes of the Kingdom, and the security and ease of a retirement amongst Gown-men, had drawn thither.
>
> Their first purpose was no more, then onely the satisfaction of breathing a freer air, and of conversing in quiet one with another, without being ingag'd in the passions, and madness of that dismal Age . . .
>
> Nor were the good effects of this conversation, onely confin'd to *Oxford*: But they have made themselves known in their printed Works, both in our own, and in the learned Language: which have much conduc'd to the Fame of our Nation *abroad*, and to the spreading of profitable Light, *at home*. This I trust, will be universally acknowledg'd, when I shall have nam'd the Men. The principal, and most constant of them, were Doctor *Seth Ward*, the

3 Thomas Sprat, *History*, p. 52.   4 Ibid., pp. 52–3.

present Lord Bishop of *Exeter*, Mr. *Boyl*, Dr. *Wilkins*, Sir *William Petty*, Mr. *Mathew Wren*, Dr. *Wallis*, Dr. *Goddard*, Dr. *Willis*, Dr. *Bathurst*, Dr. *Christopher Wren*, Mr. *Rook*: besides several others, who joyn'd themselves to them, upon occasions . . .

Their *meetings* were as frequent, as their affairs permitted: their proceedings rather by action, then discourse; cheifly attending some particular Trials, in *Chymistry*, or *Mechanicks*: they had no Rules nor Method fix'd: their intention was more, to communicate to each other, their discoveries, which they could make in so narrow a compass, than an united, constant, or regular inquisition . . .

Thus they continued without any great Intermissions, till about the year 1658. But then being call'd away to several parts of the Nation, and the greatest number of them coming to *London*, they usually met at *Gresham* College, at the *Wednesdays*, and *Thursdays* Lectures of Dr. *Wren*, and Mr. *Rook*: where there joyn'd with them several eminent persons of their common acquaintance: The Lord *Viscount Brouncker*, the now Lord *Brereton*, Sir *Paul Neil*, Mr. *John Evelyn*, Mr. *Henshaw*, Mr. *Slingsby*, Dr. *Timothy Clark*, Dr. *Ent*, Mr. *Ball*, Mr. *Hill*, Dr. *Cro[o]ne*: and divers other Gentlemen, whose inclinations lay the same way. This Custom was observ'd once, if not twice a week, in Term time; till they were scatt'red by the miserable distractions of that Fatal year;[5] . . . For then the place of their meeting was made a *Quarter* for *Soldiers*. But, . . . upon this follow'd the *King's* Return; and . . . the *Royal Society* had its beginning in the wonderful pacifick year, 1660.[6]

Wilkins had a magnetic personality and a stature which attracted others and commanded attention. In addition he possessed outstanding personal courage and a magnanimous disposition. Part of his great contribution, deriving from the

[5] By 'that Fatal year' Sprat of course means 1659, when the Protectorate collapsed. Some historians have supposed that Sprat mistakenly thought 1658 to have been 'that Fatal year', but that is an error due to a misreading of Sprat's text. Following the dispersal of the club from Oxford in 'about the year 1658', Sprat says that the meetings were held 'once, if not twice a week, in Term time' at Gresham College. This cycle of term-time meetings, with vacations coming between, continued 'till', he says, 'they [the club members] were scatt'red by the miserable distractions of that Fatal year;'— that is, towards the end of 1659. 'But', he continues, 'upon this follow'd the *King's* Return', which was of course in the spring of 1660.

[6] Thomas Sprat, *History*, pp. 53–8.

quality of his character, was the generous and unimpassioned liberality which marked the society from the start. A Puritan throughout the Civil War, and married to Cromwell's sister in 1656, at the Restoration he became reconciled with the Royalists. Both as a Puritan cleric, and later, as an Anglican bishop, Wilkins used his powers to temper the authorities towards religious and civil toleration. Walter Pope, Wilkins's half-brother, explaining that his close relationship to Wilkins prevents him from saying much in praise of a man who was, in any case, 'so well known', says:

> therefore I shall say no more of him at present, but that he was a Learned Man, and a Lover of such; he was of a Comely Aspect, and Gentleman-like Behavior; . . . He had nothing of Bigottry, Unmannerliness, or Censoriousness, which were then in the *Zenith*, amongst some of the Heads, and Fellows of Colleges in *Oxford*. For which Reason many Country Gentlemen, of all Persuasions, but especially those then stiled Cavaliers and Malignants, for adhering to the King and the Church, sent their Sons to that College [Wadham] that they might be under his Government. I shall instance[7] but in two eminent Sufferers for that Cause, Colonel *Penruddoc* who was murder'd at *Exeter*, and Judge Jenkyns, who was kept a close Prisoner till the Kings Return, for not owning the Parliaments usurp'd Authority, these two had their Sons there.[8]

Seth Ward, ejected from his Fellowship at Sidney Sussex College, Cambridge, for refusing to take the Covenant, had been elected Savilian Professor of Astronomy at Oxford in 1649. He chose to enter Wadham, 'invited thereto by the Fame of Dr. *Wilkins* Warden thereof'.[9] The next year Laurence Rooke, who later became a Gresham College Professor of Astronomy and then of Geometry, took up residence at Wadham. Anthony Wood recalls that 'being much addicted to experimental Philosophy, he retired to *Wadham* College in 1650 for the sake of Dr. *Wilkins* Warden, and of Dr. *Ward* Astronomy Professor'.[10]

[7] By a misprint this word appears as 'instant'.
[8] Walter Pope, *The Life of the Right Reverend Father in God, Seth, Lord Bishop of Salisbury*, London, 1697, pp. 27–8.
[9] Ibid., pp. 15–16.
[10] Anthony Wood, *Athenae Oxonienses*, 1721, vol. II, p. 297.

Christopher Wren had entered Wadham in 1649,[11] when he was nearly seventeen, and under Wilkins's auspices had found the means to stimulate and develop his natural inventiveness. It was through Wilkins that Robert Boyle joined the group, five or six years after its formation. Wilkins pressed Boyle to come to Oxford, saying, '. . . you will be a means to quicken and direct us in our enquiries', and added, 'I . . . shall be most ready to provide the best accommodations for you, that this place will afford'.[12]

Although Wilkins possessed 'a very mechanical head',[13] and took an active part in the club's experimental work, his real contribution was not as a scientist, but as an intellectual leader of great perception and determination. Like Francis Bacon, he had a remarkable sense of direction, and an integrating vision which enabled him to engage the problem as a whole. Like Bacon, Wilkins also had the necessary intellectual energy to discard a traditional mode of thought and to confront what was unfamiliar and difficult; and in action he had the tenacity of purpose to stay a long course in the face of continual opposition.

In 1638, at the age of twenty-six, he had published *The Discovery of a World in the Moone* in which he discussed the physical nature of the moon, and incidentally gave it as his opinion that man might eventually reach it. In his second edition, which came out two years later, he expanded this point.[14] After considering what he believed to be some of the probable obstacles to such a flight—for example man's weight, and the low temperature and rare atmosphere of the upper regions—he thought that given sufficient 'motive faculty' to carry the vehicle beyond the sphere of the earth's attraction, 'tis possible for some of our posteritie, to find out a conveyance to this other world'.

In the Epistle to the Reader in the original edition, repeated in the second, he said:

It is my desire that by the occasion of this discourse, I may raise up some more active spirit to a search after other hidden and

---

[11] Wadham College Register.
[12] Robert Boyle, *Works*, ed. Thomas Birch, 1744, vol. V, pp. 629–30.
[13] Bodleian Library MS. Aubrey 6, fol. 92ʳ (and John Aubrey, *Brief Lives*, ed. Andrew Clark, vol. II, p. 299).
[14] John Wilkins, *The Discovery of a New World*, London, 1640, pp. 203–42.

unknowne truths. Since it must needes be a great impediment unto the growth of sciences, for men still so to plod on upon beaten
principles, as to be afraid of entertaining any thing that may seeme
to contradict them. An unwillingnesse to take such things into
examination, is one of those errours of learning in these times
observed by the judicious *Verulam*. Questionlesse, there are many
secret truths, which the ancients have passed over, that are yet
left to make some of our age famous for their discovery.

He knew that prejudice dies hard; that the human mind tends
to accept what is familiar and easy, even when this is demon-
strably inaccurate or incomplete, rather than make the
strenuous mental effort necessary to reach a more satisfactory
view:

> Things are very hardly received which are altogether strange to
> our thoughts and our senses. The soule may with lesse difficulty
> be brought to beleeve any absurdity, when as it has formerly
> beene acquainted with some colours and probabilities for it; but
> when a new, and an unheard of truth shall come before it,
> though it have good grounds and reasons, yet the understanding
> is afraid of it as a stranger, and dares not admit it into his beleefe,
> without a great deale of reluctancie and triall. And besides,
> things that are not manifested to the senses, are not assented unto
> without some labour of minde, some travaile and discourse of the
> understanding; and many lazie soules had rather quietly repose
> themselves in an easie errour, than take paines to search out the
> truth.[15]

Wilkins admitted the greatness of Aristotle's achievement, but
deplored the mental lethargy of later ages which were un-
willing to make their own contribution to knowledge:

> I thinke the world is much beholden to him [Aristotle] for all its
> sciences. But yet 'twere a shame for these later ages to rest our
> selves meerely upon the labours of our Fore-fathers, as if they had
> informed us of all things to be knowne, and when we are set upon
> their shoulders, not to see further than they themselves did.
> 'Twere a superstitious, a lazie opinion to think *Aristotles* works the
> bounds and limits of all humane invention, beyond which there
> could be no possibility of reaching. Certainely there are yet many

[15] John Wilkins, *The Discovery of a New World*, pp. 17–18.

things left to discovery, and it cannot be any inconvenience for us, to maintaine a new truth or rectifie an ancient errour.[16]

He believed that his contemporaries were on the edge of discoveries not fully to be realized in their generation; that it was the way of Providence 'not presently to shew us all, but to leade us on by degrees', and that

> Time will come, when the indeavors of after ages, shall bring such things to light as now lie hid in obscuritie. Arts are not yet come to their solstice. But the industrie of future times, assisted with the labors of their forefathers, may reach that height which wee could not attaine to.[17]

Wilkins here shows, ten years before it was to bear fruit in practice at Oxford, the quality of mind which was to be a vital element in the conception and definition of the Royal Society. Having seen the whole scope of the problem, at Oxford he found the milieu, and himself provided the leadership, necessary to give it focus and body.

The statement in the *History* that the 'first *Elements*, on which the *Royal Society* arose, and supported its beginnings'[18] were the meetings at Oxford, is solidly confirmed by contemporary evidence and opinion, which also reinforce the *History*'s implication that John Wilkins was the personality at their centre.

John Evelyn was in close touch with the Oxford experimenters, and, though a Royalist, was a friend and admirer of the Parliamentarian Wilkins. He became a foundation member of the Royal Society and was nominated one of its first Council by Charles II. It was Evelyn who suggested the title 'Royal Society', which was assumed at the time of its incorporation.[19] Under 6 January 1660/61 he recorded in his diary that he was a member of this

> assembly of divers learned Gent: It being the first meeting since

[16] John Wilkins, *The Discovery of a New World*, pp. 27–8.

[17] Ibid., pp. 203–4. This passage, like the others quoted from this book, appears in the text of the first edition (under the title *The Discovery of a World in the Moone*), published two years earlier, in 1638. The second edition has been used here for the advantage of its slightly revised punctuation, which is more familiar to the modern reader.

[18] Thomas Sprat, *History*, p. 124.

[19] *The Diary of John Evelyn*, ed. E. S. De Beer, London, 1955, vol. III, p. 306.

the returne of his *Majestie* in *Lond*: but begun some years before at *Oxford*, & interruptedly here in *Lond*: during the Rebellion.[20]

In a letter to Dr. William Wotton, dated 30 March 1696, Evelyn again mentions the origin of the Royal Society, in answer to an inquiry about the life of Boyle, on which Wotton was working. Evelyn says:

> Now as he [Boyle] had an early inclination to learning (so especially to that part of philosophy he so happily succeeded in), he often honour'd Oxford, and those gentlemen there, with his company, who more peculiarly applied themselves to the examination of the so long domineering methods & jargon of the scholes. You have the names of the learned junto, most of them since deservedly dignified in that elegant History of the Royal Society, which must ever owne its rise from that assembly . . .[21]

On 12 September 1703 Evelyn gave Wotton further details of 'the famous assemblage of virtuosi at Oxford'. He listed some of the chief members, recalling that Edmund Dickenson[22] of Merton had also been a member, and concluding emphatically:

> . . . and especially Dr. Wilkins (since Bishop of Chester): the head of Wadham Coll: where these and other ingenious persons used to meete to promote the study of the new philosophy which has since obtained.[23]

Another familiar of the group, John Aubrey, also affirms that the Royal Society originated in the Oxford club, and that Wilkins, following his intellectual exemplar Francis Bacon, was its leader. Aubrey says:

> The beginning of Philosophical Experiments was at Oxon 1649, by Dr. Wilkins, Seth Ward, Ralph Bathurst &c.[24]

and:

> He [Wilkins] was the principall Reviver of Experimentall Philosophy (secundum mentem Domini Baconi) at Oxford,—

[20] *The Diary of John Evelyn*, ed. E. S. De Beer, London, 1955, vol. III, p. 266.
[21] *The Diary and Correspondence of John Evelyn*, ed. William Bray, London, 1906, vol. III, p. 481.
[22] See Joseph Foster, *Alumni Oxonienses 1500–1714*, vol. I, p. 401.
[23] *The Diary and Correspondence of John Evelyn*, ed. William Bray, London, 1906, vol. IV, pp. 33–4.
[24] Bodleian Library MS. Aubrey 6, fol. 87^r [marginal note] and John Aubrey, *Brief Lives*, ed. Andrew Clark, 1898, vol. II, p. 288.

where he had weekely an experimentall philosophicall Clubbe: wch began 1649. and was the Incunabula of the Royall Society. When he came to London they mett at ye Bullhead taverne in Cheapside (e.g. 1658, 1659, and after); till it grew to big for a Clubb, and so they came to Gresham Colledge Parlour.[25]

The first Secretary and tireless promoter of Royal Society interests, Henry Oldenburg, speaking from his own knowledge of the Oxford club, referred to its vitality, calling it 'the *Oxonian Sparkles*'. He further identified it by saying:

I mean, that Meeting, which may be called the *Embryo* or First Conception of the *Royal Society*: . . .[26]

Gilbert Burnet, through Sir Robert Moray, his 'second father',[27] who sponsored his election as a Fellow, was very close to the centre of things when the Society was emending the form of its incorporation by Royal Charter in 1663. Writing about the period which immediately preceded this, when the Society was establishing itself in London after leaving Oxford, Burnet said:

And the meetings that Wilkins had begun at Oxford were now held in London to such a degree, that the king himself encouraged them much, and many experiments were made before him . . .[28]

Wilkins may justly be called the architect of the Royal Society, for he was not only the pivot of the Oxford club; he was instrumental in achieving its metamorphosis. In 1653 he had given £200 towards a College for Experiments and Mechanics to be set up over the Examination Schools or long gallery of the University.[29] It is unlikely that this plan was ever

[25] Bodleian Library MS. Aubrey 6, fol. 92ᵛ (and John Aubrey, *Brief Lives*, ed. Andrew Clark, vol. II, p. 300).
[26] *Philosophical Transactions*, London, March 1668/9, Dedication (see below, pp. 115–16 and note 60). Oldenburg became a member of Oxford University in June 1656 (Anthony Wood, *Fasti Oxonienses*, 1691–2, vol. II, 729). He was still at Oxford on 15 April 1657 (Boyle, *Works*, V, p. 299) when he was acting as tutor to Boyle's nephew, Richard Jones.
[27] Gilbert Burnet, *The History of My Own Time*, ed. Osmund Airy, Oxford, 1897 and 1900, vol. I, p. 533.
[28] Ibid., p. 342.
[29] Published, from a private collection of Samuel Hartlib's manuscript papers, by Professor G. H. Turnbull, *Notes and Records of the Royal Society of London*, vol. 10, no. 2, p. 114, 1953. See also below, p. 113 and note 48.

realized, for in 1657 he was still intent on founding a 'Chymico-Mathematico-Mechanical School'.[30] About a year later the Oxford club, with additional members, reassembled in London. There, at its meeting on 28 November 1660, 'Something was offered about a designe of founding a Colledge for the Promoting of Physico-Mathematicall, Experimentall Learning', and under Wilkins's chairmanship it was decided formally to inaugurate a society 'for the promoting of Experimentall Philosophy'.[31] The Royal Society proper, in fact if not in name, dates from this meeting.

Wilkins's career, like that of Seth Ward and very many others, reflected the political flux of his time. Although both later became Anglican bishops, in their Oxford days they incurred the disapproval of 'peevish People', and were publicly preached at from the pulpit of the University church.[32] Walter Pope, recalling this embarrassment, impartially remarks, 'Dr. *Ward* rid out this Storm, but Dr. *Wilkins* put into the Port of Matrimony, marrying the Protectors Sister'. Pope adds laconically, 'but after the Kings Return, it was for a while a Spoke in his Cart'.[33] It was doubtless this obstacle which prevented Wilkins from becoming President when the Society was formally constituted with Charles II's approval. Royal support for the Society was negotiated by Sir Robert Moray, a Royalist who had followed Charles into exile.[34]

Seth Ward, who had found refuge at Oxford, was also in trouble at the Restoration. Only recently elected President of Trinity College, he felt obliged to resign. Walter Pope, his great friend said:

> . . . he left *Trinity College*, and *Oxford* . . . with an unwilling willingness, for he was contented with his Condition, and so pleas'd with a Collegial Life, and the Charms of that sweet place, that he would willingly have remain'd there the rest of his days . . .[35]

---

[30] Robert Boyle, *Works*, ed. Thomas Birch, 1744, vol. V, p. 397. By a slip Evelyn calls Wilkins 'Wilkinson'. For further correspondence on this proposition, see *The Diary and Correspondence of John Evelyn*, ed. William Bray, 1906, vol. IV, p. 32.

[31] Journal Book of the Royal Society, vol. I, p. 1.

[32] Walter Pope, *Life of Seth, Lord Bishop of Salisbury*, p. 43.

[33] Ibid., p. 45.

[34] Below, pp. 131, 139, 140–1.

[35] Walter Pope, *Life of Seth, Lord Bishop of Salisbury*, p. 48.

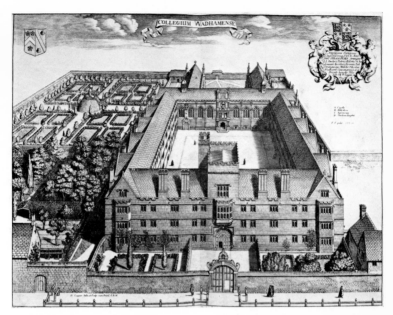

5. Meeting places of the Oxford experimental science club.
Top. Wadham College, Oxford, where the club met in the Lodgings of
the Master, John Wilkins. *By courtesy of the Bodleian Library, Oxford.*
Bottom left. Buckley Hall, in the High Street, Oxford (from the south).
The doors shown inside the entry, on the right, opened into the house
(now 106 High Street) where the club met in William Petty's lodgings.
By courtesy of the Bodleian Library, Oxford.
Bottom right. Deep Hall, in the High Street, Oxford (small gabled house on
the left), where the club met in Robert Boyle's lodgings. The house was
demolished in 1810. *By courtesy of the Museum of the History of Science, Oxford.*

Octob. 23. 1651.

Ordered

1. That no man be admitted but by the consent of the major pt of the company.

2. That the votes for admission (to the intent they may be free, & about physicia) be given in present, affirmations by blanks, negatives by black papers, put into the box.

3. That every mans admission be proposed & concluded the same day after it is proposed, so as at the passing of it there be at the least eleven present.

4. That every one pay for his admission an equall share in money, and two third parts for the instruments in stock, answerable to the number of the company.

5. If any of the company (being resident in the Univ^ty) do willingly absent himself from the weekly meeting without speciall occasion, by the space of six weeks together, he shall be reputed to have left the company & his name from thenceforth to be left out of the catalogue.

6. That if any man does not duly upon the day appointed perform such exercise or in such experiments as shall be appointed for that day or in case of weary attendance provide that course be supplyed by another. He shall ... to the use of the company for his default 2s. 6d. & shall perform his task notwithstanding within such reasonable time as the company shall appoint.

6. Rules of the Oxford experimental science club, dated 23 October 1651, written in the hand of Gerard Langbaine, then Provost of The Queen's College, Oxford. *By courtesy of the Bodleian Library, Oxford.*

But Pope (a Wadham man himself) viewing this episode philosophically, could not resist a playful dig at Trinity. He said that for Seth Ward the change

> ... turn'd ... not only to his private Emolument, but to the public good also: For had he kept that Headship, I mean been buried alive in *Trinity College*, hiding his glorious Light under that Bushel, *Exeter* and *Salisbury* could not have boasted of so good a Bishop ...[36]

In explaining the policy of the Royal Society, Sprat had pointed out that its ultimate value could not be estimated merely in terms of its practical achievement in the first few years, considerable though that was, and this criterion applies even more to the pioneer work at Oxford. Not only were the Oxford men innovators; they were fully conscious of their role. They knew that they had taken on themselves 'the first *drudgery* and *burden* of *Observation*, which is needful for the *Beginning* of so difficult a work'.[37] As Seth Ward said at the time, '... the paines is great, the reward but slender'.[38] The work at this preparatory stage, made more arduous by the difficulties of the times, was necessarily on a modest scale. Sprat says that they could do little more than communicate to each other what they had discovered 'in so narrow a compass'.[39]

Although, as the work progressed, some members of the group revealed a greater faculty for research than others, and though particular names were necessarily attached to outstanding discoveries, the essential nature of the undertaking was corporate, 'a conjunction of both Purses and endeavours'.[40]

On 23 October 1651 the Oxford club regulated its meetings to increase its efficiency. Its list of eight rules[41] concerns such matters as admission to membership, contributions towards instruments, and fines for failure to carry out experiments according to a rota. The time of meeting was to be 'every Thursday before two of the clock'. But it was not rigidly organized. A member could 'willingly absent himself from the

---

[36] Walter Pope, *Life of Seth, Lord Bishop of Salisbury*, p. 49.
[37] Thomas Sprat, *History*, p. 7.
[38] *Vindiciae Academiarum*, Oxford, 1654, p. 50. See above, pp. 64-7, for an account of this publication.
[39] Thomas Sprat, *History*, p. 56; and above, p. 103.
[40] *Vindiciae Academiarum*, p. 35; and below, p. 113.
[41] Bodleian Library MS. Ashmole 1810.

E

weekly meeting without speciall occasion, by the space of six weeks, together' before his name was 'left out of the Catalogue', and then the order was to take effect only if he were resident in the University. There were no rules about the conduct of the work itself.

Comparison with other manuscripts shows that this list was written by Gerard Langbaine, at that time Provost of The Queen's College, Oxford.[42] The discovery of this document, lightly stuck inside the first volume of the Minute Book of the Oxford Philosophical Society, which was founded in 1683, has led, from the nineteenth century onwards, to some unfounded assumptions.[43]

By February 1652 the Oxford club consisted of 'about 30 persons'. Writing from Wadham College on 27 February, Seth Ward gave this information to Sir Justinian Isham, together with further details.[44] Within the club was a group of eight members which had chosen to make chemical experiments its particular concern. An arrangement had been made whereby each person in turn took charge of the experiments for a week at a time.

> Besides this Greate Clubb we have a combination of a lesser number viz: of 8 persons who have joyned together for the furnishing an elaboratory and for makeing chymicall experiments wch we doe constantly every one of us in course undertakeing by weeks to manage the worke.

On the same occasion Seth Ward defined their general aim. It was, he said,

> according to our opportunityes to make inquisitive experiments, the end is that out of a sufficient number of sure[45] experiments, the way of nature in working may be discovered.

Ward also said that the club wanted to compile an index of publications on discoveries made by earlier experimenters, so

---

[42] Comparison with Bodleian Library MS. Ballard 11, fol. 23, for example, proves this conclusively.   [43] Below, pp. 126–7.

[44] The text of this letter is published in *Notes and Records of the Royal Society of London*, vol. 7, no. 1, pp. 69–70, 1950. See also below, p. 122. The manuscript is now with the Northamptonshire Record Society.

[45] The published text (above, note 44) gives 'such', but as the late Professor G. H. Turnbull pointed out in *Notes and Records of the Royal Society of London*, vol. 10, no. 2, p. 113, 1953, the correct reading is 'sure'.

that as the occasion arose, reference could easily be made to a given subject.[46] At the same time a list could be made of 'those wch are still inquirenda'. For this purpose the group had begun to catalogue the books in the Bodleian Library, 'everyone takeing his part'.

In 1654 Seth Ward made public reference to the club in declaring that Aristotelianism[47] was being combated in the approach to science at Oxford University:

Chymistry you know is not neglected here, there being a conjunction of both Purses and endeavours of severall persons towards discoveries of that kind, such as may serve either to the discovery of light or profit, either to Natural Philosophy or Physic [i.e. Medicine] . . . The practice of Physic hath been bottomed upon experience and observation . . . I have formerly given some intimation of our Chymical Society, so that I hope it will be charitably concluded that we are not ignorant of those hypostaticall principles . . . Magneticall Philosophy is not neglected here . . . and . . . it is a reall designe amongst us, wanting only some assistance for execution, to erect a Magneticall, Mechanicall, and Optick Schoole,[48] furnished with the best Instruments, and Adapted for the most usefull experiments in all those faculties.[49]

Robert Hooke, who had worked with some of the members, affirms the practical, informal nature of their researches. The

[46] This was attempted again, by the Royal Society proper. In the *History*, p. 252, Sprat says:

Having well succeeded in this their purpose of *collecting* divers patterns of all *Natural*, and *Artificial* things: they have also (amongst others) appointed a *Committee*, whose chief employment shall be to read over whatever *Books* have been written on such subjects. By this means they hope speedily to observe, and digest into *Manuscript volumes*, all that has been hitherto try'd, or propounded in such studies. This is the only help that an *Experimenter* can receive from *Books*: which he may still use, as his *Guides*, though not as his *Masters*. For this end they have begun a *Library* consisting only of such *Authors*, as may be serviceable to their *Design*.

For a further reference to cataloguing by the Oxford club, see below, pp. 121 ff.

[47] For his refutation of Aristotelianism, see above, pp. 64–7.

[48] The plan mentioned here is probably Wilkins's proposed College for Experiments and Mechanics (above, p. 109).

[49] *Vindiciae Academiarum*, Oxford, 1654, pp. 35–6.

following account was found by Richard Waller, then Secretary of the Royal Society, among Hooke's manuscripts before the publication in 1705 of his posthumous works. Speaking of the 'philosophical meetings' at Oxford, Hooke says:

> At these Meetings, which were about the Year 1655 (before which time I knew little of them) divers Experiments were suggested, discours'd and try'd with various successes, tho' no other account was taken of them but what particular Persons perhaps did for the help of their own Memories; so that many excellent things have been lost, some few only by the kindness of the Authors have been since made publick; among these may be reckon'd the Honourable Mr. *Boyle's Pneumatick Engine* and Experiments, first printed in the Year 1660.[50]

Another reference to the nature of the work done by the Oxford experimental science club, while it was actually going on, was made by Matthew Wren, a cousin of Sir Christopher Wren, in *Monarchy Asserted or the State of the Monarchicall & Popular Government*, published at Oxford in 1659. In the dedication to Wilkins, Matthew Wren explains that he is answering an oblique attack on the virtuosi in general and on Wilkins in particular. This attack had been made during the previous year by James Harrington,[51] who thought that a challenge to his *Commonwealth of Oceana*,[52] published anonymously by Wren in 1657,[53] had been sponsored by the whole group of virtuosi inspired by Wilkins, and that all were members of the University.

Wren explains that he is not a member of the University,[54] though he is proud to belong to the group led by Wilkins. He says:

> We are to understand that a Gentleman in the *University* who is

[50] Robert Hooke, *Posthumous Works*, ed. Richard Waller, London, 1705, p. iii.

[51] James Harrington, *The Prerogative of Popular Government*, London, 1658.

[52] James Harrington, *The Commonwealth of Oceana*, London, 1656.

[53] Matthew Wren, *Considerations on Mr. Harrington's commonwealth of Oceana: restrained to the first part of the preliminaries*, London, 1657.

[54] He was a Cambridge (Peterhouse) man. Anthony Wood (*Fasti Oxonienses*, vol. II, 819) explains his position at Oxford: 'This person . . . was originally a Student in Cambridge, and afterwards a Student for several years (in the time of Usurpation) in this University, not in a Coll. or Hall, but in a private House'.

both a Divine, A Doctor, an head of a College, and a Mathematician, has the Satisfaction to see frequently at his Lodging an assembly of Men who are known both at home and abroad to be of the most learned persons of this Age; The imployment of this Company is by making Experiments and by communicating their Observations to carry on a discovery of Nature.[55]

Information on the work done at Oxford is fragmentary, but from various sources it is possible to gain a good idea of the range and resourcefulness of the club's activities. Evelyn mentions the collection of instruments and apparatus in the gallery and Warden's Lodgings 'at Dr. *Wilkins's*, at Waddum', where most of the exhibits belonged to Wilkins '& that prodigious young Scholar, Mr. *Chr: Wren*'.[56] Wilkins and Wren also worked together in constructing a telescope eighty feet long, 'to see at once the whole moon'.[57]

Seth Ward did much to improve telescopes, and carried out many experiments with them. We have his own word for it that in February 1652, while a member of the club, he was 'building a slight observatory' and 'procuring and fitting Telescopes and other instruments for observation'.[58] This work gave rise to his theory of planetary motion, which he published, first at Oxford, and later, more fully, in London.[59] Although this work was done, in the first place, in his capacity as Professor of Astronomy, his professional work, like that of other members of the club, enriched the common stock of their knowledge, while gaining reciprocally from the work of the club. Oldenburg refers to this in dedicating the fourth volume of the *Philosophical Transactions* of the Royal Society to Seth Ward in 1669. Mentioning the time, about fifteen or sixteen years before, when Ward 'Geometrized *Astronomy*' and 'added Life to the *Oxonian* Sparkles . . . that Meeting, which may be called the Embryo or First Conception of the *Royal Society*: . . .'

---

[55] Matthew Wren, *Monarchy Asserted or The State of Monarchicall & Popular Government*, The Preface to the Reader, Oxford, 1659.
[56] *The Diary of John Evelyn*, ed. E. S. De Beer, vol. III, pp. 110–11.
[57] G. H. Turnbull, *Notes and Records of the Royal Society of London*, vol. 10, no. 2, p. 116, 1953.
[58] He referred to this in his letter to Sir Justinian Isham, above, p. 112, note 44.
[59] Seth Ward, *In Ismaelis Bullialdi Astronomiae Philolaicae Fundamenta Inquisitio Brevis*, Oxford, 1653; and *Astronomia Geometrica*, London, 1656.

Oldenburg goes on to speak of Ward's contribution, 'both by your own private studies, and in Juncture with the said *Society* since its *Institution*'.[60]

Walter Charleton, a former pupil of Wilkins,[61] writing during the period of the Oxford club, and carried away by admiration for Ward's *Astronomia Geometrica*, rather headily assigns him the role of a Copernicus. Charleton says:

> . . . were I worthy to have this Gentlemans Picture in my study, I should desire to have it drawne in this manner. I would have *Hipparchus*, *Ptolemy*, and *Tycho*, standing in a triangle, and supporting the whole Cœlestial Machine on their heads; on one side, *Copernicus* turning all the Orbs about with his right hand; and this *Heros* on the other side, with a Table in his left hand containing the Figures in *Euclids* Elements, and with the Forefinger of his right, pointing to the Planetary Spheres, as demonstrating the theory of their Motions by the maxims of Geometry.[62]

Besides achieving a great improvement in '*Optick Tubes*, or *Telescopes*', the club possessed '*Microscopes*, that magnify the dimensions of minute and otherwise undiscernable bodies, even to an incredible rate, and bring the sight to a familiar acquaintance with the shapes of not only whole small Flies and other Insects, but also of the smallest part of them'.[63] This provoked the jibe by James Harrington, that the Oxonians were 'good at two Things, at diminishing a Commonwealth and at Multiplying a Louse'.[64] In repudiating this charge Matthew Wren denied that their purpose was to examine the 'little Animals'. It was an experiment in measurement, 'a limbe of Mathematiques'.[65] Collation of the references to these experiments reveals that the author of them was Christopher Wren, and that his drawing of magnified flies, fleas and lice were 'seen with Delight and Instruction by all Strangers; and not

[60] *Philosophical Transactions*, London, March 1668/9, Dedication. This dedication is missing from some copies.

[61] Anthony Wood, *Athenae Oxonienses*, 1721, vol. II, p. 1112.

[62] W. Charleton, *The Immortality of the Human Soul, Demonstrated by the Light of Nature*, London, 5167, pp. 43-4.

[63] Ibid., pp. 47-8.

[64] James Harrington, *The Prerogative of Popular Government*, London, 1658, The Epistle Dedicatory. See above, p. 114, for Matthew Wren's answer to Harrington's *Commonwealth of Oceana*.

[65] Matthew Wren, *Monarchy Asserted*, 1659, The Preface to the Reader.

only so, but have been received with applause by Foreign Princes'.[66]

Christopher Wren's genius as an architect is widely recognized. It is less well known that had he not found his *métier* in this medium with the great opportunities offered by the rebuilding of the City after the Fire of London, he might well have made scientific research his life-work. So outstanding was he as an originator that in the *History* Sprat pays him the unique compliment of naming him and of listing his many discoveries 'on the meer consideration of Justice'. One is of particular interest. Sprat says:

> *He* was the first Author of the Noble *Anatomical Experiment* of *Injecting Liquors into the Veins of Animals.* An *Experiment* now vulgarly known; but long since exhibited to the Meetings at *Oxford* . . . By this *Operation* divers Creatures were immediately purg'd, vomited, intoxicated, kill'd or reviv'd, according to the quality of the Liquor injected: Hence arose many new *Experiments,* and chiefly that of *Transfusing Blood,* which the *Society* has prosecuted in sundry Instances, that will probably end in extraordinary Success.[67]

Boyle and Oldenburg, on separate occasions, also confirmed that the credit for initiating this research belonged to Wren.[68]

Another member of the Oxford club with an 'admirable Inventive head, and practicall parts',[69] William Petty, is now

---

[66] Matthew Wren, *Monarchy Asserted,* 1659. Matthew Wren said on the same occasion:

> The pictures of these Animals in that enlarged proportion which the Glass represents them in are drawn by a Mathematician, a member of this Assembly, who has invented a way to measure the apparent magnitude of them . . .

In his 'Ephemerides' of 1655 Hartlib records that Mercator told him that Christopher Wren had 'brought a great perfection into microscopes to make them multiply exceedingly and geometrically to measure the things in them'. (G. H. Turnbull, *Notes and Records of the Royal Society of London,* vol. 10, no. 2, p. 112.)

[67] Thomas Sprat, *History,* p. 317.

[68] *Philosophical Transactions,* 1665, pp. 128–30; and Robert Boyle, *Some Considerations touching the Usefulnesse of Experimental Naturall Philosophy,* Oxford, 1663, Part II, Essay II, Postscript, pp. 62–3. Further evidence on this point is given in *Parentalia,* ed. Stephen Wren, 1750, pp. 231–2.

[69] Bodleian Library MS. Aubrey 6, fol. 14ᵛ (and John Aubrey, *Brief Lives,* ed. Andrew Clark, vol. II, p. 144).

chiefly remembered as the pioneer of political economy, which involved the application of scientific principles to a contiguous field of knowledge, as envisaged by Bacon.[70]

Petty's time with the club was short, and little evidence of his actual work survives, but his impact was powerful, and continued to bear fruit long after he had left Oxford. In 1649 he had 'entred himselfe of Brasen-nose Coll:' where with characteristic energy he revolutionized the teaching of anatomy.[71] Anthony Wood says that he was created a Doctor of Physic by the University Delegates early in 1650 because they 'had received sufficient testimony of *his rare qualities* and gifts'.[72] At about the same time he was made a Fellow of Brasenose College. Thomas Hearne, who considered the replacement of 'Loyal Persons' deplorable, implies that Petty's only qualifications were that he had 'studied Physick, cut up doggs and taught Anatomy in the War';[73] but in less than a year he was unanimously elected to the University Chair of Anatomy.[74] In 1652 he left for Ireland, where he was Physician-General to the Army. While there, Petty guided Boyle in his researches before he joined the Oxford club.[75]

It was at Petty's lodgings in an apothecary's house that the club met for a time, 'because of the convenience of inspecting Drugs, and the like',[76] soon after its establishment at Wadham. After Petty had left Oxford the meetings reverted to Wadham, where they were held for most of the club's total existence.

The house where Petty lodged was evidently convenient for practical experiments, including anatomy, as it was here that a woman's body was brought for dissection after she had been hanged 'on Oxford Gallowes' in December 1650. An anatomy lecture was to have been read over her 'being usual upon the

[70] Above, pp. 50–1 and note 122.
[71] Bodleian Library 175 Aubrey 6, fol. 13ʳ (and John Aubrey, *Brief Lives*, vol. II, p. 141).
[72] Anthony Wood, *Fasti Oxonienses*, 1691–2, vol. II, 770. This was on 7 March 1649/50 (Joseph Foster, *Alumni Oxonienses*, Oxford, 1891, vol. III, p. 1153).
[73] Bodleian Library MS. Hearne's Diaries 5, p. 106 (and Thomas Hearne, *Remarks and Collections*, ed. C. E. Doble and H. E. Salter, Oxford, 1885, vol. I, p. 78).
[74] Anthony Wood, *Athenae Oxonienses*, 1691–2, vol. II, 610.
[75] Robert Boyle, *Works*, 1744, vol. V, p. 242.
[76] Below, pp. 167.

anatomising of either man or woman', but to the astonishment of all those present, which included a group of physicians, she began to breathe. Petty applied various remedies, some of which she might better have been without, and she recovered completely.[77] This episode appears to have enhanced Petty's professional reputation, as there is frequent mention of it in contemporary sources.

It has not before been known where this meeting-place of the Oxford club was. John Wallis had said that it was in an apothecary's house.[78] Anthony Wood mentioned it in his *History and Antiquities of Oxford*, which was published posthumously in 1796, but the reference there does not make sense. The text represents Wood as saying, 'Their meetings were at Mr. Pettie's Lodgings in an Apothecary's house against [i.e. opposite] All Souls'. The footnote to this gives it as 'John Clerk Apoth. at Buckley Hall'.[79] But Buckley Hall (as it was then called) is not opposite All Souls College, but some fifty yards farther along the High Street. The answer is to be found in an examination of Wood's manuscript,[80] together with documentary evidence of the holdings and leases of that part of 'Buckley Hall' usually referred to in legal documents as 'The Tavern', a name which survived from its medieval function. 'Buckley Hall' appears to have been the name colloquially applied at this period to the building as a whole, which dates from the fourteenth century, and now comprises 106 and 107 High Street. At the time in question 'The Tavern' (106), abutting on the east side of the property then legally referred to as 'Buckley Hall' (107), belonged to Oriel College.

In his manuscript Wood had scored a line under 'House against Allsoules', and as an afterthought had written over the top 'at Buckley Hall', adding, in the margin, 'Joh. Clerk apoth'. At his first attempt at recollection Wood had probably confused the meetings at Petty's lodgings with those (in the club's last phase) which were in fact, for a short time, held opposite All Souls, at Boyle's lodgings, also in an apothecary's

77 W. Burdet, *A Wonder of Wonders*, London, 1650/1.

78 Below, p. 167.

79 Anthony Wood, *The History and Antiquities of the University of Oxford*, ed. John Gutch, Oxford, 1786–92, vol. II, pt. II, p. 633.

80 Bodleian Library MS. Wood F.1. A double sheet has been inserted between pp. 1065 and 1066. The relevant passage is on the first folio, verso, of this inserted sheet.

house.[81] But the name of the house and the apothecary's name leave no doubt about the location of Petty's lodgings. Oriel College records show that at this period John Clarke, the apothecary, was the sub-tenant of the property, which is now 106 High Street.[82] This is opposite the back of Brasenose College, where Petty was a Fellow, and is now faced by the New Quadrangle gateway, built in the nineteenth century.

Another remarkable experimenter was Thomas Willis, who gave his name to the Circle of Willis in the brain. While a member of the Oxford club he published his researches on fermentation and fevers.[83] Much of his experimental work on the anatomy of the brain and the nervous system was carried out at Oxford, too, with the help of Christopher Wren (whose beautiful drawings illustrate the published work), Thomas Millington and Richard Lower,[84] who himself became an anatomist of renown.

Robert Boyle, the most illustrious experimenter of them all, in 1660 published his main findings of this period, *New Experiments Physico-Mechanicall, Touching the Spring of the Air and its Effects*. It was in the house where Boyle lived and worked in his laboratory for fourteen years, until 1668, that the Oxford club met for a time after Wilkins became Master of Trinity College, Cambridge, shortly before it reassembled in London. The house, described by Anthony Wood as 'next on the west side of University Coll. sometime knowne by the name of Deep hall' belonged to John Cross, an apothecary.[85] The building no longer exists, the Shelley Memorial now standing on its site, but the grounds still form part of the Fellows' Garden.

Sprat, obliged to limit himself to a brief account of the embryo society, listed its 'principal, and most constant'[86] members. Obviously, over the ten or eleven years of the club's existence, with its background of the Civil War and other

[81] Below, note 85.
[82] *Oriel College Records*, ed. C. L. Shadwell and H. E. Salter, Oxford, 1926, p. 215.
[83] Thomas Willis, *De Fermentatione . . . altera . . . De Febribus*, London, 1659.
[84] Thomas Willis, *Cerebri Anatome cui accessit Nervorum Descriptio et Usus*, London, 1664, Epistola Dedicatoria.
[85] Bodleian Library MS. Wood F.1, on a sheet inserted between pp. 1110 and 1111; and Anthony Wood, *Life and Times*, ed. Andrew Clark, Oxford, 1891, vol. I, p. 290.
[86] Thomas Sprat, *History*, p. 55.

vicissitudes, many memberships must have been temporary, others spasmodic. Sprat said that from the time of its inception the club 'continued without any great Intermissions' until its migration to London.[87] One brief suspension is mentioned by Petty in a letter to Boyle, dated 17 February 1657/8: 'I have not, amongst all my intelligence, heard better news, than that the club is restored at *Oxford*'.[88]

The fact that the list of rules of the Oxford experimental science club in 1651 was written by Gerard Langbaine, at that time Provost of The Queen's College, raises the question of the part he played. Langbaine has never been mentioned in connexion with the club, and his activities were not in the field of experimental science. He was a scholar, and while Keeper of the University archives, although not a Bodleian Librarian, he took on himself the task of attempting to catalogue the printed books in the Bodleian Library, in addition to cataloguing manuscripts.[89] There is also the question whether the group organized by Langbaine to catalogue these books was the group mentioned by Seth Ward as cataloguing the books in the Bodleian Library for the purposes of the Oxford experimental science club.[90] If so, the list of twenty or so persons given by Langbaine constitutes two-thirds of the Oxford club, and names members who have not hitherto been known to belong to it.[91]

The club had decided to begin cataloguing more than a year before Seth Ward's reference to it, and had already come to the conclusion that it would be necessary to tackle the Bodelian Library itself. Between 19 January and 12 February 1651/52, William Petty had written to Samuel Hartlib:

The Club-men have cantonized or are cantonizing their whole Academy to taske men to several imploiments and amongst others to make Medullas of all Authors in reference to experimental learning. Thus they intend to doe with Kircherus Workes and others whatsoever.

[87] Thomas Sprat, *History*, p. 57.
[88] Robert Boyle, *Works*, 1744, vol. V, p. 298.
[89] See R. W. Hunt, *A Summary Catalogue of Western Manuscripts in the Bodleian Library at Oxford*, Oxford, 1953, vol. I, p. xviii.
[90] Above, pp. 112–13.
[91] Bodleian Library MS. Wood donat 1, pp. 1–3.

The club was also to make 'an accurate Catalogue upon Oxford Library'.[92]

In his letter of 27 February 1651/2 to Sir Justinian Isham,[93] Seth Ward said that the club had started, and intended to complete, a catalogue for its own use, of Philosophy (which included Natural Philosophy), Medicine and Mathematics books in particular, but also those of other Faculties. At that date it had already gone through the Natural Philosophy and Applied Mathematics books. Ward said:

. . . As for those things wherein you were pleased to desire an intelligence I can onely give you this account, for what concernes our Clubb wch consists of about 30 persons we have (every one takeing a portion) gone over all or most of the heads of naturall philosophy & mixt mathematics collecting onely an history of the phenomena out of such authors as we had occasion and opportunity, our first business is to gather together such things as are already discovered and to make a booke with a generall index of them, then to have a collection of those wch are still inquirenda and according to our opportunityes to make inquisitive experiments, the end is that out of a sufficient number of sure experiments, the way of nature in workeing may be discovered, but because (not knoweing what others have done before us) we may probably spend our labour upon that wch is already done, we have conceived it requisite to examine all the bookes of our public library (everyone takeing his part) and to make a catalogue or index of the matters and that very particularly in philosophy physic mathematics & indeed in all other facultyes, that so that greate numbers of books may be serviceable and a man may at once see where he may find whatever is there concerneing the argument he is upon, and this is our present business wch we hope to dispatch this Lent.

Gerard Langbaine, who at this time appears to have been a member of the Oxford club, wrote from The Queen's College, Oxford, to John Selden on 16 March 1651/2 that he was organizing the cataloguing of the Bodleian Library:

[92] Published from a private collection of Samuel Hartlib's manuscript papers, by Professor G. H. Turnbull, *Notes and Records of the Royal Society of London*, vol. 10, no. 2, p. 113, 1953.
[93] This letter is referred to above, pp. 112–13 and note 44.

For myself, I have engaged a matter of a score of our ablest men in that kind, to undertake a thorough Survey of our Publick Library, intending to make a perfect Catalogue of all the books according to their Severall Subjects in severall kinds; and when that's done to incorporate in it all the Authors in any of our private College Libraries, which are wanting in the Public, so as he that desires to know, may see at one view, what we have upon any subject, Dr. James made some beginnings in this kind; but none yet has ventur'd either to perfect his or begin anew.[94]

What Langbaine here said he intended to do is similar to what Seth Ward described as the aim of the Oxford club—the making of a subject-catalogue of all the books in the Bodleian Library (and in addition, of those in the college libraries which the Bodleian Library did not possess). But Langbaine did not imply that there was to be special emphasis on Natural Philosophy and allied subjects, or that these books were to be catalogued first. In fact he made it clear that this was an impartial effort to do what was long overdue: to make a systematic catalogue of the whole Library, for the convenience of readers in general.

This would have been an enormous task, and it is evident that before a subject-catalogue could be made, a complete list of the books was necessary. Whether Langbaine decided to attempt this first, with the intention of making a subject-catalogue from it, or whether he changed his mind and decided to make an author-catalogue in alphabetical order, that is what the evidence shows he did. This attempt must have trailed on for years, but little of its result has survived, and Anthony Wood said that Langbaine died before it was half done.

Langbaine made lists of the cataloguers and the sections of the Library each of them was to cover. On his death these papers passed into the hands of Thomas Barlow. In 1672 Anthony Wood retrieved these lists from among waste paper. Wood wrote a note of explanation in the beginning of each of three manuscript volumes of Langbaine's papers,[95] which

94 Bodleian Library MS. Selden supra 109, fol. 465. R. W. Hunt, in *A Summary Catalogue of Western Manuscripts in the Bodleian Library at Oxford*, Oxford, 1953, vol. I, pp. xxi–xxii, publishes this text and gives information about it.
95 Bodleian Library MSS. Wood donat 1–5. He wrote an explanation in volumes 1, 3 and 5 (as they are now bound and numbered).

among others, he gave to the Bodleian Library. Wood's note in the first volume says:

Fragmenta Langbainiana
Severall collections of Dr. Gerard Langbaine of Queens College wch I found among the wast pap[er]s of Dr. Thom. Barlow of the said coll. an 1672
Written in ord to ye making of a universal catalogue in all kind of Learning—but he died before he could go half through with it.

At the beginning of the first volume are three lists of names, and against each name a section of books to be catalogued. The first list is for folio books, the second for quarto and the third for octavo. Langbaine simply began with the first of the books (which already had numbers), A1, and allocated a certain section to each person. The books were in four categories— Theology, Jurisprudence, Medicine and Arts. Langbaine's own record of the sections he catalogued was also rescued by Wood.[96] It covers about three hundred volumes, and confirms that Langbaine entered the books just as they stood on the shelves. This was broadly, though by no means strictly, in alphabetical order. But the books had been numbered in unbroken sequence, and Langbaine retained this arrangement, even when an occasional quarto book was found among folios.

The names of a number of prominent members of the Oxford club appear—'Dr. Wilkins', 'Mr. Wallis', 'Mr. Bathurst', 'Mr. Ward Wad[ham]' and 'Mr. Willis', as well as Langbaine himself. Many of those helping appear on all the lists, thus, though there are three lists, each containing twenty names, there are only twenty-three persons besides Langbaine taking part. John Wilkins, followed by John Owen,[97] both Heads of Houses, are the first two named. Wilkins does not appear on the other two lists, but the other Oxford club members already mentioned, and Langbaine himself, are on all three. Of the rest of the persons named, some cannot be identified with certainty[98] and little is known about others. 'Dr. Crosse' is

[96] Bodleian Library MS. Wood donat 1, pp. 3–338. He did not complete the third section assigned him.
[97] Dean of Christ Church (Joseph Foster, *Alumni Oxonienses 1500–1714*, vol. III, p. 1100, no. 7).
[98] Further research on these lists would probably make identification more definite.

Joshua Crosse, Sedleian Professor of Natural Philosophy at Oxford from 1648–60.[99] 'Dr. Barkesdale' is Francis Barksdale, Doctor of Medicine,[100] 'Mr. Lydall jun.' is almost certainly John Lydall, connected with, if not a member of the Oxford club, and a friend of Ralph Bathurst, Thomas Willis and John Aubrey.[101] 'Mr. Lydall sen.' is probably Richard Lydall, friend of Willis and later Warden of Merton College.[102] 'Mr. Rallingson' is probably Richard Rallingson (also spelt Rawlinson) of The Queen's College,[103] described by Anthony Wood as 'an ingenious man, well skill'd in the Mathematicks'.[104] 'Mr. Ladyman' is Samuel Ladiman of Corpus Christi College, made a Fellow by the Parliamentary Visitors in 1648.[105] 'Mr. Conyers' is probably William Conyers of St. John's College, who became a Doctor of Medicine in 1653.[106] 'Mr. Gorge' is perhaps Robert Gorges, Fellow of St. John's College.[107] 'Mr. Ward jun.' is perhaps Philip Ward,[108] who was made a Proctor in 1653. 'Mr. Wood' is Robert Wood, appointed a Fellow of Lincoln College by the Parliamentary Visitors in 1650, and licensed to practise medicine in April 1656. Aubrey mentions him as one of the 'vertuosi' of the Oxford club.[109]

Langbaine's list of 'a score of our ablest men in that kind' included a number of the best-known members of the Oxford experimental science club, and it would be reasonable to suppose that the club's wish to catalogue the Library in order to

[99] Joseph Foster, *Alumni Oxonienses 1500–1714*, vol. I, p. 356, no. 27.
[100] Ibid., p. 72.
[101] Ibid., vol. III, p. 952, no. 6. (Letters from Richard Lydall to Aubrey, mentioning these friends and experimental work at Oxford during the time of the club, are in Bodleian Library MS. Aubrey 13, especially ff. 308–16.)
[102] Ibid., vol. I, p. 952, no. 10. Aubrey says that Richard Lydall and Willis shared a horse before Willis received his M.D.—which was on 8 December 1646 (MS. Aubrey 8, fol. 16ᵛ, and *Brief Lives*, ed. Andrew Clark, vol. II, p. 303).
[103] Ibid., vol. III, p. 1230.
[104] Anthony Wood, *Fasti Oxonienses*, 1691–2, vol. II, p. 822.
[105] Joseph Foster, *Alumni Oxonienses, 1500–1714*, vol. III, p. 869.
[106] Ibid., vol. I, p. 318, no. 28.
[107] Ibid., vol. II, p. 588, no. 16.   [108] Ibid., vol. IV, p. 1570.
[109] Bodleian Library MS. Aubrey 6, fol. 13ᵛ (and *Brief Lives*, vol. II, p. 141). Samuel Hartlib, after a visit from Robert Wood on 3 July 1658, says of him: 'He was appointed by the Club to make a Catalogue of matter for all Trades, Artificers &c. in Oxf. Library, of which he hath collected some sheets'. (G. H. Turnbull, *Notes and Records of the Royal Society of London*, vol. 10, no. 2, p. 114, from Hartlib's manuscript 'Ephemerides'.)

facilitate its work in the natural sciences, may have stimulated Langbaine to make his attempt at that particular time. But Langbaine had already been cataloguing manuscripts for some years[110] and probably saw this as an opportunity, which provided willing helpers,[111] to catalogue the printed books as well. Undoubtedly Langbaine was an organizer, who liked things done in an orderly way, and who wanted the University Library to be of the maximum use to its readers.

Whether or not the rules of the Oxford experimental club were made on his initiative or were merely written out by him, there is a strong resemblance between that piece of organization and the draft of rules he later made for borrowing books from the Bodleian Library.[112] There is the same drive, businesslike regard for details of procedure, and manner of presentation. This seems to indicate that Langbaine was something of an administrator in the Oxford club, whose members, in general, appeared to be intent on carrying out their experimental work rather than on making rules for procedure.

This club was given an entirely illusory extension of life by a nineteenth-century historian, Charles Weld,[113] whose mistake has continually been repeated. The misunderstanding arose because Weld found Langbaine's list of rules—merely a double sheet of writing paper—placed inside the cover of the first volume of the Minute Book of the Philosophical Society of Oxford,[114] which was founded by Robert Plot in 1683 and

---

[110] See R. W. Hunt's account of Langbaine's cataloguing in *A Summary Catalogue of Western Manuscripts in the Bodleian Library*, pp. xviii–xxiv.

[111] Samuel Hartlib, in his 'Ephemerides' for 1655, says: 'At Oxford Dr. Wallis with divers others began to collect Catalogos Materiar [um] but left of again'. Hartlib gives his informant as 'Mr Brewerton' (William Brereton, above, p. 10, note 4). Langbaine's own cataloguing went on until his death in 1658.

[112] Langbaine's list of Bodleian Library rules is written on the second sheet of a draft of a letter from him to Sir Kenelm Digby in Paris, dated 28 August 1656, from The Queen's College, Oxford. The whole document is Bodleian Library MS. Ballard 11, ff. 22–3.

[113] C. R. Weld, *A History of the Royal Society*, 1848, vol. II, pp. 33–5.

[114] Bodleian Library MS. Ashmole 1810. The Minute Book records the first formal meeting of this society on 26 October 1683. The first informal meetings were begun by Plot in about 1681. Plot's preliminary club is mentioned in a letter to Plot from Edward Tyson on 25 April 1681 (Bodleian Library MS. Ashmole 1813, fol. 94^v; and R. T. Gunther, *Early Science in Oxford*, Oxford, 1939, vol. XII, p. 5). The society came to an end in

lasted until 1690. There was, of course, a gap of about twenty years between the migration of Wilkins's club to London in 1658–9 and the formation of Plot's society, which was modelled on the Royal Society itself, Plot having been elected a Fellow in 1677. Wilkins's club, in fact, adopted no formal name at all until it finally emerged, on incorporation by Royal Charter in 1662, as the Royal Society. Boyle remarked on this shortly before the charter was received. Referring to 'the Illustrious Company that meets at *Gresham* Colledge',[115] he said that the members 'have hitherto suspended the Declaring themselves as a Society'.[116] Until incorporation, even in their own records, the members referred to the club unspecifically as 'the Society' or 'the Company'.

The picture of the Oxford experimental science club revealed by the evidence, fragmentary though that is, shows this society to be the prototype of the Royal Society proper, which itself, from the first, acknowledged the fact. Undoubtedly, earlier societies with an interest in 'the New Philosophy' had helped to create the climate in which the Oxford club originated and developed, but this society alone constituted the model on which the Royal Society was formed.

[115] Robert Boyle, *An Examen of Mr. T. Hobbes his Dialogus Physicus De Natura Aeris*, London, 1662, The Preface.
[116] Ibid., p. 3.

1690 when Plot left Oxford. The last entry in the Minute Book is 3 June 1690. On 26 March 1694 Plot wrote reproachfully to Arthur Charlett, Master of University College, Oxford, and a former member of the society, urging the society's revival. Plot said that it could easily be done if Charlett and John Wallis, who had been a nominal President (below, p. 181, note 88) would 'cordially set about it' (Bodleian Library MS. Ballard 14, fol. 58).

5

ESTABLISHMENT AS A
ROYAL FOUNDATION

The Royal Society officially 'had its beginning in the wonderful pacifick year, 1660'.[1] This point, 'where they began to make it a form'd, and *Regular Assembly*', marks the end of the first stage, which was 'the *preparation*'.[2] So far as its constitution is concerned the Society now entered on a period of transition, in which, as Sprat says, the members were 'ord'ring their platform'.[3] Here it is important to remember what the Society stood for, and to consider what it wanted in order to establish itself satisfactorily.

What it stood for was the gradual evolution of new, developing sciences—not as an end, but as a means—towards a much fuller understanding of man's physical environment, 'for the service of mankind'.[4] And it was concerned to emphasize its preoccupation with science as distinct from other fields of knowledge.

What it wanted at this stage were public recognition and security for the future. In other words it was concerned about the need for two things—satisfactory status and permanence—

[1] Thomas Sprat, *History*, p. 58; (and above p. 103).
[2] Ibid., p. 52 (and above, p. 101).
[3] Ibid., p. 59. [4] Ibid., p. 76.

because both were necessary for carrying out its work with reasonable hope of success.

At its formal inauguration in 1660 the Society had passed some simple rules for its internal administration, similar to those made at Oxford.[5] What it now sought, primarily concerned its external aspects, and here again it followed Bacon in his idea of a 'King's Charter'

> containing gift of revenue, and many privileges, exemptions and points of honour.[6]

A Royal Charter, as its members well knew, could confer two kinds of benefit which would enormously strengthen their position: prestige and legal standing.

They were realistic enough not to expect from an impecunious king, lately returned from exile, what would have eased their burden considerably—financial help; and it is one of the remarkable facts about this whole undertaking from the beginning, that its vast and courageous project was conceived and carried on without external financial resources.[7] In the *History* Sprat put the most constructive view of these difficulties, but in doing so was careful not to give the impression that financial help was not wanted:

> Of the Stock, upon which their *Expence* has been hitherto defraid, I can say nothing, that is very *magnificent*: seeing they have rely'd upon no more than some small *Admission-money*, and *weekly Contributions* amongst themselves. Such a *Revenue* as this, can make no great sound, nor amount to any *vast summ*. But yet, I shall say this for it, that it was the onely way, which could have been begun, with a security of success, in that condition of things. The *publick Faith* of *Experimental Philosophy*, was not then strong enough, to move Men and Women of all conditions, to bring in their

---

[5] Journal Book, vol. I, p. 1. For the rules of the Oxford club, see above, pp. 111–12.

[6] Francis Bacon, *New Atlantis: Works*, vol. III, p. 149.

[7] Charles II did give the Royal Society a claim to lands and other interests in Ireland, but he allowed them to pass into other hands. A letter from the President of the Royal Society (Lord Brouncker) to the Lord Lieutenant of Ireland (the Duke of Ormonde) on 3 January 1662/3, pressing the Royal Society's claim, is in the Society's archives (Supplement to the Letter Book, vol. 1, pp. 142–5). Thomas Birch, *The History of the Royal Society*, 1756–7, vol I, pp. 168–9, publishes this letter and refers to Sir William Petty's unavailing efforts on behalf of the Royal Society to get this grant honoured.

Bracelets and Jewels, towards the carrying of it on . . . It was therefore well ordain'd, that the first Benevolence should come from
the *Experimenters themselves.* If they had speedily at first call'd for
mighty Treasures; and said aloud, that their Enterprise requir'd the
Exchequer of a Kingdom; they would onely have been contemn'd, as
vain *Projectors.*

. . . And yet I shall presume to assure the World; that what
they shall raise on these mean Foundations, will be more answerable to the *largeness* of their intentions, than to the *narrowness* of
their beginnings . . .

There is scarce any thing, has more hindred the *True Philosophy*;
than a vain opinion, that men have taken up, that nothing could
be done in it, to any purpose, but upon a *vast charge*, and by a
mighty Revenue . . . But this imagination can now no longer prevail. Men now understand, that Philosophy needs not so great a
prodigality to maintain it: that the most *profitable* Tryals are not
always the most *costly*: that the best Inventions have not been
found out by the *richest*, but by the most *prudent* and *Industrious*
Observers: that the right *Art* of *Experimenting*, when it is once set
forward, will go near to sustain it self. This I speak, not to stop
mens future Bounty, by a Philosophical Boast, that the *Royal
Society* has enough already: But rather to encourage them to cast
in more help; by shewing them, what return may be made from a
little, by a wise administration.[8]

During this stage Wilkins, formally, could do little. At the
Restoration he had lost his Mastership of Trinity College,
Cambridge, to which, in 1659, he had been appointed from
the Wardenship of Wadham College, Oxford; and although
personally well liked by his colleagues in the Society, he was
certainly not in a position to represent them in an approach to

---

[8] Thomas Birch, *The History of the Royal Society*, 1756-7, vol. I, pp. 77-80.
In the early years of the Royal Society the need for subscriptions (and the
improvement that greater prestige might be expected to bring) caused the
Society to admit men of rank and position who were by way of being
patrons, and were not actively engaged in scientific research. In the *History*,
after the list of Fellows, Sprat says (pp. 433-4):

In this number perhaps there may some be found, whose *employments* will
not give them leave to promote these *Studies*, with their own *Hands*. But it
being their part to *Contribute*, joyntly towards the *Charge*, and to pass
judgment on what others shall *try*: they will appear to be well-nigh as useful, as those that *Labor*, to the main end of this *Enterprize*.

the King.[9] Sir Robert Moray, a Royalist who had been in exile with Charles, and had first enlisted his interest in the Society,[10] now took on the task of negotiating incorporation by Royal Charter.

Meantime the immediate practical need was that of somewhere suitable to meet. The Society simply had not got the resources necessary to erect or buy and maintain a building of its own. When the Oxford experimental science club, dispersed by the various fortunes of most of its prominent members during 1658-9, had reassembled in London, it met for a time after the Wednesday and Thursday lectures of Christopher Wren and Laurence Rooke, respectively, at Gresham College, in term time only.[11] Wren and Rooke had been outstanding members of the Oxford club, and on their appointments from Oxford University to Gresham College—Rooke in 1652 and Wren in 1657—had maintained close contact with the club. This arrangement in London continued until it was interrupted, as Sprat implies, towards the end of 1659 'by the miserable distractions of that Fatal year',[12] when 'the place of their meeting was made a *Quarter* for *Soldiers*'.[13]

At the Restoration the club had resumed its meetings as before, adjourning after the lectures to Rooke's room in Gresham College. It was there, on 28 November 1660, that the Society had been formally constituted.[14]

At the meeting which formally inaugurated the Society it was decided to continue the weekly meetings on Wednesdays in Rooke's room at Gresham College in term time, and to meet in the vacations in William Ball's room at the Middle Temple,[15] one of the four Inns of Court, to which he had been admitted in 1646.[16] Ball, the eldest son and heir of Sir Peter Ball, also of the Middle Temple, is mentioned by Sprat as one of 'several eminent persons of their common acquaintance' who joined

[9] Above, p. 110.
[10] Journal Book, vol. I, p. 3, where it is recorded that on 5 December 1660 Moray 'brought in word from ye Court that The King had been acquainted with the designe of this meeting. And he did well approve of it, & would be ready to give an encouragement to it'.
[11] Thomas Sprat, *History*, pp. 57-8.
[12] See above, p. 103, note 5.   [13] Thomas Sprat, *History*, p. 58.
[14] Journal Book, vol. I, pp. 1-2.   [15] Ibid.
[16] *Register of Admissions to the Honourable Society of the Middle Temple*, ed. Sir Henry F. MacGeagh and H. A. C. Sturgess, London, 1949, vol. I, p. 143.

the club in London.[17] Obviously this arrangement could only be a temporary measure, and discussions on possibilities for a suitable, permanent meeting-place began immediately.

At the next meeting, on 5 December 1660, a committee was set up to discuss the question of the Society's constitution.[18] Two days later, at this committee's first sitting, it was suggested that the College of Physicians 'would afford convenient Accomodation for the meeting of this Society'.[19] At the following general meeting, which was on 12 December, a special group was formed to consider the matter. The Journal Book records:

> It was then referred to My Lord Brouncker, Sir Robert Moray, Sir Paul Neile, Mr. Matth: Wren, Dr. Goddard, and Mr. Ch: Wren, to consult about a convenient place for the weekely meeting of the Society.[20]

On the same occasion the suggestion made by the committee that the College of Physicians would be a suitable meeting-place for the Society was discussed and accepted. Various conditions were set out in the proposal to be made to the College. Gresham College was not even considered:

> Whereas it was suggested at the Comittee that the Colledge of Physitians, would afford convenient Accomodation for the meeting of this Society, upon supposition, that it be graunted & accepted of; It was thought reasonable, That any of the fellowes of the said Colledge, if they shall desire it, be likewise admitted as Supernumerarys, they submitting to the Lawes of the Society, Both as to the pay, at their admission & the weekely allowance; as likewise the particular works, or tasks yt may be allotted to them.
>
> That the Publick Professors of Mathematicks; Physick, & Naturall Philosophy of both Universitys, have the same priviledge, with the Colledge of Physitians, They paying as others at their admission, & contributing their weekely allowance & assistance, when their occasions doe permitt them to be in London.[21]

---

[17] Thomas Sprat, *History*, p. 57.
[18] Journal Book, vol. I, p. 3.
[19] Ibid., p. 4.
[20] Ibid. At this meeting it was decided that the number of the society should be 55, but that persons of, or above, the degree of baron might be admitted as supernumeraries. This number was increased from time to time (below, p. 138, note 42).
[21] Ibid.

However, the proposal was evidently not accepted by the College of Physicians, for at the following meeting of the Society on 19 December, the first resolution was

> that the next meeting should be at Gresham Colledge, & so from weeke to weeke till further order.[22]

The decision to hold all the meetings for the time being at Gresham meant that the arrangement to use William Ball's room at the Middle Temple in the vacations was rescinded. This is confirmed by Samuel Hartlib. Writing to John Worthington on 17 December Hartlib had said:

> Thus much is certain, that there is a meeting every week of the prime virtuosi, not only at Gresham College in term time, but also out of it, at Mr. Ball's chambers in the Temple.[23]

But on 1 January 1660/1, again writing to Worthington, Hartlib had given him the latest news that the Society had moved back to Gresham, temporarily (although it was in the vacation), and was meeting in Goddard's lodgings:

> Mr. Boyle, one of them [the virtuosi] told me that for the present they are removed to Gresham Coll., to Dr. Goddard's lodging.[24]

Failure to obtain headquarters at the College of Physicians had forced the Society to take the only possible course which would ensure week-to-week continuity for its experimental work. But it still had no place to meet in, except the private room of one of its members.

Even in these precarious and extremely limiting conditions it was desirable that as far as possible the work should go on, and at the meeting of 19 December, which had decided on the temporary return to Gresham, a resolution was passed

> That every man of this Company be desir'd to bring in such Experiments to a Comittee to be appointed for that end, as he shall thinke most fit for the advancement of the generall designe of the Company.[25]

At the same time the difficulty of organizing experimental work without a room in which apparatus could be placed in

[22] Journal Book, vol. 1, p. 6.
[23] *The Diary and Correspondence of Dr. John Worthington*, ed. James Crossley (Chetham Society Publications no. XIII), Manchester, 1847, vol. 1, p. 246.
[24] Ibid., p. 257.   [25] Journal Book, vol. I, p. 6.

readiness for the meetings had to be dealt with. This was done by enlisting the help of the members of the Society who held academic appointments at Gresham, and therefore had rooms of their own in the building:

> That Dr. Wilkins, & as many of the Professors of Gresham Colledge, as are of this Society, or any three of them, be a Comittee for the receiving of all such experiments.[26]

As John Ward remarks in this connexion:

> The Gresham professors, who at that time were members of this society, besides Mr. Wren and Mr. Rooke, were Mr. Petty (afterwards Sir William) Dr. Goddard, and Mr. Croune.[27]

Of these, all except Croone had been leading members of the Oxford club. Sprat names Croone, who at this time was Professor of Rhetoric at Gresham College, among 'the several eminent persons of their common acquaintance' who had joined the club in London.[28] At the inaugural meeting of 28 November 1660 Croone had been elected Registrar of the Society.

On 16 January 1660/1 the Society was still having to make use of the fact that some of its members happened to be Gresham professors. At that meeting it was ordered

> That those of this Society who belong to Gresham College, together with Sir Robert Moray & as many others of this Company as will meete, be a Committee about Magneticall enquiries.[29]

But by 20 March 1660/1 the extremely unsatisfactory state of affairs had improved a little, with the Society's acquisition of a room for its use at Gresham. At the meeting that day it was voted

> that the Number of the Society be enlarged . . . That the Gentlemen of Gresham Colledge [i.e. members of the Society who were Gresham professors] be Overseers for the accomoding the roome, for the Society's Meeting.[30]

Writing about four years later, Sprat showed that the Royal Society had acquired the use of further accommodation there:

[26] Journal Book, vol. I, p. 6.
[27] John Ward, *The Lives of the Professors of Gresham College*, London, 1740, Preface, p. xii.
[28] Thomas Sprat, *History*, p. 57; (and above, p. 103).
[29] Journal Book, vol. I, p. 8.   [30] Ibid., vol. I, p. 13.

Here the *Royal Society* has one *publick Room* to meet in, another for a *repository* to keep their Instruments, Books, Rarities, Papers, and whatever else belongs to them: making use besides, by permission, of several of the other Lodgings, as their occasions do require.[31]

Sprat refers to Gresham in courteous terms, but he makes it clear that the Society was indebted to the College only for its hospitality.

The Royal Society continued to meet at Gresham College, maintaining its entirely separate entity, until the meetings were disrupted, first by the Plague in 1665, when the Society went into recess for eight months, and then by the Fire of London in the following year.[32] The Society's efforts to find suitable accommodation continued far beyond the period considered here;[33] and it is perhaps not irrelevant to emphasize that its character, which had first been determined at Oxford, experienced no change on its incidental contacts with Gresham College. Soon after the Fire, when the Society was attempting to raise money to build its own college, the President, Council and individual Fellows all stressed the need for improved facilities for the Society, in order to maintain its function. While these plans were being considered, Oldenburg, writing to Boyle at Oxford, said:

. . . the building a college for the Royal Society is conceived to be by the council, as being that, which will in all likelihood establish our institution, and fix us (who are now looked upon but as wanderers, and using precariously the lodgings of other men) in a certain place, where we may meet, prepare and make our experiments and observations, lodge our curators and operators, have our laboratory, and operatory all together. It is a maxim, I learned in my logick, when a boy; *Qui amat finem, amat & media ad finem.*[34]

[31] Thomas Sprat, *History*, p. 93.
[32] After several attempts to find other accommodation, the Royal Society accepted the offer of Henry Howard (sixth Duke of Norfolk 1677) to hold their meetings at Arundel House in the Strand, and on 4 January 1666/7 the Council ordered a form to be printed stating that in future the weekly meetings would be at Arundel House at the usual time. (Council Book, vol. I, p. 120.)
[33] See below, pp. 190–1.
[34] Robert Boyle, *Works*, 1744, vol. V, p. 389; the letter was written in March 1667/8.

After the immediate problem of a meeting-place for the newly instituted, but still nameless, society came plans for a charter. The first Royal Charter, granted in 1662, was certainly a landmark in the history of the Society. Under the terms of incorporation it received many privileges.[35]

It was granted various external privileges: legal standing, so that it had the same rights and obligations before the law as any individual subject; permission to meet in London or within ten miles of it; the right to appoint printers and engravers, and the power to authorize them to print matters relating to the Society (i.e. the right to grant an imprimatur); the same right as that possessed by the College of Physicians and the Corporation of Surgeons of London to demand and anatomize the bodies of executed criminals; the right to correspond on scientific subjects with any foreigners; permission to build a college or colleges in London or within ten miles of it; and the appointment of certain persons of high position as arbiters if disputes should arise within the Society, that could not be resolved there.

The Society had the right, through its President, Council and Fellows, to order its own internal affairs. The President and Council were authorized to make laws, statutes and orders, and to manage all the affairs of the Society, the only proviso being that such action should be reasonable and not contrary to the laws of the realm.

Yet, despite the formal expressions of pleasure and gratitude, the Society was not satisfied, and within a few months announced that alterations were to be made to the Letters Patent.[36] It has often been stated that the Royal Society obtained 'further privileges' in the Royal Charter of 1663, without specifying what these were. But the only privilege which the Society did not already possess was the grant of a coat-of-arms, which might well have been made separately, without the considerable labour of preparing and passing another comprehensive charter, particularly so soon after the original Charter.

Except for the addition of the coat-of-arms there is very little difference in the practical terms of the two charters. Such differences concern only minor matters and relate to internal administration, which the Society already had the right to

[35] The Charter, drawn up in Latin, is in the Royal Society archives.
[36] Journal Book, vol. I, pp. 110–11 (26 November 1662).

alter at will. The real difference, and it is a most significant one, of which the grant-of-arms, with its motto 'Nullius in Verba' (nothing in words) was symptomatic, was not one of further privileges but of definition. This Charter embodied the official declaration of the Royal Society's purpose and status, which had not been made sufficiently clear in the original document.

The name by which the Society had first been incorporated was simply 'the Royal Society', without qualification, and there was no mention of the King as Founder.

That the Society had wanted its purpose made clear, and that it had meant the King to be its formal Founder is evident from various sources. Even before he suggested the name 'Royal Society', Evelyn, as a member of the Society, had joined in the efforts to gain Charles's support for a Royal Charter. In *A Panegyric to Charles the II*, published to celebrate the Coronation on 23 April 1661, Evelyn said:

> Nor must I here forget the honour You have done our *Society* at *Gresham Colledge* by Your curious enquiries . . . which concern *Philosophy* . . . [F]or You is reserv'd the being Founder of some thing that may improve practical and Experimental knowledg, beyond all that has been hitherto attempted, for the Augmentation of Science, and universal good of Mankind, and which alone will consummate Your Fame and render it immortal.[37]

For this service Evelyn was formally thanked by the Society for mentioning 'this Company & its designe'.[38]

When the original Charter had been received by the Society, the President's official speech of thanks to the King strikingly recalled Evelyn's words. Charles was referred to as 'the Royal Founder', which, legally, he was not, and the general purpose for which the Royal Society had been founded, as 'the advancement of the knowledge of natural things, and of all usefull arts, by Experiments'.[39]

The second form of the Charter, passed in 1663,[40] made good the omissions. In it the Society's legal title was altered to 'the Royal Society of London for Promoting Natural Knowledge' and the King declared himself its Founder and Patron.

[37] P.14.   [38] Journal Book, vol. I, p. 42.
[39] Supplement to the Letter Book, vol. I, p. 139.
[40] This Charter, in Latin, is also in the Royal Society archives.

This Charter, which legally embodied these points that the Society considered very important, did not merely qualify or extend the first; it superseded and literally nullified the original Charter, which in practice had never really been implemented.

Under the terms of the original Charter a Council of twenty-one Fellows had been appointed. This Council never sat officially, nor did the election of Fellows to it, which under the terms of the Charter was due on 30 November 1662, take place. Instead, nineteen of those already named were put forward, with two changes, making the same total of twenty-one, and these were nominated in the new form of the Charter of incorporation. It was not until the occasion when the new form of the Charter was read before the assembled Society on 13 May 1663 that the Council sat; and that this was its first sitting is officially recorded in the Council Book, in which this meeting is the first entry.[41]

Of further significance is the fact that Fellows who had been elected or admitted under the authority of the original Charter were no longer regarded as valid Fellows. Most of those who had thus formerly been accepted as Fellows were named by the Council under the new form of the Charter, and together with others who had not belonged to the Society before, were declared Fellows on the new foundation.[42] Any person who had been a Fellow under the original form of the Charter, and for some reason had not been admitted to the Society under its new constitution had to be re-elected, and his Fellowship dated from this election.

One notable example is that of Thomas Willis, the eminent physician and surgeon. Willis had been a leading member of the Oxford experimental science club, and at the formal inauguration of the Society in London on 28 November 1660 had been named on the list of those who 'if they should desire it, might be admitted before any others'.[43] He became a mem-

---

[41] Council Book, vol. I, p. 1.

[42] On 20 May 1663 the Council issued a list of those who were to be 'Received, Admitted, and ordered to be registered Fellows of the Royal Society (Council Book, vol. I, pp. 3–6). These numbered 115, only 12 of whom (excluding the President) had the standing of a baron or above (see above, p. 132, note 20). Sprat's list in the *History*, pp. 431–3, at the time of going to press in 1667 contains a total of 191 names (including that of the King). [43] Journal Book, vol. I, p. 2.

ber of the Society on 13 November 1661,[44] and a Fellow of the
Royal Society on its incorporation in 1662. Owing to an over-
sight he was not admitted a Fellow under the new form of the
Charter, and, his existing Fellowship being no longer valid,
he had to be elected again. This was done on 18 November
1663, in the following terms:

> Dr. Willis was chosen, having been forgot to be chosen again, at
> the time, when, upon the renewall of the Charter, the Council,
> according to the power graunted them therein, did receive and
> admitt into the Society such persons, as had been elected Fellows
> afore, upon the first Charter.[45]

Dr. Henry More was another Fellow under the original Charter
whose Fellowship had become invalid. He was elected a Fellow
on the new Foundation on 25 May 1664.[46]

With the passing of the new form of the Charter the terms of
incorporation sprang to life: the nominated Council now sat;[47]
a list of Fellows was drawn up;[48] work began on the long
business of making the Statutes, which were to govern the
internal organization of the Society;[49] the Council exercised
its right to appoint printers to the Society;[50] and to issue its
warrant for the body of an executed criminal for the purpose of
anatomy.[51]

The day after the new Charter had been formally received
by the assembled Society, Sir Robert Moray wrote to Huygens.
He said that they would be able to work more effectively for
the establishment of the Society than had been possible hitherto; the constitution of the Society had now been set up as they
intended.[52] This sentiment is repeated by Sprat in the *History*.
Giving a comprehensive 'epitome' of the main points of the
'Letters Patents', he uses the new form, and makes no mention
of the earlier one. This, he says, is the Royal Society's '*Legal*

[44] Journal Book, vol. I, p. 40.   [45] Ibid., vol. II, p. 1.

[46] Ibid., p. 83.

[47] Above, p. 138. (Council Book, vol. I, p. 1.)

[48] Above, p. 138, note 42.

[49] Council Book, vol. I, p. 6.

[50] Terms of the Charter.   [51] Ibid.

[52] Christiaan Huygens, *Oeuvres Complètes*, The Hague, 1889–, vol. IV, p. 343.
The Council elected Huygens to a Fellowship about a month later, on 22
June 1663.

Ratification.[53] Thanking the prominent lawyers who had given their services, he makes the point that 'the *Profession* of the *Law*' is not, as sometimes supposed, 'an Enemy to *Learning* and the *Civil Arts*', and takes the opportunity to reaffirm that Bacon was the Royal Society's intellectual source:

> But it is enough to declare, that my Lord *Bacon* was a *Lawyer*, and that these eminent *Officers* of the *Law*, have compleated this foundation of the *Royal Society*: which was a work well becoming the largeness of his Wit to devise, and the greatness of their Prudence to establish.[54]

In the original Charter provision had been made for two Sergeants-at-Mace to attend on the President, though this had not been put into practice; nor did the Society possess a mace. This clause was repeated in the new Charter, and on 23 May 1663, only ten days after the Council sat for the first time, the Royal Jewel House received a warrant from the King to deliver to the Society 'one guilt Mace'.[55] On 13 July 1663 the Council ordered that the arms of the Society should be engraved on it, and an inscription which recorded the Society's new title; that the King was its Founder and Patron; and the year, 1663.[56]

The Royal Society now had the charter it wanted; the end of the second period had been reached. It was therefore natural that from this relatively firm ground the leaders should look about them and take stock of their position. Partly as a 'plain History' and partly as an explanation and justification to those who misunderstood or were hostile to the Society, they now wanted to put on record what their point of departure had been, the route by which they had come, and the direction they hoped to take.[57]

In his letter to Huygens, written the day after the Society had received the new Charter, Sir Robert Moray had expressed his satisfaction with it.[58] He added:

[53] Thomas Sprat, *History*, pp. 133–43.
[54] Ibid., pp. 143–4.
[55] C. R. Weld, *A History of the Royal Society*, London, 1848, vol. I, pp. 164–5 and note 28.
[56] Council Book, vol. I, p. 21.
[57] Thomas Sprat, *History*, An Advertisement to the Reader.
[58] See above, p. 139.

We are soon going to have a tract printed which will give information on all that concerns the Society[59]

It was intended that the History of the Society should be published with the Statutes, which were still being compiled, a process which, as it turned out, took about eighteen months from the time the Society received its revised Charter. Writing to Huygens on 28 October 1663, William Brereton, a member of the Council, said:

As for the History of the Society, it should accompany the Statutes when they are printed, which will be, I believe, very soon.[60]

Whether Sprat had been elected a Fellow for the primary purpose of writing the history of the Society is not known, but the date of his election rather points to this. On 25 March 1663 Sir Robert Moray informed the Society that Sir Henry Bennet had received the King's signature to the Patent.[61] At the next meeting, on 1 April, Sprat was proposed as a Fellow by John Wilkins, and a fortnight later elected.[62] On 22 April the new Charter passed the Great Seal. Sprat was admitted to the Society on 29 April, and was therefore in time to be included on the list of Fellows drawn up under the new foundation and brought out on 20 May 1663.[63]

Bringing his account of the Society up to the Charter, Sprat said:

I have hitherto describ'd the first *Elements*, on which the *Royal Society* arose, and supported its beginnings: I have trac'd its progress from the first private indeavours of some of its *members*, till it became united into a *Regular constitution*: and from thence I have related their first *conceptions*, and *practices*, towards the setling of an universal, constant, and impartial survey of the whole *Creation*. There now remains to be added . . . an Account of the *Incouragements* they have receiv'd from abroad, and at home; and a Particular Enumeration of the *Principal Subjects*, about which they have been emploi'd since they obtain'd the *Royal Confirmation*.[64]

---

[59] Nous faison estat de faire publier dans peu de temps un petit traitté par lequel on sçaura tout ce qui concerne la Societé. (Published in Christiaan Huygens, *Oeuvres Complètes*, The Hague, 1889–, vol. IV, p. 343.)

[60] Pour l'Histoire de la Societé elle doit accompagner les Statuts quand on les imprime, ce que sera (comme je crois) bien tost. (Ibid., vol. V, p. 4.)

[61] Journal Book, vol. I, p. 153.   [62] Ibid., p. 156.

[63] Above, p. 138, note 42.   [64] Thomas Sprat, *History*, p. 124.

A general survey of the Society's achievements, as summarized in the *History*, has already been given in Chapter 3, and it is not the purpose of this study to follow the course of the Society's progress in its later stages.

Naturally, as in the history of any other human institution, the Society had its times of apparent recession. On occasion there was cause to lament the thinness of the attendance at meetings, or that the work lacked focus.[65] But by now the Society was too firmly established to succumb to these hazards, and was able to continue, as its promoters had intended, with its work towards 'raysing a *new Philosophy*'.[66]

[65] See above, p. 86.   [66] Thomas Sprat, *History*, p. 323.

7. Some notable Fellows of the early Royal Society.
Top left. Sir Christopher Wren. *By courtesy of the Ashmolean Museum, Oxford.*
Top right. John Wallis. *By courtesy of the Bodleian Library, Oxford.*
Bottom left. Sir William Petty. *By courtesy of Brasenose College, Oxford.*
Bottom right. Robert Boyle. *By courtesy of the Ashmolean Museum, Oxford.*

8. Some notable Fellows of the early Royal Society.
Top left. Thomas Willis. *By courtesy of the Bodleian Library, Oxford.*
Top right. Seth Ward. *By courtesy of Trinity College, Oxford.*
Bottom left. Henry Oldenburg. *By courtesy of the Royal Society.*
Bottom right. Viscount Brouncker, P.R.S. *By courtesy of the Royal Society.*

6

THE RELIGIOUS POLICY
OF THE ROYAL SOCIETY

Bacon's vision of new sciences was down to earth; the facts of nature were the subject of his study. Yet the impulse behind it was essentially a religious one, and the Royal Society, as a body, followed his precepts on religion in its relation to science.

Man, said Bacon, should understand his role as a scientist: he was only 'the servant or interpreter of nature':

> For the chain of causes cannot by any force be loosed or broken, nor can nature be commanded except by being obeyed.

Man might discover laws and apply them for his use, but he had not created those laws, and unless he acknowledged the Creator as such, he was a victim of self-delusion. Man's intellect itself was 'the crown and consummation' of the physical universe, and his extending knowledge of nature should be to the glory of God, not to the inflation of his own ego.[1] This temptation should be kept in mind, said Bacon, 'that we do not so place our felicity in knowledge, as we forget our mortality'.[2]

[1] Francis Bacon, *Instauratio Magna*, Distributio Operis: *Works*, vol. IV, pp. 32–3.
[2] Ibid., *The Advancement of Learning* I: *Works*, vol. III, p. 266; and *De Augmentis Scientiarum* I: *Works*, vol. I, p. 435.

F

He addressed himself to those who were to build the new sciences, urging this humility:

> I would address one admonition to all; that they consider what are the true ends of knowledge, and that they seek it not either for pleasure of the mind, or for contention, or for superiority to others, or for profit, or fame, or power, or any of these inferior things; but for the benefit and use of life; and that they perfect and govern it in charity. For it was from lust of power that the angels fell, from lust of knowledge that man fell; but of charity there can be no excess, neither did angel or man ever come in danger by it.[3]

Of his own intention Bacon said:

> And for myself, I am not raising a capitol or pyramid to the pride of man, but laying a foundation in the human understanding for a holy temple after a model of the world. That model therefore I follow. For whatever deserves to exist deserves also to be known, for knowledge is the image of existence.[4]

His College in the *New Atlantis* was 'dedicated to the study of the Works and Creatures of God' and was 'for the finding out of the true nature of all things, (whereby God might have the more glory in the workmanship of them, and men the more fruit in the use of them)'.[5]

God was known to man in two ways, through his Word, 'the kingdom of heaven', and through his Works, 'the kingdom of man'. The *Novum Organum* was a gateway into that temporal heritage conferred by God on man—*Aphorismi de Interpretatione Naturae et Regno Hominis*[6]—and Bacon repeated his warning on the need for humility in entering it:

> the understanding [must be] thoroughly freed and cleansed; the entrance into the kingdom of man, founded on the sciences, being not much other than the entrance into the kingdom of heaven, whereinto none may enter except as a little child.[7]

Historians have often considered that Bacon saw religion as an impediment to the scientist's entry into his kingdom. That

---

[3] Francis Bacon, *Instauratio Magna*, Praefatio: *Works*, vol. IV, pp. 20–1.

[4] Ibid., *Novum Organum* I, Aph. CXX: *Works*, vol. IV, pp. 106–7.

[5] Ibid., *New Atlantis*: *Works*, vol. III, pp. 145–6.

[6] This was a sub-title of the *Novum Organum*.

[7] Francis Bacon, *Novum Organum* I, Aph. LXVIII: *Works*, vol. IV, p. 69.

is not so. His view that the scientist should 'give to faith that only which is faith's' was simply an injunction to look for the facts of nature in nature itself, not in the figurative language which the Scriptures, written in an earlier day, sometimes used to express physical phenomena.[8] Religion put no prohibition on scientific research so long as it did not offend the moral law;[9] divine law could not be in opposition to scientific knowledge, since the one set forth the Will, the other the Works of God. At the same time, warned Bacon—and this is the reverse of the coin—science was not in a position to dictate to, or overrule, the truths of revealed religion:

> for if any man shall think by view and inquiry into these sensible and material things to attain that light whereby he may reveal unto himself the nature or will of God, then indeed is he spoiled by vain philosophy.[10]

Natural Philosophy was

> rightly given to religion as her most faithful handmaid, since the one displays the will of God, the other his power.[11]

Francis Bacon has not perhaps been regarded as a mystic, yet a mystical recognition of the Creation as a manifestation of the Divine Intelligence, and a concomitant belief that its physical laws were to be made intelligible to man, is at the heart of his philosophy of science. In the *New Atlantis* a mystical ark contained the warrant by which the society had been transformed, lived and worked; this authority consisted of a Book and a Letter, symbolizing the Word and the Works of God. Both could be read by every inhabitant of New Atlantis, whether native or immigrant, as though written in his own language, for both transcended the barriers of race, being the heritage of mankind as a whole. From time to time immigrants from many countries had settled there, including 'Hebrews, Persians, and Indians'; some immigrants in antiquity such as

---

[8] Francis Bacon, *Instauratio Magna*, Praefatio: *Works*, vol. IV, p. 20; and *Novum Organum* I, Aph. LXV: *Works*, vol. IV, p. 66.
[9] Ibid., *Instauratio Magna*, Praefatio: *Works*, vol. IV, p. 20; and *Novum Organum*, Aph. LXXXIX: *Works*, vol. IV, pp. 88–9.
[10] Ibid., *Advancement of Learning* I: *Works*, vol. III, p. 267; and *De Augmentis Scientiarum* I: *Works*, vol. I, p. 436.
[11] Ibid., *Novum Organum* I, Aph. LXXXIX: *Works*, vol. IV, p. 89.

the Chaldeans and Arabs were still represented by their descendants.[12]

The symbolic imagery of this part of the narrative is derived from the Apocalypse of St. John. Bacon's Book and Letter stand respectively for the two books in the Apocalypse. The Book (which contained the Old and New Testaments) stood for the apocalyptic book or scroll 'sealed with seven seals', that is, the Word of God;[13] and the Letter represented the small book or scroll which was open in the hand of the angel who stood with one foot on the sea and the other on the land. This little book contained God's secret design, which was to be revealed in a new prophecy affecting many peoples, races, languages and kings.[14]

Bacon's interpretation of this prophecy was realistic: 'For God forbid', he said in his 'Plan of the Work',

> that we should give out a dream of our own imagination for a pattern of the world; rather may he graciously grant to us to write an apocalypse or true vision of the footsteps of the Creator imprinted on his creatures.[15]

Explaining this, he said that it should be realized 'how vast a difference' there was between the illusions of the human mind and 'the Ideas of the Divine'. It was the latter which should be sought, for they were 'the creator's own stamp upon creation, impressed and defined in matter by true and exquisite lines'.[16] In the most profound sense of the term Bacon was urging 'the gospel of scientific truth', and he summed up his precept in these words:

> I want this primary history to be compiled with a most religious care, as if every particular were stated upon oath; seeing that it is the book of God's works, and (so far as the majesty of heavenly may be compared with the humbleness of earthly things) a kind of second Scripture.[17]

---

[12] Francis Bacon, *New Atlantis*: *Works*, vol. III, pp. 137–9 and 141.
[13] *The Apocalypse of St. John (Revelation)*, Chapter V.
[14] Ibid., Chapter X.
[15] Francis Bacon, *Instauratio Magna*, Distributio Operis: *Works*, vol. IV, pp. 32–3.
[16] Ibid., *Novum Organum* I, Aph. CXXIV: *Works*, vol. IV, p. 110.
[17] Ibid., *Parasceve ad Historiam Naturalem et Experimentalem*, IX: *Works*, vol. IV, p. 261.

Bacon expressed the belief, not merely that such a study of nature as he proposed was permissible, but that it was part of the divine plan that man should 'approach with humility and veneration to unroll the volume of Creation'.[18] The silent language of the laws and working of nature, he said, was that referred to by the Psalmist:[19]

> For this is that sound and language which went forth into all lands, and did not incur the confusion of Babel; this should men study to be perfect in, and becoming again as little children condescend to take the alphabet of it into their hands, and spare no pains to search and unravel the interpretation thereof, but pursue it strenuously and persevere even unto death.[20]

Bacon, then, saw science as the notation of a universal language to be learnt by the scientist in the service of God for the benefit of man. He saw also that this view could not be reconciled with the disqualification from his projected scientific institution of any person on grounds of race or indeed of religion. Thus although the kingdom of New Atlantis was Christian, Jews, 'whom they leave to their own religion', lived there in freedom and friendship.[21]

The question of religious freedom was far from merely academic to Bacon; the problem was on his doorstep, for he lived in an age of intense religious intolerance, when religion was often another name for party. A member of the Established Church of England himself, Bacon had a deep distaste for religious intolerance on the part of the authorities, unless it was sincerely believed that the safety of the state or civil peace was at stake. In his essay 'Of Unity in Religion', published in 1625,[22] the year before his death, he deplored the quarrels and violence engendered by differences of interpretation among Christians, and thought it reprehensible 'so to consider men as Christians, as we forget that they are men'.[23] Moreover, he saw that

[18] Francis Bacon, *Historia Naturalis et Experimentalis ad Condendam Philosophiam: sive Phaenomena Universi: Works*, vol. V, p. 132.
[19] *Vulgate*, Psalm XVIII. 4 (*A.V.* XIX. 4).
[20] Francis Bacon, *Historia Naturalis et Experimentalis: Works*, vol. V, pp. 132–3.
[21] Ibid., *New Atlantis: Works*, vol. III, p. 151.
[22] Ibid., *Essayes or Counsels Civill and Morall* III, 'Of Unity in Religion': *Works*, vol. VI, pp. 381–4.
[23] Ibid., p. 384.

differences in belief which gave rise to this friction were often either trivial in nature, or, on more important questions, sometimes more apparent than real:

> Men ought to take heed of rending God's church by two kinds of controversies. The one is, when the matter of the point controverted is too small and light, not worth the heat and strife about it, kindled only by contradiction . . . The other is, when the matter of the point controverted is great, but it is driven to an over-great subtilty and obscurity . . . A man that is of judgment and understanding shall sometimes hear ignorant men differ and know well within himself that those which so differ mean one thing, and yet they themselves would never agree.[24]

The subject of disunity among Christians had occurred continually in Bacon's works, and, where it concerned differences between the Roman Catholic and Protestant faiths, had been treated, for the most part, in terms of Protestant indignation and justification. It was towards the end of his life that he extended his own boundaries to take a more comprehensive view, and this was closely connected with the intention that his 'new philosophy' should have the widest possible reception. He was well aware that insularity would penalize it in the eyes of foreigners, and he was anxious that it should not be ignored in Italy and France. For this reason, to avoid giving offence to the Roman Catholic Church, he made many changes and omissions in the text when his *Advancement of Learning*, first published in 1605, was republished in its much expanded Latin version, *De Augmentis Scientiarum*, in 1623.[25] He sent a copy to James I, saying:

> It is a translation, but enlarged almost to a new work . . . I have been also mine own *Index Expurgatorius*, that it may be read in all places. For since my end of putting it into Latin was to have it read everywhere, it had been an absurd contradiction to free it in the language and to pen it up in the matter.[26]

To Prince Charles he wrote:

> I send your Highness in all humbleness my book of 'Advancement of Learning' translated into Latin, but so enlarged as it may

---

[24] Francis Bacon, *Essayes or Counsels Civill and Morall* III, 'Of Unity in Religion': *Works*, vol. VI, pp. 382–3.
[25] A long list of such emended or omitted passages is given in *The Letters and the Life of Francis Bacon*, ed. James Spedding, 1874, vol. VII, p. 436, note 2.
[26] Ibid., p. 436.

go for a new work. It is a book I think will live, and be a citizen of the world, as English books are not.[27]

It was not that Bacon wanted Roman Catholic scholars and experimenters merely to read his work; he wanted their help. He knew that the actual work of compiling the 'Natural History', the stuff of which the new sciences were to be formed, would be vast, and he was eager to engage all the best talents. Following the publication of the *Novum Organum* in 1620, he had received inquiries from the distinguished French mathematician, Father Redemptus Baranzan, Professor of Philosophy and Mathematics at Annecy. In his answer Bacon had written on 31 July 1622:

A Natural History out of which philosophy may be built is (as you also observe) what I desire before anything else; nor shall I be wanting to the work, so far as in me lies. I wish I may have fit assistants. Nor can anything in this department fall out more happily than that you, being what you are, should contribute the first-fruits of the work, by composing a history of the Heavens, in which only the phenomena themselves, and the different astronomical instruments, with their uses, and then the principal and most celebrated hypotheses, both ancient and modern, and at the same time the exact calculations of the periodic returns, and other things of that kind, shall be set forth plainly and simply, without any doctrine or theory whatever. And if to this history of the Heavens you would add a history of Comets (concerning the composition of which I send herewith certain articles and as it were particular topics), you will have erected a truly magnificent frontispiece for Natural History, and done the greatest service to the Instauration of the Sciences, and a very great favour to myself.

I am getting a translation made of my book of the *Advancement of Learning*. It will be finished, please God, by the end of this summer; and I will send you a copy.[28]

In a letter to an Italian correspondent, Father Fulgenzio Micanzio, in about the autumn of 1625, Bacon gave a full account of his plans, already partly accomplished, for the

[27] *The Letters and the Life of Francis Bacon*, ed. James Spedding, vol. VII, p. 436.
[28] Ibid., p. 377, note 1.

publication of the 'Instauration'. Concerned, as always, about the amount of work to be done, he said:

> As for the third part, namely the 'Natural History', that is plainly a work for a King or Pope, or some college or order.[29]

By the time the Royal Society came into being, civil war had immeasurably complicated and intensified religious divisions in England, and the Society's religious policy is all the more remarkable in such an explosive situation. Sprat devotes a considerable part of the *History* to explaining and defending the Society's position. He begins:

> I will now proceed to the weightiest, and most solemn part of my whole *undertaking*; to make a defence of the *Royal Society*, and this new *Experimental Learning*, in respect of the *Christian Faith*. I am not ignorant, in what a slippery place I now stand; and what a tender matter I am enter'd upon. I know that it is almost impossible without offence, to speak of things of this Nature, in which all *Mankind*, each *Country*, and now almost every *Family*, do so widely disagree among themselves. I cannot expect that what I shall say will escape misinterpretation, though it be spoken with the greatest simplicity, and submission, while I behold that most men do rather value themselves, and others, on the little differences of *Religion*, than the main substance itself; . . .[30]

The Royal Society followed Bacon in its attitude to religion, but here distinction must be made between the Society as a body and its members as individuals. From the time of its formal institution at the Restoration in 1660, many of its members were Anglicans, with a high proportion of clerics and dignitaries, and from 1667 included Gilbert Sheldon, Archbishop of Canterbury.[31] This, together with the fact that Charles II, the head of the Established Church of England, was the Society's formal founder, might give the impression that the Society was a manifestation of the Establishment. But that is not so. While it supported Christian principles of conduct, it was not, as an institution, even Protestant. In its own *History* the Royal Society declared its position in these unequivocal terms:

[29] *The Letters and the Life of Francis Bacon*, ed. James Spedding, vol. VII, pp. 532–3, note 2.
[30] Thomas Sprat, *History*, pp. 345–6.
[31] Above, p. 13, note 18.

As for what belongs to the *Members* themselves, that are to constitute the *Society*: It is to be noted that they have freely admitted
Men of different Religions, Countries, and Professions of Life.
This they were oblig'd to do, or else they would come far short of
the largeness of their own Declarations. For they openly profess,
not to lay the Foundation of an *English, Scotch, Irish, Popish,* or
Protestant Philosophy; but a Philosophy of *Mankind.*[32]

Sprat pointed out the importance to the nation of this example:

Nor is it the least commendation the *Royal Society* deserves, that
designing a union of mens *Hands* and *Reasons*, it has proceeded so
far in uniting their *Affections*: For there we behold an unusual
sight to the *English Nation*, that men of disagreeing parties, and
ways of life, have forgotten to hate, and have met in the unanimous advancement of the same *Works*. There the *Soldier*, the
Tradesman, the *Merchant*, the *Scholar*, the *Gentleman*, the *Courtier*,
the *Divine*, the *Presbyteryan*, the *Papist*, the *Independent*, and those of
Orthodox Judgment, have laid aside their names of distinction, and
calmly conspir'd in a mutual agreement of *labors* and *desires*: ...
For here they do not only endure each others presence without
violence or fear; but they *work* and *think* in company, and confer
their help to each others *Inventions.*[33]

When the Society was incorporated by Royal Charter in
1662, it took the opportunity to make its intentions clear.
Its Council, formally nominated by the King, represented a
wide range of Christian allegiance—Roman Catholic and non-
conformist Protestant, as well as Anglican.[34] Politically its
Council was also inter-denominational, including in its number
Royalists who had gone into exile with Charles, Royalists who
had remained loyal throughout the Commonwealth, and supporters of Cromwell.[35] Similarly, foreigners had been readily
admitted as Fellows:

[32] Thomas Sprat, *History*, pp. 62–3.   [33] Ibid., p. 427.
[34] The membership of the Council was displayed prominently in that it
formed a part of the text of the Chapter itself, as it did in the Charter of
1663 which superseded the original one. Sir Kenelm Digby, a Roman
Catholic, appeared on both, together with Jonathan Goddard and Robert
Boyle, who were among the 'Low Church' element.
[35] Sprat mentions three of those who had gone into exile with Charles—
William Erskine, Sir Robert Moray and Sir Gilbert Talbot (*History*, p. 58);
others such as Viscount Brouncker (the President), John Evelyn and Sir

. . . the *Royal Society* has made no scruple, to receive all inquisitive strangers of all Countries, into its number. And this they have constantly done, with such peculiar respect, that they have not oblig'd them to charge of contributions: they have always taken care, that some of their Members, should assist them in interpreting all that pass'd, in their publick Assemblies: and they have freely open'd their Registers to them; thereby inviting them, to communicate forein Rarities, by imparting their own discoveries.[36]

Patriotism was neither to be identified with Protestantism nor with insularity; the Society looked outwards, to Europe and beyond. Calling on France's newly instituted Académie Royale des Sciences to help in the great task, the Royal Society stated its position:

To them, and to all the Learned World besides, they call for aid. No difference of *Country*, *Interest*, or profession of *Religion*, will make them backward from taking, or affording help in this enterprize. And indeed all *Europe* at this time, have two general Wars, which they ought in honor to make: The one a *holy*, the other a *Philosophical*: The one against the common Enemy of *Christendom*, the other also against powerful, and barbarous Foes, that have not been fully subdu'd almost these six thousand years, *Ignorance*, and *False Opinions*. Against these, it becomes us, to go forth in one common expedition: All civil Nations joyning their *Armies* against the one, and their *Reason* against the other; without any petty contentions, about privileges, or precedence.[37]

The supposition that the Royal Society was a manifestation of 'the Puritan ethic'[38] is refuted by the Society's own testimony, as well as by its conduct in action. Both in its embryo stage at Oxford and, after the Restoration, in London, this group was moving against the stream. It was in opposition to the boundaries set by party divisions, provincialism and

[36] Thomas Sprat, *History*, pp. 64–5.   [37] Ibid., p. 57.
[38] R. K. Merton, 'Science, Technology and Society in Seventeenth Century England', *Osiris*, 1938, vol. IV, pp. 360–632. Merton derived the term from 'the Protestant ethic', his source being Max Weber, *The Protestant Ethic and the Spirit of Capitalism* (translated from the German by T. Parsons), New York, 1930. Merton's inference is that the Royal Society was an expression of the Puritan movement in England in the seventeenth century.

Paul Neile had remained Royalists at home; John Wilkins and Jonathan Goddard had been prominent supporters of Cromwell.

nationalism, in a religious as well as a political connotation; as already seen, it wanted a two-way traffic with the outside world, particularly the countries of the Continent.

Nor was an active interest in experimental science and scientific exchange peculiarly Protestant. One outstanding illustration of this is the famous Florentine academy, the Cimento, founded in 1657, whose patron and leader Prince Leopoldo de' Medici, brother of the Grand Duke of Tuscany, had taken the initiative in approaching the Royal Society, as yet nameless, in 1661.[39] The Prince had asked just such an exchange as the Society was hoping for, and continued his correspondence with the Royal Society even after he became a Cardinal in 1667.[40] In the *History* Sprat says:

> In *Italy* the *Royal Society* has an excellent priviledge of receiving, and imparting *Experiments*, by the help of one of their own *Fellows*,[41] who has the opportunity of being *Resident* there for them, as well as for the *King*. From thence they have been earnestly invited to a mutual intelligence, by many of their most *Noble* Wits, but chiefly by the *Prince Leopoldo*, Brother of the Great Duke of *Thuscany*; who is the Patron of all the *Inquisitive Philosophers* of *Florence*: from whom there is coming out under his Name an account of their proceedings call'd *Ducal Experiments*.[42] This application to the *Royal Society* I have mention'd, because it comes from that Country, which is seldome wont to have any great regard, to the *Arts* of these *Nations*, that lye on this side of their mountains.[43]

Historians who have adopted the theory of 'the Puritan ethic' usually explain that they mean the term to apply less to a specific religious standpoint than to a philosophy of life which was secular and social in character, representing the freedom and initiative of the individual, typically of middle or yeoman class, against authoritarianism; and that this way of life was essentially utilitarian in its aspirations and activities. But while Puritanism may have produced a more secular society, it did not produce what appears to be assumed in this theory—a more democratic society; for it effected a shift of

---

[39] Above, p. 17.   [40] Above, p. 18.
[41] Sir John Finch. See above, pp. 17–18.
[42] This was published under the title *Saggi di Naturali Esperienze*. The Prince sent a copy to the Royal Society (above, p. 18).
[43] Thomas Sprat, *History*, p. 126.

control which diminished the civil and religious liberty of those who did not subscribe to it. At the same time, the character of rigorous intolerance which some other historians, mainly in the past, have attributed to this movement in its entirety, is exaggerated. During the brief tenure of Puritan government there were certainly some Puritans, like John Wilkins himself, who do not conform to that image. But the real point concerning this question is that the general outlook on life to which the term 'Puritan ethic' has been applied, did definitely tend to be class-conscious, insular and self-sufficient, characteristics which were inextricably bound up with the genuine (if limited) concern for liberty, stalwart independence and resourcefulness, which have been emphasized in the theory of 'the Puritan ethic'. The Royal Society, however, was without distinction of class, party, creed or race; outward-looking, and not utilitarian in the immediate sense.

The Royal Society might have pursued Bacon's scientific policy while ignoring its religious implications. That his concept as a whole was put into action, not only against the practice of the time, but in spite of the personal intolerance of some of the Fellows, was largely due to Wilkins. In the Society's earliest days at Oxford, Wilkins had shown unusual sympathy to those who were subject to political or religious discrimination by the authorities.[44] His own friends belonged to contending groups, but met amicably at Wadham College under his aegis.[45] While Master of Trinity College, Cambridge,

he joined with those who studied to propagate better thoughts, to take men off from being in parties, or from narrow notions, from superstitious conceits, and a fierceness about opinions.[46]

In 1668 Wilkins was a leader of those who

set on foot a treaty for a comprehension of such of the dissenters as could be brought into the communion of the church [of England], and a toleration of the rest.[47]

[44] Above, pp. 103–4.
[45] John Evelyn was one of Wilkins's Royalist friends who visited him at Wadham (above, p. 115).
[46] Gilbert Burnet, *The History of My Own Time*, ed. Osmund Airy, Oxford, 1897 and 1900, vol. I, p. 332.
[47] Ibid., p. 465.

But the opposition was too strong, and the attempt failed. Seth Ward was one of those who opposed it:

> [Ward and Wilkins] continued their old Friendship [from their Oxford days] till death, tho' it is not to be deny'd, that they after-wards differ'd in their Opinions concerning the Bill of Compre-hension, the Bishop of *Salisbury* opposing it, and the Bishop of *Chester* with great zeal espousing it.[48]

In 1670 the Conventicle Act, which had fallen into disuse, was revived. This Act was directed against all non-Anglicans, who by it were subject to indignities and severe penalties, Roman Catholics in particular.[49] Wilkins, who by this time was Bishop of Chester, withstood the hostility of his fellow-bishops and the opposition of the King, to speak most forcibly against the Act in the House of Lords, while it was being debated before becoming law. Gilbert Burnet, who knew Wilkins, records:

> When the act against conventicles was in that house, Wilkins argued long against it. The king was much for having it pass, not that he intended to execute it, but he was glad to have that body of men at mercy, and to force them to concur in the design for a general toleration. He spoke to Wilkins not to oppose it. He an-swered, he thought it an ill thing both in conscience and policy: therefore both as he was an Englishman and a bishop, he was bound to oppose it. The king then desired him not to come to the house while it depended. He [Wilkins] said, by the law and constitution of England, and by his majesty's favour, he had a right to debate and vote: and he was neither afraid nor ashamed to own his opinion in that matter, and to act pursuant to it. So he went on: and the king was not offended with his freedom.[50]

Again Seth Ward was among those on the other side:

> 'Tis true, he [Ward] was for the Act against Conventicles, and labour'd much to get it pass, not without the Order and Direction of the greatest Authority, both Civil and Ecclesiastical, not out of Enmity to the Dissenters Persons, as they unjustly suggested, but of Love to the repose and welfare of the Government; for he

---

[48] Walter Pope, *Life of Seth, Lord Bishop of Salisbury*, p. 54.
[49] For the terms of this Act see *Statutes of the Realm* (1625–80), 1819, vol. 5, pp. 648–51.
[50] Gilbert Burnet, *The History of My Own Time*, ed. Osmund Airy, Oxford, 1897 and 1900, vol. I, pp. 493–4.

believ'd if the growth of them were not timely suppressed, it would either cause a necessity of a standing Army to preserve the Peace, or a general Toleration, which would end in Popery, whether [i.e. whither] all things then had an apparent tendancy.[51]

An examination of the *Journals of the House of Lords* for the period that this Act was under consideration shows that Wilkins was present for every debate on it. Well might Burnet say of him: 'He had a courage in him that could stand against a current'.[52]

Wilkins's tolerance earned him the censure of the bigoted, but the praise of the discriminating. Anthony Wood, admiring all else about him, saw it as a deficiency in 'a constant mind and setled principles'.[53] To John Evelyn he was 'this incomparable man, the most universaly beloved of all that knew him'.[54]

At a time when public office and the learned professions were barred to all those who did not conform to the Established Church of England, the Royal Society had publicly repudiated such a limit on its membership, and 'openly professed'[55] its policy. This aroused resentment among some of the Anglicans outside the Society, notwithstanding the presence of the Archbishops of Canterbury and York and several bishops within it. The grounds of complaint were not that the Society was Puritan, but that it was 'Papist'. Henry Stubbe was extremely vociferous on this subject. In *Legends no Histories*, published in 1670, he attacked the opinion expressed in Sprat's *History* that 'It is dishonorable, to pass a hard Censure on the Religions of all other Countries',[56] Sprat's tacit reference being to the Roman Catholic Church. Stubbe continued:

Mr. *Sprat*, Mr. *Sprat* let me tell you and some of your fellow-*Virtuosi*, that there is tenderness *for those without* which is *Cruelty* to *those within*: . . .

[51] Walter Pope, *Life of Seth, Lord Bishop of Salisbury*, p. 68.
[52] Gilbert Burnet, *The History of My Own Time*, ed. Osmund Airy, vol. I, p. 455.
[53] Anthony Wood, *Athenae Oxonienses*, 1691–2, vol. II, p. 371.
[54] *The Diary of John Evelyn*, ed. E. S. De Beer, vol. III, p. 518.
[55] Above, p. 151.
[56] Thomas Sprat, *History*, p. 63. Stubbe refers to this passage in a marginal note in *Legends no Histories*, p. 19.

Stubbe then said pointedly that the *History* gave the impression that the Royal Society was 'making way for the Introducing of som thing else besides a *New Philosophy*'.[57] In *Campanella Revived*, also published in 1670, Stubbe contended that the Royal Society was intent on 'reducing *England* unto *Popery*'.[58]

Another complaint came from Thomas Barlow, in 1675, shortly before he became Bishop of Lincoln. He was writing, he said, '*sub sigillo*', to a friend who had sent him a published copy of a lecture read before the Royal Society by Sir William Petty on 26 November 1674:

> I confess I am, and (a long time) have been not a little troubled, to see Protestants, nay Clergy-men, and Bishops, approve and propagate, that which they miscall *New-Philosophy*; so that our Universities begin to be infected with it, little considering the Cause or Consequences of it, or how it tends evidently to the advantage of *Rome*, and the ruine of our Religion.[59]

He declared that:

> It is certain this *New-Philosophy* (as they call it) was set on foot, and has been carried on by the Arts of *Rome* . . . for the great Writers and Promoters of it are of the Roman Religion: (such as *Des Cartes, Gassendus, Du Hamel,* . . . *Mersennus,* . . . &c.)[60]

and said that their aim was to bring about the fall of Protestantism by causing theological division and confusion among Protestants. This, he considered, had been very successful:

> and what divisions this new Philosophy has caused amongst Protestants in *Holland* and *England*, cannot be unknown to any considering person.[61]

How a paper on *Duplicate Proportion together with a New Hypothesis of Springing or Elastique Motions* (explained as Petty said, 'in a way which the meanest Member of adult Mankind is capable of understanding')[62] could give rise to such alarm, is

---

[57] Henry Stubbe, *Legends no Histories*, p. 20.
[58] This is part of the sub-title, and indicates the entire theme.
[59] *The Genuine Remains of that Learned Prelate Dr. Thomas Barlow*, ed. P. Pett, London, 1693, p. 157. The editor was Sir Peter Pett, who published these papers about two years after Barlow's death.
[60] Ibid., pp. 157–8.   [61] Ibid., p. 158.
[62] In 'The Epistle Dedicatory' of his book.

hard to see; but it does illustrate the fantastic nervous fears which the Royal Society had to contend with. The President and Council of the Royal Society, who had formally ordered the publication of the lecture,[63] would doubtless have been exasperated, though hardly surprised, by Barlow's commentary on Petty's text, of which one example will suffice to show its tenor. 'I suppose', Petty had said, 'all the *First Matter* of the World to be *Atoms*; that is, Matter Immutable in Magnitude and Figure . . . and that all *Juncture* of *Atomes* is made by their *Innate motions*'.[64] Scolding Petty, in what amounts to several pages of small print, for being atheistic and (perhaps worse) for quoting from Gassendi, Barlow ended triumphantly, '*In the beginning God Created the Heaven and the Earth*, &c no mention of Atomes'![65]

The Royal Society was, in fact, what it said it was, independent of party, and, not least, of party in religion. It was an upholder of Christian principles, while insisting on the right of the individual to follow his conscience in religious practice. It was a minority group which nevertheless attracted to itself many of the most gifted and powerful minds of that age, and mitigated the neurosis engendered by party divisions and national isolationism, at the same time constituting a highly-civilized movement towards the full liberty of the subject.

[63] This is stated in the Royal Society's imprimatur, which is placed before the text.
[64] William Petty, *Duplicate Proportion together with a New Hypothesis of Springing or Elastique Motions*, 1674, pp. 17–18.
[65] *The Genuine Remains of that Learned Prelate Dr. Thomas Barlow*, ed. P. Pett, 1693, p. 155.

PART TWO

I

JOHN WALLIS'S ACCOUNTS OF
THE ORIGIN OF THE ROYAL
SOCIETY

In 1678, eleven years after Sprat's *History* was published, John Wallis, in a dispute with another Fellow about something else, gave it as his opinion that the Royal Society had not started at Oxford, but in London several years earlier. Little contemporary notice seems to have been taken of this, the first of Wallis's two similar versions of the origin, which was contained in a self-defensive tract published by Wallis himself.[1]

He wrote a second version in 1697,[2] differing somewhat in its details, which remained in manuscript until more than twenty years after his death. This version, included in an

[1] John Wallis, *A Defence of the Royal Society*, Oxford, 1678. The only seventeenth-century reference to Wallis's account appears to be in the MS. of Anthony Wood's *The History and Antiquities of the University of Oxford*, which was not published until it was edited by John Gutch in 1796. Wood merely quotes Wallis's tract, giving the page numbers (Bodleian Library MS. Wood F.1, on a double sheet of writing paper inserted between pp. 1065 and 1066). In the printed text (vol. II, pt. II, pp. 632–3) no indication is given that Wood was merely quoting this tract.

[2] Bodleian Library MS. Smith 31, pp. 47–8. The amanuensis is Humfrey Wanley (1672–1726).

account of his life which he sent to Dr. Thomas Smith,[3] a collector of rare books and manuscripts, was among miscellaneous papers which on Smith's death passed to Thomas Hearne, the historical antiquary.[4] In 1725 Hearne inserted Wallis's autobiography in the preface to his edition of *Peter Langtoft's Chronicle*.[5] By this means Wallis's opinion on the origin of the Royal Society reached a much wider public than before, and one which was no longer contemporary.

Hearne made no comment on the contents of the document, but in 1756 Thomas Birch, writing on the origin of the Royal Society, quoted from Hearne's preface and said that 'upon the authority of Dr. Wallis' it was evident that Sprat had not traced the Royal Society to its source.[6] This view has been repeated ever since.

The circumstances in which Wallis wrote the first version of this account were very different from those in which Sprat had written his. Sprat's work had been subject to a methodical scrutiny by a wide range of informed persons, whose business was a calm appraisal of facts; Wallis wrote in passionate self-defence, trying to invalidate by argument all the statements made by his opponent.

The situation had arisen in this way. In 1659–60 Dr. William Holder, the brother-in-law of Sir Christopher Wren, had taught a deaf mute to speak. This was a ten-year-old boy, Alexander Popham, who had been deaf and dumb all his life. It seems to have been the first experiment of its kind in this country.[7]

---

[3] 1638–1710.

[4] Bodleian Library MS. Smith 132, p. 74. This manuscript contains a catalogue of the papers left by Thomas Smith to Hearne. Those relating to the life of Wallis are listed as 'Num. cxxi 1'.

[5] Thomas Hearne, The Publisher's Appendix to his Preface, *Peter Langtoft's Chronicle*, London, 1725, pp. clxi–clxiv.

[6] Thomas Birch, *The History of the Royal Society*, London, 1756–7, p. 1. John Ward, *The Lives of the Professors of Gresham College*, London, 1740, p. x, quoting Wallis's account from Hearne, had already said: 'Dr. Wallis has traced this matter farthest back of any writer I know of; and, as what he sais, is from his own knowledge, his relation is the more authentic'. But Ward saw in this no contradiction to Sprat's account. Instead, curiously, he took Sprat's (which was written much earlier) to confirm Wallis's account: 'This account is confirmed by another celebrated writer . . .' (ibid., p. xi).

[7] Sir Kenelm Digby in *The Nature of Bodies*, London, 1645, p. 308, says that a priest in Spain had done this. Digby adds that he told Charles I about it, and that he was greatly interested.

Holder published a short description of it in the *Philosophical Transactions* of the Royal Society in 1668[8] and mentioned it in an appendix to his book *Elements of Speech* in the following year.[9] In the dispute eighteen years after the treatment, Holder said that Wallis knew what had been done and had even been to see and hear the boy.

Two years after Holder's experiment, Wallis, having raised the question whether it would be possible to teach a dumb person to speak, as though he had never heard of this case, successfully taught a young man to speak, who had been deaf only since he was five years old. Wallis brought his achievement to the notice of the Royal Society, which asked him to bring the young man before one of its meetings. This Wallis did, and was greatly commended for his skill.[10] Then he treated Holder's former patient, who after a lapse of two years had lost his earlier ability to speak, but who quickly regained it with further help. Wallis gave his account of these cases to Henry Oldenburg in 1670, for inclusion in the *Philosophical Transactions*,[11] of which he was the editor. No mention was made of Holder's earlier treatment.

Holder knew nothing about this article until 1678, when someone showed it to him, and then he took exception to it as failing to give a full account of the facts. Later that year he published a tract entitled *A Supplement to the Philosophical Transactions of July 1670*, giving his view of the case. He related how the original patient, Alexander Popham, had been sent to him, and incidentally mentioned the origin of the Royal Society:

> Some years immediately before His Majesties happy Restauration, divers ingenious persons in *Oxford* used to meet at the Lodgings of that excellent Person, and zealous promoter of Learning, the late Bishop of *Chester*, Dr. *Wilkins*, then Warden of *Wadham* College, where they diligently conferred about Researches and

---

[8] *Philosophical Transactions*, London, 1668, pp. 665–8.

[9] William Holder, *Elements of Speech: an Essay of Inquiry into the Natural Production of Letters: with an Appendix concerning Persons Deaf and Dumb*, London, 1669. The book carries the imprimatur of the Royal Society, and is published by '*J. Martyn* Printer to the *R. Society*'.

[10] Journal Book (14 May 1662), vol. I, pp. 60–1.

[11] *Philosophical Transactions*, 1670, no. 61, pp. 1087–99. (The pagination is incorrect, repeating that in an earlier part of the volume.)

Experiments in Nature, and indeed laid the first Ground and
Foundation of the Royal Society. In that time, *viz.* in the Year
1659, *Alexander Popham* Esq; being deprived of Hearing from his
Birth, and consequently of Speaking, about the Tenth year of his
Age, by the Instance of Dr. *Ward*, now Lord Bishop of *Sarum*, and
the said Bishop *Wilkins*, and Dr. *Bathurst*, the present Dean of
Wells, was recommended to the care of Dr. *William Holder*, then
Rector of *Bletchington*, near *Oxford*, and brought thither to him.[12]

Wallis, in an angry reply, rather oddly entitled *A Defence of the
Royal Society*, contradicted everything Holder had said, including his reference to the origin of the Royal Society. In his
opinion, said Wallis, the Royal Society had begun in London
in about 1645.

Anthony Wood, in characteristic style, had something to
say about this business:

> Dr. *Wallis* (who, at any time, can make black white, and white
> black, for his own ends, and hath a ready knack of sophistical
> evasion, as the writer of these matters doth know full well) did
> soon after publish an answer to that *Supplement*.[13]

Even John Aubrey, whose judgment was much more impartial
than Wood's generally was, came to much the same conclusion.
He said:

> Dr. John Wallis unjustly arrogates the glory of teaching the sayd
> young gentleman to speake, in the Philosophical Transactions.[14]

In the same manuscript, a few pages farther on, Aubrey says
of Wallis:

> Tis certaine that he is a person of reall worth and may stand with
> much glory upon his owne basis, needing not [to] be beholding
> to any man for fame, of which he is so extremely greedy, that
> he steales flowers from others to adorne his own cap,—e.g. he
> lies at watch, at Sir Christopher Wren's discourse, Mr. Robert
> Hooke's, Dr. William Holder, &c.; putts downe their notions in
> his note book, and then prints it, without owneing the authors.
> This frequently, of which they complaine.[15]

[12] William Holder, *A Supplement to the Philosophical Transactions of July 1670*,
London, 1678, p. 4.
[13] Anthony Wood, *Fasti Oxonienses*, 1691–2, vol. II, p. 816.
[14] Bodleian Library MS. Aubrey 6, fol. 88 (and *Brief Lives*, vol. I, p. 404).
[15] Ibid., ff. 94ᵛ–5 (and *Brief Lives*, vol. II, pp. 281–2).

Wallis's second, modified, version is fuller, though there is a significant omission. He had previously said that these meetings in London from about 1645 were organized according to rules: that there was a penalty for non-attendance, and that members paid a weekly contribution to cover the cost of experiments.[16] It seems not unlikely that in his first version, writing hurriedly in a very defensive and excited frame of mind, and a considerable time after the events he was recalling, Wallis had genuinely confused what had been done at those meetings with what was later done at Oxford, or even at the modest start of the Royal Society proper in London in 1660.[17] In his second version there is no mention at all of rules, penalties, or of arrangements for weekly experiments.

The whole question turns on the *nature* of these meetings described by Wallis; and, notwithstanding the unavoidable inference that Wallis, in his first version, was a very defensive man, and in his second version a very stubborn one, he implicitly answers this question himself. It was an informal society which met at a number of places, wherever it happened to be convenient,[18] to discuss, collect and disseminate information on various learned subjects, including topics of general interest relating to 'the New Philosophy'. Wallis begins:

About the year 1645, while I lived in *London* (at a time, when, by our Civil Wars, Academical Studies were much interrupted in both our Universities:) beside the Conversation of divers eminent Divines, as to matters Theological; I had the opportunity of being acquainted with divers worthy Persons, inquisitive into Natural Philosophy, and other parts of Humane Learning; And particularly of what hath been called the *New Philosophy* or *Experimental Philosophy*.[19]

[16] John Wallis, *A Defence of the Royal Society*, 1678, p. 7.
[17] When the Society was formally established in 1660 it made rules for attendance, subscriptions, etc., which resembled those made earlier, at Oxford (above, p. 129), and recorded them in its Journal Book on 5 December 1660, vol. I, p. 1.
[18] Wallis says in his second version that the meetings were held 'sometimes at Dr. Goddard's lodgings in *Woodstreet* . . . sometime at a convenient place in *Cheap-side*; sometime at *Gresham College* or some place near adjoyning' (below, p. 166).
[19] Bodleian Library MS. Smith 31, p. 47, and Thomas Hearne, *Peter Langtoft's Chronicle*, 1725, p. clxi.

Wallis here shows that experimental science was only one of the subjects under the general heading of 'Humane Learning', which they discussed. It appears to have been a special interest, but it was not their sole purpose for meeting. When he lists the topics considered under the specific heading of 'the New Philosophy', even more is revealed about the nature of the meetings. Analysis of this list shows that the subjects they discussed were some of the most notable examples of practical discovery and speculation in that age, and were a talking point in Europe generally—discoveries made independently by individual experimenters, who were not members of that club, in widely differing times and places. As Wallis himself says of them:

> Some . . . were then but New Discoveries, and others not so generally known & imbraced, as now they are. . . .[20]

Wallis continues his narrative:

> We did by agreement, divers of us, meet weekly in *London* on a certain day, to treat and discourse of such affairs. Of which number were *Dr. John Wilkins* (afterward *Bp. of Chester*) *Dr. Jonathan Goddard, Dr. George Ent, Dr. Glisson, Dr. Merret,* (Drs. in Physick,) *Mr. Samuel Foster* then Professor of Astronomy at *Gresham College, Mr. Theodore Hank*[21] (a German of the *Palatinate* and then Resident in *London,* who, I think gave the first occasion, & first suggested those meetings) & many others.
>
> These meetings we held sometimes at *Dr. Goddards* lodgings in *Woodstreet* (or some convenient place near) on occasion of his keeping an Operator in his house, for grinding Glasses for Telescopes & Miscroscopes;[22] and sometime at a convenient place in *Cheap-side*; sometime at *Gresham College* or some place near adjoyning.
>
> Our business was (precluding matters of Theology & State Affairs) to discourse and consider of *Philosophical Enquiries,* and such as related thereunto; as *Physick, Anatomy, Geometry, Astronomy, Navigation, Staticks, Magneticks, Chymicks, Meckanicks,* and *Natural*

[20] Below, p. 167.   [21] A slip, by the amanuensis, for 'Haak'.
[22] Seth Ward, in the dedication to *In Ismaelis Bullialdi Astronomiae Philolaicae Fundamenta, Inquisitio Brevis,* Oxford, 1653, refers to Goddard's interest in telescopes and other instruments, and thought that he was the first Englishman to construct a telescope: 'Diu est ex quo telescopia praestantissima primus, quantum ego scio, Anglorum ipse fecisti'.

Experiments; with the State of these Studies, as then cultivated, at home and abroad. We there discoursed of the *Circulation of the Bloud, the Valves in the Veins, the Venæ Lacteæ, the Lymphatick Vessels,* [23] *the Copernican Hypothesis, the Nature of Comets, and New Stars, the Satellites of Jupiter, the Oval Shape* (as it then appeared) *of Saturn, the spots in the Sun, and its Turning on its own Axis,* [24] *the Inequalities & Selenography of the Moon, the several Phases of Venus & Mercury, the Improvement of Telescopes, and grinding of Glasses for that purpose, the Weight of Air, the Possibility or Impossibility of Vacuities, and Natures Abhorence thereof, the Torricellian Experiment in Quicksilver, the Descent of heavy Bodies, and the degrees of Acceleration therein*; and divers other things of like nature. Some of which were then but New Discoveries, and other not so generally known & imbraced, as now they are, with other things appertaining to what hath been called *The New Philosophy*; which, from the times of *Galileo* at *Florence*, and *Sr. Francis Bacon* (*Lord Verulam*) in *England*, hath been much cultivated in *Italy, France, Germany*, & other Parts abroad, as well as with us in *England*.

About the year 1648, 1649, some of our company being removed to *Oxford* (first *Dr. Wilkins*, then I, and soon after *Dr. Goddard*) our company divided. Those in *London* continued to meet there as before (and we with them, when we had occasion to be there;) and those of us at *Oxford*; with *Dr. Ward* (since *Bp. of Salisbury*) *Dr. Ralph Bathurst* (now *President of Trinity College in Oxford*) *Dr. Petty* (since *Sr. William Petty*) *Dr. Willis* (then an eminent Physician in Oxford) and divers others, continued such meetings in Oxford; and brought those Studies into fashion there; meeting first at *Dr. Petties* Lodgings, (in an Apothecaries house) because of the convenience of inspecting Drugs, and the like, as there was occasion; And after his remove to *Ireland* (tho' not so constantly) at the Lodgings of *Dr. Wilkins*, then Warden of *Wadham Coll*. And after his removal to *Trinity College in Cambridge*, at the Lodgings of *the Honourable Mr. Robert Boyle*, then resident for several years in *Oxford*.

Those meetings in *London* continued, and (after the Kings Return in 1660) were increased with the accession of divers worthy &

[23] Wallis inserted 'the Venæ Lacteæ, the Lymphatick Vessels' in this version (in his own hand, between the lines of the text written by his amanuensis).
[24] Wallis also inserted 'the spots in the Sun, and its Turning on its own Axis' in this version.

Honourable Persons; & were afterwards incorporated by the name of *the Royal Society*, &c. and so continue to this day.[25]

Wallis's list of subjects discussed by this club is very important in revealing its nature; they will therefore be considered in order.

The first topic on Wallis's list is '*the Circulation of the Bloud*'. William Harvey (1578–1657) had published his treatise *Exercitatio anatomica de motu cordis et sanguinis in animalibus* at Frankfurt in 1628, proving the circulation of the blood.

In an earlier passage in this autobiography, Wallis had already made some revealing remarks on his attitude to this discovery, and indeed to 'the New Philosophy' itself. Recalling his own experience of science as taught at Cambridge University in the early 1640s, he showed that at that period 'the Schoolmen' still dominated the natural sciences, and that even Dr. Francis Glisson was still teaching anatomy by the medieval method of disputation. In teaching Harvey's discovery in this way, Glisson illustrated a danger against which Bacon had warned—that of reducing the effectiveness of such new discoveries as had been made, by absorbing them into the old framework,[26] disputation being incapable of producing any further development of scientific knowledge. Wallis had said:

> From Logick, I proceeded to *Ethicks*, *Physicks* and *Metaphysicks*, (consulting the Schoolmen on such points) according to the Methods of *Philosophy*, then in fashion in that University. And I took into it the Speculative part of *Physick & Anatomy*; as parts of *Natural Philosophy*; and as *Dr. Glisson*, (then *Publick Professor of Physick* at that University) hath since told me, I was the first of his Sons, who (in a publick Disputation) maintain'd the Circulation of the Bloud, (which was then a new Doctrine,) tho' I had no Design of Practising *Physick*. And I had then imbib'd the Principles of what they now call the *New Philosophy*.[27]

This was the situation at that time among the most advanced of university teachers, but since Wallis wrote this passage more than fifty years later, in 1697, it seems to indicate that

[25] Bodleian Library MS. Smith 31, pp. 47–8, and Thomas Hearne, *Peter Langtoft's Chronicle*, 1725, pp. clxi–clxiv.
[26] Above, pp. 33–4.
[27] Bodleian Library MS. Smith 31, pp. 41–2 and Thomas Hearne, *Peter Langtoft's Chronicle*, pp. cxlix–cl.

he never did fully appreciate the state of affairs which John Wilkins and those closest to him in his group at Oxford sought to remedy.

Wallis's second topic is '*the Valves in the Veins*'. Hieronymo Fabrizio ab Aquapendente, also known as Fabricius (1537–1619), the Italian anatomist and former teacher of Harvey, had already published his *De venarum ostiodis* at Padua in 1603, describing the 'valves in the veins', though it was Harvey who realized their function.

The third topic mentioned, '*the Venæ Lacteæ, the Lymphatick Vessels*', was a discovery made by Gaspero Aselli (1581–1626) of Pavia. His discovery of the lacteal or lymphatic vessels which collect and carry the fatty content of food from the intestine into the bloodstream was made known in his *De lactibus sive lacteis venis*, published posthumously in 1627.

Wallis's list continues with a classic of philosophical as well as of scientific controversy, '*the Copernican Hypothesis*'. In 1543 Nicolaus Copernicus (1473–1543), a Polish astronomer, expounded the theory, in his *De Revolutionibus Orbium Coelestium*, that the earth moved round the sun (which was static) and revolved on its own axis,[28] in contradiction to the Ptolemaic conception of the universe with the earth at rest at the centre, surrounded by concentric spheres. Thus the conflicting claims of these theories had been argued for a hundred years before this club began.

Galileo Galilei (1564–1642) in his *Sidereus Nuntius* (1610) helped to confirm the main contention of the Copernican theory (that the earth revolved round the sun) by observations made with the use of an improved telescope of his own invention, which he described in detail. His discoveries included the four satellites of Jupiter and the mountainous surface of the moon ('mapped' by Hevelius in *Selenographia*, 1647). In the same year he discovered that Venus has phases like the moon.

Martinus Hortensius of Amsterdam observed the phases of Mercury, and published his *Dissertatio de Mercurio in Sole viso, et Venere invisa, instituta cum Petro Gassendo* in 1633.

Galileo discussed the nature of sun-spots in his *Discorso intorno alle cose che stanno in su l'acqua o che in quella si muovono*

---

[28] This was basically a revival of the theory of Aristarchus of Samos, a Greek who lived in the third century B.C. Copernicus had proposed the hypothesis many years earlier, but this was the occasion of its publication in full.

published in 1612. In 1619, after the appearance of three comets, he wrote *Discorso della Comete di Mario Guiducci*, where he discussed their nature. All these discoveries were also considered at the meetings in London, as they were in very many other places; and doubtless, as Wallis implies, when on occasion the members met at Goddard's lodgings, the opportunity was taken to look through his telescopes and microscopes.[29]

Wallis's next topic was another innovation which had caused argument among philosophers even more than among experimenters. Aristotle had flatly denied the possibility of a void, but Evangelista Torricelli (1608–47), an Italian, had proved, with his 'tube' or barometer containing mercury, that a vacuum (in the sense of a space without air) could be obtained. He also maintained, what Galileo had already asserted, that the atmosphere had weight. This was in 1643, and was therefore one of the most recent of the classic experiments discussed by the group. Boyle later referred to 'that famous controversy about vacuum in which the *Aristotelians* were great champions for the negative'.[30]

The last topic on Wallis's list arises from the publication in 1632 of Galileo's *Dialogo sopra i due massimi sistemi del mondo* in which the Ptolemaic and Copernican systems are discussed in the form of a dialogue, to the greater justification of the latter, and where Galileo enunciated the law of the acceleration of freely falling bodies.

If any original research was carried out by this club as a body, Wallis does not mention it; and it is obvious from this list that even in the discussions concerned with experimental science (which was only one of the subjects the members considered), their basic purpose was the collection, discussion and dissemination of information on discoveries made by others.

Francis Bacon had no particular significance to this group. Wallis merely associates him with Galileo in marking the time when interest in the subject first became general in Europe. Wallis concludes the list by saying:

> . . . with other things appertaining to what hath been called *The New Philosophy*; which, from the times of *Galileo* at *Florence*, and

[29] Above, p. 166 and note 22.
[30] Robert Boyle, *Works*, 1744, vol. V, p. 674. By a slip 'negative' has been rendered 'affirmative', but this is corrected in the second edition, 1772, vol. VI, p. 701.

Sr. Francis Bacon (Lord Verulam) in England, hath been much cultivated in *Italy*, *France*, *Germany*, & other Parts abroad, as well as with us in *England*.[31]

Wallis's list, published in 1678, and rewritten with additions in 1697,[32] closely follows part of Joseph Glanvill's *Plus Ultra*, published in 1668, where Glanvill enumerated, and at times discussed, discoveries which he considered of particular significance in the study of physical phenomena. Concerned with developments in science up to the time he went to press, Glanvill's catalogue of discoveries included recent work done by the Royal Society, and went twenty years past the period of the meetings referred to by Wallis.

Practically every item in Wallis's list, including the additions[33] made in 1697, twenty years after his first version, is present in Glanvill's catalogue, almost entirely in the same order, and at times expressed in strikingly similar language. Whether or not Wallis actually followed Glanvill's text when listing topics of scientific interest discussed at those meetings so many years before, is unimportant. The point is that, having compiled a list similar to Glanvill's, Wallis used it for a very different purpose, and one which Glanvill's exposition completely invalidates.

In making his catalogue at all, Glanvill was of course naming actual discoveries and discoverers, not listing items which were merely debated or considered by others, as Wallis was. And Glanvill had stressed the point that while, in themselves, these '*Inventions of single Endeavourers*' were of great value, the Royal Society, with its much wider scope, had the means to promote scientific research on a scale previously undreamed of:

> Now whoever considers with the Noble Verulam, how much the *state* of things in the World hath been *altered* and *advanced* by these THREE EXPERIMENTS alone [the inventions of printing, the compass and gunpowder],[34] will conceive great hopes of Modern *Experimental Attempts*, from which greater matters may be looked for, than those which were the *Inventions* of *single Endeavourers*, or the *results* of *Chance*.

[31] Above, p. 167.   [32] Above, p. 161.   [33] Above, p. 167, notes 23, 24.
[34] Bacon refers to these discoveries in the *Novum Organum* I, Aph. CXXIX: *Works*, vol. IV, p. 114.

And of all the *Combinations* of Men that ever met for the *Improvement* of *Science*, there were never any whose *Designs* were better laid, whose *Encouragements* were *greater*, whose *Abilities* were more *promising*, or whose *Constitution* was more *judiciously* or *advantageously* formed, than the *ROYAL SOCIETY*.[35]

In his section on 'the Study, Use, and vast Improvements of *ANATOMY*' Glanvill considered the discovery of the Circulation of the Blood to be of the first importance, and he dealt with it at length at the end of a catalogue of other 'anatomical' discoveries:

> But of all the *modern Discoveries, Wit* and *Industry* have made in the *Oeconomy* of *humane Nature*, the Noblest is that of the *Circulation* of the *Blood*, which was the Invention of our deservedly-famous *Harvey*.[36]

Wallis, who did not discuss any of the topics he mentioned, gave this subject prominence by placing it first on the list. After that, his order is almost exactly the same as Glanvill's, which in the relevant items is as follows:

> The *Valves* of the *Veins*, discover'd by *Fabricius ab Aquapendente*; . . . The *Lymphatick Vessels*, by Dr. *Joliffe, Bartholin* and *Olaus Rudbeck*; . . . [*Plus Ultra*, p. 14; in the summary, p. 74, 'the *Venæ Lacteæ*, the *Vasa Lymphatica*'].[37]

After a section on Geometry, in which Wallis was highly praised for his contribution to Mathematics, Glanvill went on to Astronomy:

> *Copernicus* restored the *Hypothesis* of *Pythagoras* and *Philolaus,* and gave far more *neat* and *consistent Accounts* of the *Phænomena*. . . . *Galilæo* . . . discovered the *Nature* of the *Galaxy*, . . . *New Stars* . . . the *Asseclæ* [*Satellites*] of *Jupiter* . . . the strange *Phases of Saturne*, on while *oblong*, and then *round*; the *increment* and *decrement* of

---

[35] Joseph Glanvill, *Plus Ultra*, pp. 82–3.   [36] Ibid., p. 15.
[37] Further observations on these ducts (mentioned above, p. 169) were made, apparently independently of each other, in 1651 by Thomas Bartholinus, a Dane, whose *Vasa Lymphatica* was published in Copenhagen in 1653, and Olaus Rudbeck, a Swede, who published his *Hepaticos Aquosos et Vasa Glandularum Serosa* at Westeräs in 1653. Dr. George Joyliffe (1621–58) may have made similar independent observations at about the same time, though the first public announcement of it was in 1654, by Francis Glisson in his *Anatomia Hepatis*, London, Chapter XXXI, pp. 266–7.

Venus, like the *Moon*; the *Spots* in the *Sun*, and its *Revolution* upon its own *Axis* . . . *Hevelius* [in his *Selenographia*] drew a *Graphical Description* of the *Moon* in all its *Phases*, as it appear'd in the *Telescope* . . . shewing the *inequality* and *mountanous protuberances* of its surface . . . *Martinus Hortensius* found *Mercury* to have variety of *Phases*, like the *Moon*; . . .[38]

Glanvill next discussed the importance of the telescope and said that 'several ingenious Members of the ROYAL SOCIETY are now busie about improving them to a greater height'.[39]

After this came discussion of other instruments for measuring, including the barometer, by which

the way is found to measure all the *degrees* of *Compression* in the *Atmosphere*, and to estimate exactly any *accession* of *weight*, which the Air receives . . .[40]

Glanvill explained how to make a barometer, and the principle of it. He continued:

This *Experiment* was the *Invention* of *Torricellius*, and used to little more purpose at first, but to prove a *Vacuum* in Nature . . .[41]

Wallis's list, which so closely resembles Glanvill's, is obviously worthless as evidence of an earlier date for the prototype of the Royal Society, for it reveals that the club in question was quite different from the Royal Society in nature and purpose.

Wallis's inadvertent evidence on the nature and purpose of the London meetings, and his stated belief that Theodore Haak inspired them, is corroborated by Haak himself. This information comes from his correspondence with Father Marin Mersenne in Paris, while the London meetings were going on.[42] Haak, a native of Neuhausen in the Palatinate, who had settled in this country, was a man of considerable intellectual

---

[38] Joseph Glanvill, *Plus Ultra*, pp. 40 and 42–6; see also pp. 39, 72.
[39] Ibid., p. 55.   [40] Ibid., p. 59.   [41] Ibid., p. 61.
[42] Five letters, which survive from the correspondence between Haak and Mersenne during the period of the London club, were written by Haak, the first dated 24 May/3 June 1647, and the last 3/13 July 1648. These are MS. Bibliothèque Nationale Nouv. acq. françaises 6206 ff. 89, 167, 91, 168 and 64 in chronological order. Harcourt Brown, *Scientific Organizations in Seventeenth Century France*, Baltimore, 1934, Chapter III, refers to this correspondence.

curiosity, and interested in 'the New Philosophy' as an important aspect of 'the republic of letters' which was his permanent preoccupation.[43]

Mersenne,[44] a friar of the Order of Minims, was a theologian and mathematician, and at that time provided one of the main centres in France for the discussion and exchange of news about 'the New Philosophy'. But since this term has often been used loosely, it is well to be aware that Mersenne's connotation was not that of Bacon and the Royal Society.

At the time that Bacon's *Novum Organum* was published, Mersenne was still essentially Aristotelian in outlook, and in his *Quaestiones in Genesim*, published in 1623, condemned as false any hypothesis which challenged that system.[45] To ensure what he considered to be the proper intellectual control of knowledge, and no doubt to offset Bacon's proposal of colleges on an international scale for 'arts and sciences at large',[46] Mersenne recommended that an Academy of Sciences should be founded in France. This institution was, of course, to be for 'the sciences' according to the scholastic system, not for sciences in the modern sense.[47] Mersenne wanted this foundation to be under the patronage of the Pope and the princes, an academic centre of international importance, which distinguished scholars from other European countries would be invited to join.[48]

Rejecting Bacon's concept of science, Mersenne, in *La Verité des Sciences*, published in 1625, said that man's investigation of nature was incapable of penetrating beyond his sense perceptions to interior structures and processes, whose study Bacon had urged. 'For that reason', said Mersenne, 'I consider that Verulamius's plan is impossible.'[49]

Mersenne's idea of a scholastic academy was never realized, but in 1635 he formed a small group which he named 'Academia Parisiensis'.[50] By that time he had discarded the Aristotelian philosophy for a 'mechanical philosophy' much influenced by Descartes. This theory rationalized all the

---

[43] Below, pp. 196–7.   [44] 1588–1648.

[45] Marin Mersenne, *Quaestiones in Genesim*, Paris, 1623, Praefatio, et Prolegomena ad Lectorem.

[46] Below, p. 209.   [47] See above, p. 26, note 25.

[48] Above, note 45.

[49] Marin Mersenne, *La Verité des Sciences*, Paris, 1625, pp. 212–13.

[50] Robert Lenoble, *Mersenne ou la Naissance du Mécanisme*, Paris, 1943, p. 590.

9. Theodore Haak, leader of the London club described by John Wallis, which began in about 1645. *By courtesy of the Bodleian Library, Oxford.*

It is well more that Fifty ago [since] Discourse of this sort was
amongst us, (when the university began to be a troublesome
often the disturbance of a long Civil war) with burning of the
Inquisitive persons, did (by common Agreement) meet weekly;
And made it there business to inquire into, and promote, Philosophical Experiments, and other pieces of Experimental
Philosophy, and (what they cues) the New Philosophy which
meetings, afterwards, were divided; part of them continuing
there meetings Experimental there titen, removing to London,
but the Foundation of, what is now called, the Royal society, at
Gresham-College. And the like meeting, though with some intermission, have been here pursued to good purposes,
The like hath been done as to Anatomy; & to the like

10. John Wallis's account of the Royal Society's origin at Oxford, in
his own hand, dated 1701. *By courtesy of the Bodleian Library, Oxford.*

phenomena of nature according to mathematical rules, the assumption being that the whole of creation worked on the principle of clock-like machines. Mersenne's own interest in 'the New Philosophy' was virtually limited to mathematics, physics and astronomy, and indicated a failure to realize the fundamental importance of developing and relating all the branches of science, and, not least, the biological sciences.

At the meetings of the Academia Parisiensis, subjects including theology, philosophy, literature and natural philosophy, particularly 'the New Philosophy', were discussed, and information exchanged. Besides this, Mersenne carried on a vast correspondence with scholars of many countries.

Through his correspondence with Mersenne, Haak kept in touch with the Continent, collecting information on discoveries, inventions and publications both old and new. It was Mersenne who sent him the information for trying out the 'Torricellian experiment', which was a novelty to the English club.

Haak's accounts of the Torricellian experiment indicate that occasionally their consideration of 'the New Philosophy' included an attempt to repeat a set-piece of scientific discovery. Haak describes the setting up of this experiment, a *pièce de résistance*, put on at his suggestion before men of letters and rank who were present, not as scientists, but as persons eminent in various walks of life, assembled for an instructive diversion.[51]

An important fact that emerges from these accounts is that Haak, who was not a scientist, was leading and organizing this group; and from the whole surviving correspondence it is evident that the club's purpose was not sustained and comprehensive original research, with weekly meetings to practise this and to confer about its own discoveries, with the underlying aim of reconstructing and developing the natural sciences. If any original research was done as a group, Haak, like Wallis, does not mention it, and there is no reason to suppose that this club set up as a pioneer institution in scientific research.

The difference between this club—which Wallis alone had suggested was the beginning of the Royal Society—and the Oxford experimental science club is far from merely academic. One test of this can be made by considering what the Royal

[51] Bibliothèque Nationale MS. Nouv. acq. françaises, 6206, f. 91.

G

Society would have been like if it had simply been a continuation, on a larger scale, of what had been done at these meetings in London. Societies interested in 'the New Philosophy' had followed much that pattern in France until December 1666, when the Académie Royale des Sciences emerged from groups which derived from Mersenne, to become an experimental science club. Remarking on this in the *History*, which came out only a few months after the change, Sprat says:

> . . . they have at last turn'd their thoughts from *Words* to experimental *Philosophy*, and perhaps in imitation of the *Royal Society*.

He says that so far they have made a modest beginning, on lines similar to 'what was done at Oxford', and he expresses the hope that they will

> go on farther, and come by the same degrees, to erect another *Royal Society* in *France*.[52]

If the origin of the Royal Society is looked for in these meetings in London described by Wallis, Theodore Haak must be regarded as its originator. But nobody except Wallis either inside or outside the Royal Society, ever suggested that the

[52] Thomas Sprat, *History*, p. 56.

At the meeting of the Society on 9 October 1661 (before it had received its Charter and title) Sir Robert Moray read out a letter which he had received from Huygens. In it Huygens said that he had been informed by letter from Paris that the academy which met at M. de Montmort's wanted to emulate the London society, and would apply themselves to experiments in preference to any other employment.

On 8 June 1666 Oldenburg wrote to Boyle:

MONSIEUR *Azout* was . . . elected into the [Royal] Society, *nemine contra dicente*: and a diploma is to be dispatched to him, as was done to Mr. *Hevelius*. The same [i.e. Azout], I find by my last from *Paris*, is nominated for one of those choice persons, that are to constitute their academy; . . . I perceive, they will chiefly pursue mechanical and chemical experiments . . . I hope our Society will in time ferment all *Europe* at least: I wish only we had a little more zeal, and a great deal more assistance, to do our work thoroughly, as I am apt to believe the French will study to do theirs (they being like to be endowed) were it but out of emulation. So good be done to posterity, no great matter what passions do concur for the performance. (Robert Boyle, *Works*, 1744, vol. V, p. 357.)

Adrien Azout, the French astronomer and mathematician, was elected a Fellow of the Royal Society on 23 May 1666 (Journal Book, vol. II, p. 259).

society owed its origin to him. Certainly Haak himself made no such claim. Immediately after Sprat's *History* was published, giving the Royal Society's own account of its origin at Oxford, Haak wrote to John Winthrop, Governor of Connecticut, referring to the *History* in enthusiastic terms.[53]

In the statements which Wallis makes about the meetings at Oxford there are discrepancies. He does not mention the beginning of the Oxford club in Wilkins's Lodgings at all. This may simply be because he was not there. Wilkins had been admitted Warden of Wadham on 13 April 1648.[54] Wallis did not take up his appointment as Savilian Professor of Geometry until eighteen months later, when he was incorporated a member of Oxford University on the same day as Seth Ward, 23 October 1649, Ward having been appointed Savilian Professor of Astronomy.[55] Wallis's first recollection of the Oxford club is at the lodgings of William Petty,[56] who did not settle in Oxford until after 18 October 1649, when his brother Anthony, who had been living with him in London, was buried at the City church of St. Margaret's, Lothbury.[57] Petty then wrote to his cousin John, asking him to come to London and keep house for him;[58] but sometime in the next few months Petty moved to Oxford. On 7 March 1649/50 the degree of Doctor of Medicine was conferred on him there by the University Delegates, and at about the same time he was made a Fellow of Brasenose.[59]

Wallis seems also to have telescoped the events at the beginning of the Oxford club, as he attributes its inception to the arrival at Oxford from London of Wilkins, himself and Goddard. As already pointed out, Wallis did not arrive in Oxford until eighteen months after Wilkins, and Goddard did not take up his appointment as Warden of Merton College

[53] *Proceedings of the Massachusetts Historical Society, 1878,* Boston, 1879, p. 231. Haak had been admitted a member of the [Royal] Society on 4 December 1661.

[54] Buttery Book. Wadham College, Oxford (and R. B. Gardiner, *The Registers of Wadham College, Oxford,* London, 1889, Part I, p. 170).

[55] Joseph Foster, *Alumni Oxonienses,* Oxford, 1892, vol. IV, pp. 1561 [John Wallis] and 1570 [Seth Ward].

[56] Above, p. 167.

[57] Edmond Fitzmaurice, *The Life of Sir William Petty,* London, 1895, p. 13, note 9; and p. 313, where Anthony's death in London on 16 October 1649 is mentioned.

[58] Ibid., pp. 13–15.   [59] Above, p. 118 and note 72.

until 9 December 1651.[60] By this time the Oxford club was firmly established (as the list of rules, drawn up in the previous October, shows),[61] and had been in existence for about three years. Moreover, on Wallis's own evidence, apart from himself only two persons from Haak's club moved to Oxford—Wilkins and Goddard[62]—a point which, in retrospect, is often overlooked, the assumption being that a considerable number of persons was concerned. By the time Wallis published his version both were dead.[63]

Sprat's account is upheld without exception in all other independent contemporary accounts and opinions—whether expressed before or after Wallis published that account—in public record and in private, unpublished documents. The individual evidence of such persons as John Evelyn, John Aubrey, Henry Oldenburg and Gilbert Burnet that the Royal Society originated in the club founded by John Wilkins at Oxford University has already been considered at some length.[64] These witnesses, and those who served on the committees appointed by the Royal Society Council to supervise the writing of the *History* (also dealt with at length in an earlier chapter),[65] represented a wide range in background and position, and in religious and political views, yet their opinion is unanimous; and external evidence confirms that the *History* was indeed the expression of the Royal Society as an institution.[66]

It has also been seen that the Royal Society as an institution showed a fearless regard for impartiality at a time when, under political and religious pressures, it might more prudently have disowned its earlier Parliamentary associations at Oxford.[67]

It may be added that Sprat's advisers were well aware of the meetings which Wallis claimed to be the origin of the Royal

---

[60] Sir Nathaniel Brent had resigned as Warden of Merton on 27 November 1651 (Merton College Register 1: 3, p. 385), and a mandatory letter from the 'Committee for Reformation of the Universities', appointing Goddard in his place, has the same date (see G. C. Broderick, *Memorials of Merton College*, Oxford, 1885, p. 104).

Goddard arrived to take up his appointment on 9 December 1651 (Merton College Register 1: 3, p. 385).

[61] Above, pp. 111–12.   [62] Above, p. 167.

[63] Wilkins died in 1672, Goddard in 1675.

[64] Above, pp. 107–9.   [65] Above, pp. 10–12, 14–15.

[66] Above, pp. 13–14.   [67] Above, p. 16.

Society. Jonathan Goddard and John Wilkins, both former members of Haak's club, had served together on one of the committees set up to instruct Sprat,[68] and Wilkins had been on all of them.[69] The following former members of Haak's club, who had since joined the Royal Society, were also Fellows at that time: Theodore Haak himself, Francis Glisson, Sir George Ent and Christopher Merret.[70]

The Royal Society issued no public rebuttal of Wallis's account, but that was in keeping with its established policy of dissociating itself as an institution from the private opinions of its members.[71] And it is perhaps not without significance that the Society showed its confidence in William Holder, whose veracity Wallis had impugned in his publication of 1678, by electing him to the Council the following year.[72] Wallis, whose name had appeared on the first list of the Council (which did not sit)[73] under the Charter of 1662, had been replaced at the next election under the new Charter of 1663, and never later served on the Council.

Wallis's opinion that the Royal Society originated in Haak's meetings in London during the Civil War has been considered here in all seriousness, and rejected on the whole range of evidence, which is seen to disprove it. The crowning irony of this controversy is that Wallis, arguing, as in his first version,[74] about something else, later discarded this contention, and stated, in an account which entirely agrees with Sprat's,[75] that the Royal Society originated at Oxford, after the end of the Civil War.

In November 1700 Wallis wrote a treatise, in the form of an open letter, in opposition to a proposal to Parliament by Lewis Maidwell, a graduate of St. John's College, Cambridge, to set up a school for boys in London, near Westminster, 'design'd, amongst other Improvements, for the Sea-Service of the

---

[68] Above, pp. 11–12.   [69] Above, pp. 11–12, 14–15.

[70] Above, p. 166. Sir Charles Scarburgh, also a Fellow, had been included in Wallis's first version, but omitted in his second.

[71] See the Royal Society's reply to Henry Stubbe on this point (above, p. 14).

[72] Council Book, vol. I, p. 301 (8 December 1679). Holder had previously been elected to the Council in 1675 and 1677, and was again elected in 1682.

[73] See below, p. 138 and note 41.

[74] See above, pp. 162–4.   [75] Above, pp. 102–3.

Nation'.[76] Thomas Hearne, writing on 27 September 1732, said that Maidwell's petition was 'thrown out of the House, chiefly by Dr. Wallis's means, who wrote against it'.[77] In the course of this argument Wallis once again referred to the origin of the Royal Society.

Omitting all reference to Haak's London meetings of 1645, which had, of course, been held during the Civil War—as Wallis himself had stated, 'at a time, when, by our Civil Wars, Academical Studies were much interrupted in both our Universities'[78]—Wallis now began, as Sprat had done,[79] with the meetings which were held at Oxford in the university after the Civil War. Wallis, like Sprat, now used the termination of the Civil War to date the starting-point: it was, said Wallis, 'when the University began to be a little settled after the disturbance of a long Civil War',[80] which agrees precisely with Sprat's statement fixing the time of the inception 'some space after the end of the Civil Wars'.[81] These meetings, said Wallis, 'layd the Foundation of, what is now called, the *Royal Society*',[82] again agreeing with Sprat's statement that these meetings 'laid the foundation of all this that follow'd'.[83]

Wallis's letter and a 'supplement' (a second letter) of January 1701, together with a further exposition which had been put forward by Maidwell, were carefully written out by Wallis in his own hand.[84] These papers, which he proposed to deposit in the Savilian Library[85] at Oxford University, were, he said in a

---

[76] Bodleian Library MS. Ballard I, fol. 130. Maidwell's printed pamphlet is incorporated in the manuscript.

[77] Bodleian Library MS. Hearne's Diaries 137, p. 41 (and Thomas Hearne, *Remarks and Collections*, ed. C. E. Doble and H. E. Salter, Oxford, 1918, vol. XI, p. 113).

[78] Above, p. 165.   [79] Above, pp. 102–3.

[80] The passage is given below, p. 181.   [81] Above, p. 102.

[82] See below, p. 181.   [83] Above, p. 102.

[84] Bodleian Library MS. Savile 57. There is a heavily edited transcript, in another hand, in Bodleian Library MS. Ballard I, ff. 133–40. An edited and somewhat careless transcript of these documents, taken from MS. Savile 57, was prepared by T. W. Jackson and published under the general editorship of C. R. L. Fletcher, *Collectanea*, Oxford, 1885, pp. 309–31.

[85] Wallis died in 1703, and this manuscript, with other books which he had intended for the Savilian Library, were presented to it in about 1705 by his son (see Bodleian Library MS. Savile 101, fol. 11; and *A Summary Catalogue of Western Manuscripts in the Bodleian Library at Oxford*, Oxford, 1905, vol. V, ed. Falconer Madan, p. 187; and Sir Edmund Craster, *A History of the*

foreword, 'thought fit to be preserved; as containing Matter, which perhaps may be of Use in some after-times, if some like Occasion may again happen'. The passage on the origin of the Royal Society is as follows:

It is allso more than[86] Fifty [years] ago, since divers of the best rank amongst us, (when the University began to be a little settled after the disturbance of a long Civil War,) with many other Inquisitive Persons, did (by common Agreement) meet weekly; And made it their business to inquire into, and promote, *Mechanical Experiments*, and other pieces of *Experimental Philosophy*, and (what they call) the *New Philosophy*. Which meetings, afterward, were Divided; part of them continuing their meetings here [i.e. at Oxford]; and part of them, removing to *London*, layd the Foundation of, what is now called, the *Royal Society*, at *Gresham-College*,[87] And the like meeting[s], though with some intermission, have been here[88] pursued to good purpose.[89]

It seems that Wallis, who had always prided himself on his skill in disputation according to the traditional practice of Logic,[90] was inclined to argue the case according to his purpose at the time. In his first version[91] Wallis was attempting to invalidate all William Holder's statements on a subject which

[86] By a slip 'than' is written as 'that'.
[87] At the date of this letter the Royal Society was meeting at Gresham College. See below, p. 191.
[88] The Oxford Philosophical Society, founded in 1683 by Robert Plot on the model of the Royal Society (see above, pp. 126-7). Wallis was for some years the nominal President, though Plot, himself a Fellow of the Royal Society, actually ran the society, holding the position of Director of Experiments, an office which he had instituted (Bodleian Library MS. Ashmole 1810, ff. 1-2; and R. T. Gunter, *Early Science in Oxford*, 1929, vol. IV, p. 45).
[89] Bodleian Library MS. Savile 57, p. 7.
[90] In Wallis's account of his life (see above, pp. 161-2) he said that while studying at Cambridge University (in the early 1640s) he had studied Logic—'and I soon became Master of a *Syllogism*' and could 'manage an Argument with good Advantage, when I was to Argue or Oppose; . . . and was able to hold pace with those who were some years my Seniors; and had obtain'd the reputation of a good Disputant'.
[91] See above, pp. 162-4.

Bodleian Library 1845-1945, Oxford, 1952, pp. 183-6). Wallis's manuscript, with the rest of the contents of the Savilian Library, came under the care of the Bodleian Library in 1884, though the collection was not actually moved into the Bodleian Library until 1940.

did not concern the origin of the Royal Society, and made an issue of the origin merely because Holder had mentioned the time when the foundation of the Society had been laid at Oxford.[92] When Wallis wrote his last account, the basic situation, from his point of view, was somewhat similar; but this time Wallis's purpose was to invalidate Lewis Maidwell's case for founding a school. In order to do this, Wallis first gave a hostile and rather distorted interpretation of Maidwell's propositions;[93] he then argued that the universities were already a sufficient source of academic learning and of voluntary associations 'for particular parts of Usefull Knowledge', and that Maidwell's school was not needed. It was as an example of such voluntary initiative that the origin of the Royal Society at Oxford was mentioned.

Another ironical feature of the controversy concerning the origin of the Royal Society is that Wallis's last, and correct, account remained unpublished until 1885,[94] and that even since then it has existed in print solely in the comparative obscurity of a *collectanea* of unrelated documents, unnoticed by any historian of the Royal Society.

[92] See above, pp. 163–4.
[93] Maidwell's pamphlet (Bodleian Library MS. Ballard I, fol. 130) together with his further petition, which was copied out by Wallis (Bodleian Library MS. Savile 57, pp. 1–4), may be compared with Wallis's 'Animadversions' (MS. Savile 57, pp. 5–20).
[94] Above, p. 180, note 84.

2

THE ROYAL SOCIETY AND GRESHAM COLLEGE

A mare's nest of comparatively recent date is a theory that the Royal Society originated at Gresham College. This theory, for which there is no factual evidence, is based on misconceptions already largely dealt with here in earlier chapters; but since it has arisen from so much confusion, and continues to be repeated, it may be well to clarify the subject.

The theory that the Royal Society began at Gresham College originated in 1940 with Professor Francis R. Johnson of Stanford University, U.S.A.,[1] who 'sketched', as he said, an hypothesis.[2] Professor Johnson's aim was not to produce factual evidence (and he did not), but only to advance a line of argument 'as a rough guide for the thorough history of the antecedents of the Royal Society that may be written when English archives can again be peacefully studied by scholars'.[3]

The hypothesis rests on the erroneous assumption that the

[1] Francis R. Johnson, 'Gresham College: Precursor of the Royal Society', *Journal of the History of Ideas*, New York, 1940, vol. I, pp. 413–38. (This hypothesis has been followed by various historians, one of the most recent being Christopher Hill, *Intellectual Origins of the English Revolution*, Oxford, 1965, pp. 14 ff.)

[2] Ibid., p. 415.   [3] Ibid., p. 422.

London club, described by Wallis, was the prototype of the Royal Society.[4] By an extension of this assumption, never suggested by Wallis, Gresham College itself is made the source of this club,[5] and *ipso facto* the place of origin of the Royal Society. A hint that Gresham College was a kind of institute of technology adds to the tangle of surmise and misconception. These points will be taken in order.

Haak's meetings (that is, those described by Wallis), on Wallis's own evidence, did not start at Gresham College at all, but in Jonathan Goddard's lodgings in Wood Street. Goddard was not a member of Gresham College, but of the College of Physicians. It was merely as a matter of convenience that, later, the group at times met at Gresham College. In his first version of the meetings Wallis said that they met

> sometimes at Dr. *Goddards* Lodgings, sometimes at the *Mitre in Wood-street* hard by . . . These Meetings we removed, soon after, to the *Bull-head* in *Cheap-side*; and (in Term-time) to *Gresham-Colledge* where we met weekly at Mr. *Foster's* Lecture (then Astonomy-Professor there) and after the Lecture ended: repaired, sometimes to Mr. *Foster's* Lodgings, sometimes to some other place not far distant . . .[6]

In his second version Wallis again refers to Gresham College merely as one of the places of meeting, and not the first of them:

> These meetings we held sometimes at *Dr. Goddards* Lodgings in Woodstreet (or some convenient place near) . . . and sometime at a convenient place in *Cheap-side*; sometime at *Gresham College* or some place near adjoyning.[7]

[4] Christopher Hill, *Intellectual Origins of the English Revolution*, p. 149. Johnson (p. 416) follows Dorothy Stimson in supposing that the difference between Haak's London club and Wilkins's club at Oxford was that the latter kept minutes of the meetings. In fact it did not. Miss Stimson was one of those (following C. R. Weld, above, pp. 126–7) who attributed the minutes of Robert Plot's 'Oxford Philosophical Society' (founded in 1683) to the Royal Society's prototype at Oxford, which had left Oxford over twenty years earlier. Neither Miss Stimson nor Professor Johnson looked any farther into the Royal Society's own statement that it originated at Oxford.

[5] Francis R. Johnson, op. cit., pp. 419 ff.

[6] John Wallis, *A Defence of the Royal Society*, Oxford, 1678, p. 7.

[7] Thomas Hearne, The Publisher's Appendix to his Preface, *Peter Langtoft's Chronicle*, London, 1725, p. clxi (from Bodleian Library MS. Smith 31, p. 47).

There is not only no justification for citing Wallis's account as circumstantial evidence that this club was a product of Gresham College, but there is no evidence from any other source to support such a theory. No member of Gresham College itself ever mentioned such a club as existing there, and Haak, the originator and organizer, was not a member of Gresham. In the whole of the surviving correspondence between Haak and Mersenne during the period of Haak's meetings, and before them, there is no mention of Gresham College.[8] Moreover, only one of those named by Wallis as members of the club held an appointment at Gresham: Samuel Foster, the Professor of Astronomy. The majority were physicians, and were members of the College of Physicians—Goddard, Glisson, Ent and Merret. Scarburgh, who appears only in Wallis's first version, was also a member.

In the light of this preponderance of physicians, it is not without significance that at about the time when Haak's club began, there was in existence a private club, formed by members of the College of Physicians, to discuss medical and physiological matters, and discoveries connected with them, and that Goddard and Glisson were prominent members of it. The information comes from Francis Glisson himself, in the preface to his treatise *De Rachitide sive Morbo Puerili qui vulgo The Rickets dicitur*, published in 1650.[9]

At the meetings seven doctors had contributed written observations to the preliminary discourse on the subject of rickets, among them Glisson and Goddard. Since Glisson's publication was concerned only with this subject, he named only those who had taken part in it; so the names of the other physicians in the group are unknown.

Meetings to discuss an important aspect of natural phenomena were thus going on, but these meetings were never regarded by the Royal Society as its source either, although Goddard and Glisson, who both afterwards became Fellows of the Royal Society, were members of it. The reason is obvious:

[8] Above, p. 173 and note 42, for correspondence from May 24/June 3, 1647 to July 3/13, 1648; and British Museum MS. Birch 4279 ff. 104–24 for the period 1639–40.

[9] Writing in 1650, Glisson said that the work on rickets began five years before, at the meetings which were then going on. Thus the club began in 1645 or earlier.

although, in their respective ways these two clubs were concerned with 'the New Philosophy', their intentions fell far short of the Royal Society's purpose.

Nor did Gresham College exemplify this purpose. When, in 1620, Bacon called for the foundation of a new system of natural sciences to replace those still being taught in the universities, Gresham College had existed for twenty-three years, but he saw no potential there for the implementation of his great plan; nor, in the years following the publication of the *Novum Organum* up to the time of the inception of the Oxford experimental science club in 1648–9, was there any movement at Gresham to supersede the prevailing system of Natural Philosophy.

Sir Thomas Gresham, a merchant, had left his residence, Gresham House, to be used to accommodate lecturers who were to give formal public lectures 'for the common benefit of the people of this city [London]'.[10] Several points about the nature of this foundation and its academic appointments need to be made clear. Not only was there no question of opposition to the system of Natural Philosophy in the universities, as with the Royal Society, but, at the outset, the trustees had approached both universities, formally asking them to nominate candidates for each of the seven faculties to be represented at Gresham, saying: 'Wee have thought good to derive our choice from the verie fountaine'.[11]

Only three of the seven faculties had a bearing on Natural Philosophy—those of Geometry, Astronomy and Medicine; the other four faculties were Theology, Music, Law and Rhetoric. The City of London made the appointments for Theology, Astronomy, Geometry and Music, and the Mercers' Company for Law, Medicine and Rhetoric.[12] As each lectureship became vacant the appropriate body of trustees made a fresh election from university candidates.[13]

Soon after the college's foundation the lecturers were given the courtesy title 'Professor'. In retrospect this, too, has often

---

[10] John Ward, *The Lives of the Professors of Gresham College*, London, 1740, Preface, p. v.
[11] Ibid., p. 34 (letter to Oxford University), and p. 37 (letter to Cambridge University).
[12] Ibid., pp. 20 and 21 (from Sir Thomas Gresham's will).
[13] Ibid., p. 38.

caused confusion, for the implicit assumption has been that each 'professor' was the head of a department as in the two universities, and that each 'faculty' must be productive of much unspecified activity. In fact there were no departments at all, each 'professor' being the sole representative of that 'faculty'. The entire college consisted of seven persons, three only of whom were appointed to lecture on subjects concerning Natural Philosophy.

As far as the work itself was concerned, it was, in content, precisely what was being taught at Oxford and Cambridge, with the single concession that its presentation was adapted somewhat to the understanding and practical outlook of a non-academic audience. 'These solemn and publick lectures'[14] had to be given in English as well as in Latin 'for that the greatest part of the inhabitants within the city understand not the Latin tongue'; the Latin version was for the benefit of foreign visitors to the City.[15]

Since this audience was not conversant with the works of Hippocrates and Galen, disjointed extracts were not to be made from them, but some sequence was to be shown, according to the method of 'Fernelius',[16] that is Jean François Fernel (1497–1558), the French physician who himself followed Hippocrates and Galen. There was therefore no attempt to provide new matter, only a particular arrangement of the old.

Gresham, who had been a seaman himself, specified another allowance to be made for an audience which was largely artisan. The Professor of Astronomy was required to

> read in his solemn lectures, first the principles of the sphere, and the theoriques of the planets, and the use of the astrolabe and the staff, and other common instruments for the capacity of mariners; which being read and opened, he shall apply them to use, by reading geography, and the art of navigation, in some one term of every year.[17]

Bacon had emphatically pointed out in the *Novum Organum* that this kind of preoccupation with the immediate skills and practice of the artisan did not touch the real problem. He had already said this in *The Advancement of Learning* in 1605, and still saw need to repeat his warning eighteen years later in his

---

[14] John Ward, *The Lives of the Professors of Gresham College*, Preface, p. iv.
[15] Ibid., p. v.　　[16] Ibid., p. viii.　　[17] Ibid.

De Augmentis Scientiarum, when he again discussed 'the deficiencies which I find in public lectures', particularly those relating to Natural Philosophy.[18] Money was available to provide books for the lecturers to consult, and for some of the instruments in common use, he said, but no money was allowed for experiments, and this was essential:

> ... spheres, globes, astrolabes, maps, and the like have been provided and prepared as assistants to astronomy and cosmography, as well as books. We see likewise that some places instituted for physic have gardens for the examination and knowledge of simples of all sorts, and are not without the use of dead bodies for anatomical observations. But these respect but a few things. In general, it may be held for certain that there will hardly be any great progress in the unravelling and unlocking of the secrets of nature, except there be a full allowance for expenses about experiments; whether they be experiments appertaining to Vulcan or Dædalus (that is, the furnace or engine), or any other kind.

There was no question of scientific research in connexion with these Gresham lectureships, and the lectures were formally read, the requirement being 'that the said lecturers shall read their lectures in their hoods, according to their degrees in the universities, in such sort as they should there read the same lectures'.[19] It is a comment on the attitude of the universities to Gresham College as such, that they saw in it no rival to themselves in their domination of Natural Philosophy, reserving their hostility for the Royal Society, which, merely as a matter of convenience, met at Gresham for a time.[20]

Historians who have not understood Bacon's exposition of his project, and do not even realize that there was a need for such a vast reform, have attempted to convince themselves that in the period of fifty years from its foundation in 1595, Gresham College 'must' have been a centre of scientific

[18] Francis Bacon, *De Augmentis Scientiarum*, II, Ad Regem Suum: *Works*, vol. IV, pp. 286–8 (*Advancement of Learning* II, To the King: *Works*, vol. III, pp. 324–5).

[19] John Ward, *The Lives of the Professors of Gresham College*, London, 1740, Preface, p. viii.

[20] John Aubrey made a particular point of the fact that the Royal Society, which met at Gresham College, was quite distinct from Gresham College itself (above, p. 73).

fertility. Yet all that can be produced in support of such an hypothesis is the development of the use of logarithms, first conceived by Napier, who had no connexion with Gresham College, and a few minor contrivances such as tables for navigation and a land-measure, consisting of a chain twenty-two yards long, marked off in links.[21] When in 1634 Henry Gellibrand, then Professor of Astronomy at Gresham, verified the fact (already noted by others) that the declination of the compass further declined in a given place after an elapse of time,[22] he was intent only on the improvement of navigational tables, not on discovering the physical laws of which this was a manifestation. Professor Johnson and those who follow his lead make much of these few utilitarian inventions and improvements, but it was exactly this kind of inventiveness to which Bacon was referring when he said, 'Men of this kind, therefore, amend some things, but advance little; and improve the condition of knowledge, but do not extend its range'.[23]

What is evident is that at Gresham College there was no sign of a comprehensive view of 'the New Philosophy', and a dearth of genuine, disinterested scientific experiment. Whole fields of research opened up by the Royal Society, even in its embryo stage, were not so much as nominally represented in the 'faculties' of the foundation itself—no chemistry, no physics, none of the biological sciences, not even meteorology or geology; and as for individual performances of the professors in these great potential regions of science: in fifty years—silence.

Sprat, speaking for the Royal Society as an institution, mentions Gresham College only twice, and then very briefly. He says that when in about 1658 the Oxford club left Oxford and reassembled in London it 'usually met at *Gresham* College, at the *Wednesdays*, and *Thursdays*, Lectures of Dr. *Wren*, and Mr. *Rook*'.[24] It was an obvious thing that Wren and Rooke, who were among the most prominent members of the Oxford club, should offer the dispossessed club a place to meet.

[21] 'Gunter's chain'. Edmund Gunter was Professor of Astronomy at Gresham College from 1619 until he died in 1626, the same year as Bacon. Gunter was one of those who improved navigational tables.
[22] This treatise, *A Discourse Mathematical of the Variation of the Magneticall Needle together with its admirable diminuation lately discovered*, was published in 1635.
[23] Francis Bacon, *Instauratio Magna*, Praefatio: *Works*, vol. IV, p. 16.
[24] Thomas Sprat, *History*, p. 57.

Neither of them had connexion with Gresham College before their appointments there in the 1650s. Wren had entered Wadham College, Oxford, as an undergraduate while only a boy of seventeen,[25] and Rooke had followed his friend Seth Ward from Cambridge when he was ejected,[26] rejoining Ward at Wadham after a period of retirement to his estate in Kent.[27]

Incidentally, Laurence Rooke was the first of the Oxford club to be elected to a Gresham post, that of Astronomy Professor, in 1652. In 1657 he transferred to the Chair of Geometry there, and Christopher Wren was elected to the Chair of Astronomy, which he resigned in 1662, to return to Oxford as Professor of Astronomy. In 1657 Jonathan Goddard was elected to the Chair of Medicine at Gresham, but retained his Wardenship of Merton College, Oxford, until 1660, when, at the Restoration, he lost it, and took up permanent residence at Gresham.

The story of the Society's efforts to obtain suitable accommodation in London has already been told in an earlier chapter.[28] It is enough, here, to recall that Gresham College continued to be used as a meeting-place only as a temporary measure, after an attempt to set up the Society's headquarters at the College of Physicians in December 1660 had failed, and, for a few years, following the Society's incorporation by Royal Charter, when it was seeking permanent premises of its own. Sprat's second reference to Gresham College is to this period, when he makes courteous, though brief, acknowledgment of its hospitality in allowing the Society the use of certain rooms.[29]

On 27 November 1666 the Council again made an attempt to leave Gresham for a more convenient meeting-place. It was ordered

> That at the next Council it be considered, where the Society may meet henceforth, Gresham-college being by reason of its too great distance from the Habitations of the greatest number of the Society very inconvenient to meet in, especially at this Season of the year.[30]

[25] Above, p. 105.   [26] Above, p. 105.
[27] Anthony Wood, *Athenae Oxonienses*, 1721, vol. II, p. 297; Walter Pope, *The Life of Seth, Lord Bishop of Salisbury*, London, 1697, p. 110.
[28] Above, pp. 131–5.
[29] Thomas Sprat, *History*, p. 93. See also above, p. 135.
[30] Council Book, vol. I, p. 115.

Nothing came of this, but soon afterwards, as an effect of the Fire of London, which had occurred in September of that year, the civic authorities took over a part of Gresham College as an emergency measure to carry on the work of the Royal Exchange there. The Royal Society's accommodation was then so much reduced as to make its work almost impossible. It therefore accepted the offer of Henry Howard to make Arundel House in the Strand its headquarters.[31]

When Gresham College resumed its normal life, the Royal Society did not return, but continued to meet at Arundel House. It met there for nearly seven years, and the break with Gresham would probably have proved final, if in 1673 a deputation representing the trustees and professors of the college had not called on the Royal Society with a pressing request that it should return. This, after some deliberation, the Society decided to do.[32] There is no doubt that the presence of the Royal Society had helped to arrest Gresham College's declining fortunes. As John Ward, speaking both as a Gresham professor and a Fellow of the Royal Society, said in 1740:

> The year 1710 proved very unfortunate to the college, by the removal of the royal society; who having purchased the house of the late Dr. Brown in Crane court, Fleetstreet, began there on the 8 of November that year.[33]

Gresham professors who were also Fellows of the Royal Society had particular cause to regret the Society's removal from the College. Not only did they forfeit their exemption from paying the Society's annual subscription, but they lost the great convenience of using the Society's considerable library, Gresham having no library of its own. John Ward remarks:

> While the royal society held their meetings at Gresham college, such of the professors, who were members of it, were in civility excused from their annual payments, and felt little inconvenience from the want of a college library; but after the books of the society were removed, they became sensible of that disadvantage.[34]

[31] Above, p. 135, note 32.
[32] John Ward, *The Lives of the Professors of Gresham College*, 1740, Preface, p. xv.
[33] Ibid., p. xviii.   [34] Ibid., pp. xviii–xix.

From the time of the inception of the Royal Society's proto-type at Oxford, its founders and followers took their concept of Natural Philosophy wherever they went, including Gresham College, when they were elected to Chairs there; and it is completely beside the point to cite the achievements of such 'Gresham professors' as evidence of Gresham's scientific fertility. The Royal Society was a brilliant exotic bird of passage at Gresham College, and with its departure Gresham's brief, reflected glory vanished.

3

THE INVISIBLE COLLEGE

The 'Invisible College', which preceded the Royal Society, has been another source of confusion concerning the origin of the Royal Society. The identity of the 'Invisible College' has been a matter of conjecture, though the integration of all the existing evidence, including some which has not before been considered, points firmly to one solution. But more important in this whole context than the discovery of the identity of this society is a careful examination of the evidence in order to determine whether in nature and purpose it resembled the Royal Society; for this involves a fundamental question of concept.

The name 'Invisible College' was a private coinage of Robert Boyle's,[1] as he himself indicates, for a small society which existed in London at the time he was writing, which was during the period 1646–7.

There are only three known references by Boyle to this group, and they appear in what survives of his correspondence when he was between nineteen and twenty years old. These letters were included among those between Boyle and his friends and acquaintances which were published in 1744 by Thomas Birch, then Secretary of the Royal Society.[2] This

---

[1] Robert Boyle, *Works*, ed. Thomas Birch, London, 1744, vol. I, p. 20.
[2] Ibid., vols. I and V.

printed version is now the source for Boyle's evidence, as the manuscripts have disappeared without a trace.

Birch thought it probable (though he gave no reason for his opinion) that by 'the Invisible College' Boyle meant Theodore Haak's society,[3] which was the one described by John Wallis. Another, comparatively recent theory is that the 'Invisible College' was not Haak's club, and that it originated with Samuel Hartlib.[4]

The first of Boyle's three letters referring to the 'Invisible College', written from London on 22 October 1646 to his former tutor M. Isaac Marcombes, gives some information about the nature of the society.[5] Boyle says that besides his private reading of Aristotle's *Ethics*, 'the other humane studies' he is applying himself to, are

> natural philosophy, the mechanics and husbandry according to the principles of our new philosophical college, that values no knowledge, but as it hath a tendency to use.

He asks his correspondent to bring any information he can find about husbandry as it is practised in his part of France, and, when he sets out for England, to bring

> what good receipts or choice books of any of those subjects you can procure; which will make you extremely welcome to our *invisible college.*

This recalls Wallis's information that the group he belonged to consisted of

> divers worthy Persons, inquisitive into Natural Philosophy, and other parts of Humane Learning; And particularly of what hath been called the *New Philosophy* or *Experimental Philosophy.*

who met weekly to

> discourse and consider of *Philosophical Enquiries*, and such as related thereunto; as *Physick, Anatomy, Geometry, Astronomy, Navigation, Staticks, Magneticks, Chymicks, Mechanicks, and Natural Experiments*, with the State of these Studies, as then cultivated, at home and abroad.[6]

---

[3] Robert Boyle, *Works*, ed. Thomas Birch, 1744, vol. I, p. 25; and *The History of the Royal Society*, London, 1756, vol. I, p. 2.
[4] R. H. Syfret, 'The Origins of the Royal Society', *Notes and Records of the Royal Society*, London, vol. 5, no. 2, 1948.
[5] Robert Boyle, *Works*, ed. Thomas Birch, 1744, vol. I, p. 20.
[6] Above, pp. 165–7.

But although there are similarities there are also differences. The group described by Boyle (who on another occasion referred to it as a 'society')[7] considered itself to be a 'philosophical college' which was 'invisible', a designation which Boyle repeated in a further letter[8]—'the *invisible*, or (as they term themselves) the *philosophical college*'. The members thus appeared to regard themselves as a potential college rather than as a club which took the form of weekly meetings.

Moreover, the aim of 'the philosophical college' was utilitarian: it 'values no knowledge, but as it hath a tendency to use', and was collecting recipes and books for that purpose. Haak's club, on the other hand, was primarily a discussion group, whose interest in 'the New Philosophy' was mainly concerned with the classics of experimental discovery, which though of great importance, were not of utilitarian value.

In the next of his letters mentioning the 'Invisible College', written from London on 20 February 1646/7 to Francis Tallents, then a Fellow of Magdalene College, Cambridge, Boyle gave some further information. It was a small group of men whose ambition to 'lead the way to any generous design' was prompted by a charitable concern for the welfare of mankind:

> . . . the *invisible*, or (as they term themselves) the *philosophical college*; . . . men of so capacious and searching spirits, that schoolphilosophy is but the lowest region of their knowledge; and yet, though ambitious to lead the way to any generous design, of so humble and teachable a genius, as they disdain not to be directed to the meanest, so he can but plead reason for his opinion; persons that endeavour to put narrow-mindedness out of countenance, by the practice of so extensive a charity, that it reaches unto every thing called man, and nothing less than an universal goodwill can content it. And indeed they are so apprehensive of the want of good employment, that they take the whole body of mankind for their care.
>
> But . . . there is not enough of them.[9]

But this factor does not help to distinguish the 'Invisible College' from Haak's club, for although Wallis gave no indication of a charitable purpose in his account, Haak himself

---

7 Below, p. 198.   8 See quotation below.
9 Robert Boyle, *Works*, ed. Thomas Birch, 1744, vol. I, p. 20.

expressed a philanthropic attitude concerning this exchange of knowledge. Deploring the meanness of a person who was un-willing to share his inventions, Haak, in a letter to Mersenne from London, dated 6 August 1647, said:

> Who or what will benefit from the talent in the napkin? It is surely better to possess and to effect less, than to miss the real satisfaction which lies in communication, in doing good to others with what is mine; and sharing in the contentment which God himself pursues, in a manner of speaking, with so much ardour, without at all wearying; to do good even to the most ungrateful of people.[10]

This aim of service is, in fact, common to Haak and Samuel Hartlib, who were associated in their general activities for many years.

Both Haak and Hartlib were exiles who had settled in England, and they had a common interest in working for the Protestant cause, particularly in attempts to benefit 'the republic of letters'.[11] When Haak's *Dutch Annotations Upon the whole Bible* was published in London in 1657, a certificate issued by 'the Principal Members of the Assembly of Divines' was reproduced in it, attesting Haak's work for the Protestant faith since 1625.

The 'pansophic' schemes of Hartlib and his collaborators (the Czech educationalist Comenius, and John Dury, a Scot) are examined below in the following chapter, so the essential differences between Bacon's concept and theirs may be stated briefly here. The first difference, since this consideration dominated the aspirations of Hartlib and his collaborators, was that of religious policy. Their longed-for utopia was a world in which a united Protestant church presided over all aspects of human activity. In this collaboration Hartlib was to be 'the sollicitor of humane learning for the reformation of schooles', Dury's part was 'to promote the councells of peace ecclesiasticall', Comenius being Hartlib's 'coadiutor . . . for the

[10] MS. Bibliothèque Nationale Nouv. acq. françaises 6206 f. 167. (See above, p. 173, note 42.) This passage is here translated from the original French.

[11] John Pell (below, p. 197), in a letter to Mersenne, to whom he had been introduced by Haak, described Hartlib as 'reipublicae literariae fautori atque promotori' (*Philosophical Collections*, ed. Robert Hooke, London, 1681/82, no. 5, p. 137).

waies of schooling and pansophical learning'.[12] The second
difference was that they had no idea at all of reconstructing
the system of natural sciences as advocated by Bacon. Their
conception of 'the advancement of learning' included the collection and dissemination of practical discoveries and inventions of use to daily life, but there was no initiative to extend
the boundaries of science itself. In fact Bacon's *Novum Organum*
left them baffled and disappointed.[13]

Although there appears to be no evidence that Haak worked
for any of the particular projects sponsored by Hartlib and his
collaborators, his name was associated with Hartlib's in his
general activities over a considerable period. One incidental
way in which Hartlib had attempted to extend his work was,
by introductions and encouragement, to gain the support of
persons who might be able to contribute to learning, as he
conceived it. For this purpose, in 1638 he had introduced Haak
to the mathematician John Pell, whom Hartlib was trying to
persuade to devote his abilities to 'the publick advancement of
Learning'.[14] And in 1641 when Comenius visited England at
Hartlib's insistence, Haak was one of those who, with Hartlib
and Dury, received Comenius on his arrival. But in recounting
this in a letter to his friends at Leszno in Poland, Comenius
placed Haak's name at the end of the list, after Pell's, which
hardly suggests the role of a collaborator.[15]

On 26 April 1649 a proposal was put before the House of
Commons that Hartlib and Haak should be considered for
maintenance 'and what further shall be offered unto them, for
the Advancement of Arts and Learning'.[16] Although this
proposal was rejected, Hartlib was awarded £100 a year
maintenance on another motion,[17] and on 16 July it was

[12] Quoted by Robert Fitzgibbon Young, *Comenius in England, 1641–1642*,
London, 1932, p. 78, from a letter written by Dury in 1638. This collaboration was stated publicly when Hartlib published Dury's letters of 6 and 13
January 1642 to Sir Cheney Culpeper, under the title *Motion tending to the
Publick Good of this age and of posteritie* [etc.], London, 1642.
[13] See below, pp. 207 ff.
[14] Bodleian Library MS. Aubrey 6, fol. 53 (and *Brief Lives*, ed. Andrew
Clark, London, 1898, vol. II, p. 129).
[15] From a quotation by Robert Fitzgibbon Young, *Comenius in England,
1641–1642*, London, 1932, p. 64.
[16] *Journal of the House of Commons*, vol. 6, p. 196.
[17] Ibid., p. 227.

ordered that the same should be done for Haak.[18] On 17 August 1650 a further order was made that £50 should be paid to each of them 'for many good services in their correspondence beyond seas and to enable them to continue it'.[19]

But although it is well to be aware of this association of effort between Haak and Hartlib, the latter was concerned with his collaborators in specific, ambitious plans in which Haak was certainly not a major figure.

The theory that the 'Invisible College' was not the club led by Haak and described by Wallis, but was Hartlib's,[20] is based on the third of Boyle's letters mentioning 'the Invisible College', together with an undated letter of his referring to an unspecified 'college', both of which were written to Hartlib.

The former of these two letters was written from Boyle's manor house at Stalbridge in Dorset on 8 May 1647. In it Boyle said:

> It was very needless in your last to make apologies for the glad parliamentary news you began your letter with; for besides that its goodness authorises its nature, and were able to prefer so pleasing a disobedience to the most exact compliance with my desires; besides this, I say, you interest yourself so much in the *Invisible College*, and that whole society is so highly concerned in all the accidents of your life, that you can send me no intelligence of your own affairs, that does not (at least relationally) assume the nature of *Utopian*.[21]

On 31 March the House of Commons had voted Hartlib 'the Sum of three Hundred Pounds, in Consideration of his good Deserts, and great Services to the Parliament' and had recommended that a 'Place of Benefit' should be found for him in the University of Oxford, the request coming 'both from this Parliament and from all that are Well-wishers to the Advancement of Learning'.[22] On 2 April the necessary sanction for the monetary award had been given by the House of Lords,[23] and

[18] *Journal of the House of Commons*, vol. 6, p. 261.
[19] *Calendar of State Papers, Domestic Series* (1650), London, 1876, p. 292.
[20] See above, p. 194 and note 4.
[21] Robert Boyle, *Works*, ed. Thomas Birch, 1744, vol. I, p. 24.
[22] *Journal of the House of Commons*, vol. 5, p. 131.
[23] *Journal of the House of Lords*, vol. 9, p. 119.

on 21 April the order was passed to the Committee for Advance of Money.[24]

Another letter from Boyle to Hartlib has been thought to refer to the 'Invisible College' and thus confirm Hartlib as its originator. This letter is undated, though its subject-matter places it beyond reasonable doubt in about April 1647. In it Boyle speaks of 'your college' and 'this glorious design', which he says he would like to support:

> . . . on the score of your serious promise I am bold, not only to desire, but to expect at your hands a *Mercurius Philosophicus*, in an account of the projects and successes of that college, whereof God has made you hitherto the midwife and nurse. I shall not beg any information from you of that *diurnal* news, of which a whole sheet may be had for a peny, and yet be over-bought. No, I will stint my requests to your *Utopian* intelligence, as the only way to keep me in charity with men, by letting me see, that the degenerate world yet harbours some, that do not undeserve the name. And since you do not disdain the meanest workman, that is but willing to lay some few stones towards the building of your *college*, I shall in my following epistles . . . take the liberty to acquaint you with what thoughts and observations of mine I shall judge useful in reference to so glorious a design; to which I shall think it very much my happiness, if any endeavours of mine can have the honour in the least measure to contribute, not only as they owe a duty to the public . . . but because I know you so vastly affectionate to that public . . .[25]

Miss R. H. Syfret has suggested that this letter was written in April 1647,[26] and the subject-matter certainly indicates a date sometime before 8 May 1647, when Boyle wrote to Hartlib expressing pleasure in 'the glad Parliamentary news' received by Boyle in the previous letter from Hartlib. That letter of Hartlib's is now lost, but from Boyle's reply on 8 May we know that Hartlib had apologized for 'disobedience to the most exact compliance' with Boyle's wishes. Boyle had stipulated (in his undated letter) that Hartlib should not send him such news,

[24] *Calendar of the Proceedings of the Committee for Advance of Money, 1642–1656*, ed. M. A. E. Green, London, 1888, p. 64.

[25] Roberty Boyle, *Works*, ed. Thomas Birch, 1744, vol. I, p. 28.

[26] R. H. Syfret, *Notes and Records of the Royal Society of London*, vol. 5, no. 2, p. 120, 1948.

but this is 'so pleasing a disobedience' because it is Parliamentary news of a special kind, concerning Hartlib's 'own affairs', that is, a Parliamentary grant for his maintenance. Boyle's undated letter to Hartlib probably comes, in sequence, immediately before the letter to Hartlib of 8 May, which would place the undated letter in the period between 8 April (when Boyle had previously written to Hartlib) and 8 May. But there is nothing to prove that Hartlib was taking up a point from Boyle's latest letter. Boyle may well have written in these terms somewhat earlier than this, but it would not be until Hartlib wanted to 'disobey' him that the occasion would arise for mentioning Boyle's stipulation.

But the 'college' which Hartlib was attempting to establish during this period was his 'Office of Address'.[27] On 16 November 1647, after a lapse in the correspondence for which he apologized, Hartlib wrote to Boyle giving an account of its progress.[28] Hartlib was anxious because he had not so far received support from Parliament ('the trustees of the Kingdom') and he feared that he would be forestalled by a rival, Lord Cottington, who had already 'resolved to have erected such an office'. However, said Hartlib, he had received an offer from Sir Cheney Culpeper to help towards the cost of staffing the institution until public support was forthcoming; and, as a sample of what it would produce, Hartlib sent some 'writings' which he said Boyle could use to interest others in the project. One of these 'writings' was a 'History of Trades' (an account of crafts) by William Petty, then twenty-four years old. Only two months before this, Dury, too, had referred briefly to their difficulties when he had been approached by a friend, William Hamilton, about the possibility of an academic post: on 16 September 1647 Dury had written to Hartlib:

> I have acquainted him with the state of our college that it is like to bee stopped by evil will or frō want of authoritie or because

---

[27] Miss R. H. Syfret, expressing the view that the 'Invisible College' was not the group described by Wallis, thought it 'far more probable that Boyle's references to the Invisible College relate to the schemes of Hartlib, Dury and Comenius for a pansophic college and an Office of Address'. (*Notes and Records of the Royal Society of London*, vol. 5, no. 2, p. 128, 1948.)

[28] Robert Boyle, *Works*, vol. V, p. 256.

the Trustees doe not concurre in Counsell; and so I can promise him nothing with confidence.[29]

The following year, when Hartlib and Dury were still at the height of their efforts to establish the 'Office of Address', Boyle's words to Hartlib on his role—

... that *college* of which God has hitherto made you the midwife and nurse ... so glorious a design;[30]

—were echoed by William Petty:

We must recommend the Institution of an Office of common Addresse according to the projection of Master *Hartlib* (that painful and great instrument of this Design) ...[31]

In the first half of 1647 Hartlib and Dury had published their plan for establishing an 'Office of Address'. Hartlib was the originator, but Dury had taken, and continued to take, an active part in this grandiose project, and helped to draft it for publication.[32]

The nature of the Office of Address was explained in the first of two tracts presented to Parliament, entitled *A Brief Discourse Concerning the Accomplishment of our Reformation: tending to shew, that by an office of Publike Addresse in Spirituall and Temporall Matters, the Glory of God and the Happinesse of this Nation may be highly advanced*.[33] In the preface, addressed to Parliament, Hartlib said that others had 'concurred' with him in putting forward these proposals. The tract addressed Parliament as the 'great Trustee' of the Protestant cause, calling on it to support and effect a 'Reformation of Church and State' towards 'a Common Advancement of Religion' at home and abroad. The tract defined the central aim:

The Reformation of our Church is specified in the settlement of Truth by a Common Confession of Faith and Catechisme: in the settlement of Righteousnesse and good Order by a Common

[29] From the manuscript in the collection of Hartlib's papers, the property of Lord Delamere. A transcript is published in G. H. Turnbull, *Hartlib, Dury and Comenius*, 1947, p. 263.

[30] Robert Boyle, *Works*, ed. Thomas Birch, 1744, vol. I, p. 28.

[31] William Petty, *The Advice of W. P. to Mr. Hartlib*, London, 1648, p. 1.

[32] See below, p. 204, note 43.

[33] Published in London, 1647.

Directory of Worship, for Government, and for Discipline; and in the overthrow of Error, of Unrighteousnes, and of Disorder, by the abolishment of Popery, of Prelacy, of Superstition, of Heresie, of Schisme, and of all Profanesse.[34]

In the section 'Maximes and Reasons of a true Reformed Christian State' Hartlib expounded his object of a united Protestant commonwealth in which his schemes for the advancement of learning would flourish. He continually emphasized that the cause of the Reformed Protestant Church must be the dominant concern, 'and all other things made subordinate to it'.[35] Hartlib considered that he had been called on by God to inaugurate this ambitious scheme, and the entire tract is permeated with a sense of dedication, a conception of the glorious, 'spirituall and temporall', in the sight of the authors.

The Office of Address was to be a permanent institution consisting of 'two Parts or Branches'—the Office for Communications and the Office of Accommodations.[36] Although Hartlib conceived it as a single institution with related parts, he considered the first by far the more important of the two:

> The Office of Addresse for Communications, is as far beyond that of Accomodations in Usefulnesse, as the Matters of the Mind are above those of the Body. It is then to bee erected for Addresses and Informations in matters of Religion, of Learning, and of all Ingenuities, which are Objects of Contemplation and delight unto the Mind, for their strangenesse and usefulnesse unto the life of Man.[37]

The first duty of the Warden of this part of the Office of Address was towards religion, where he was to 'Facilitate the Meanes of Rectifying Mistakes' in unspecified ways, and endeavour to prevent 'the Increase of Divisions and Disorders about Matters of dispute whether in Opinion or Practise'. The second and third of his duties betray the misunderstanding of Bacon's practical intention which was so typical of Hartlib and his collaborators, and complete the impression of a scheme which was vast, vague, and impossible to realize profitably: 'In Matters of Humane Sciences' the Warden was to put into

[34] Samuel Hartlib, A Brief Discourse, op. cit., pp. 1–6.
[35] Ibid., pp. 13–15.   [36] Ibid., p. 42.   [37] Ibid., pp. 45–6.

practice Bacon's 'Designations, *De Augmentis Scientiarum*, amongst the Learned'. At the same time this institution was to be a huge clearing-house of

> Advices, of Proposalls, of Treaties and of all Manner of Intellectual Rarities freely to bee given and received, to and from, by and for all such as may think themselves concerned to receive or to give notice of the best Helpes and Overtures, and of the most Profitable Undertakings, Discoveries, and Occurences; wherby Godlinesse, Truth, and Peace, and all the Ways and Means tending to the harmlesse Advancement of Divine and Humane Wisdome and Perfections may be set forward in Church and Common-wealth.

The 'Professors of all Sciences in both Universities' and the Heads of Houses were to form a special committee to receive this information. Selections from it were to be made public: 'to bee put into the Publike Libraries, . . . or otherwise published in Print for the benefit of every one . . .'; and to this body of material 'by their joint advice, every yeare some stones should be added'.[38]

A passage from Boyle's letter to Hartlib on the subject of his 'college' appears to refer to this last point in Hartlib's manifesto. Boyle says:

> And since you do not disdain the meanest workman, that is but willing to lay some few stones towards the building of your *college*, I shall in my following epistles . . . take the liberty to acquaint you with what thoughts and observations of mine I shall judge useful in reference to so glorious a design; . . .[39]

What appears to be a further reference to this point is in an undated letter from Boyle to Benjamin Worsley, one of Hartlib's staunch supporters. The subject-matter indicates a date close to the above letter, and in it Boyle draws a parallel between the 'great design' and a project already put into practice by the College of Physicians. He says:

> I have fortuned upon some observations on husbandry . . . The opinion itself, together with the reasons that led me to it, you shall hear of me, God willing by the next opportunity; I being

---

38 Samuel Hartlib, *A Brief Discourse*, op. cit., pp. 47–51.
39 Robert Boyle, *Works*, ed. Thomas Birch, 1744, vol. I, p. 28 (quoted above, p. 199).

extremely mindful of my promise to transmit to you any thoughts or experiments of mine, that I shall judge conducible to the furtherance of your great design, and the enabling you to do for the great world, what the chairmen [sic] of the physicians has done for the little, publish a discourse *de usu partium*.[40]

In 1618 the College of Physicians under the chairmanship of their President, Henry Atkins, compiled and published *Pharmacopoea Londinensis, in qua Medicamenta Antiqua et Nova, usitatissima, sedulo collecto, accuratissime examinata, quotidiana experientia confirmata describuntur.* This, drawing on the resources of knowledge of the whole College, set out in recipes and remedies what they considered to be a model of medical information. With each succeeding edition new material was added, the whole undertaking being offered 'to the publique good'.

The secondary branch of Hartlib's Office of Address was called 'the Office of Accommodations', and was to be

... appointed to Meddle with al Outward Things concerning this present life, for the relations of men to each other in worldly Concernments.[41]

Hartlib suggested that the centre for the Office of Communications should be Oxford, and that for the Office of Accommodations, London. Each should be assigned a building and staff, the Warden at Oxford having 'some Colledge or Hall appointed for his Office-place'.[42]

The second tract, whose primary aim was to give further details about the Office of Accommodations, was written by Dury and published in 1648.[43] In a preface entitled 'An other Memorial on the behalf of Master Hartlib, and his negotiations for the general good of the Kingdom' Parliament was asked to 'Resolve upon these following particulars, as the

---

[40] Robert Boyle, *Works*, vol. V, p. 232. Hartlib, in his letter to Boyle of 16 November 1647 (above, p. 200) had referred to 'very dear Worsley' when giving Boyle information about the state of the proposed office of Address.
[41] Samuel Hartlib, *A Brief Discourse Concerning the Accomplishment of our Reformation* [etc.], 1647, p. 42.
[42] Ibid., p. 55.
[43] *A Further Discoverie of the Office of Publick Address for Accommodations*, London, 1648. Although this tract was issued by Hartlib, Dury was the author, as Boyle mentions this in his letter to Hartlib of 8 May 1647 (Robert Boyle, *Works*, ed. Thomas Birch, 1744, vol. I, p. 24).

Matter of an Ordinance to be passed by both Houses'. The first was that Hartlib should be appointed 'Superintendent Generall of all Offices of Addresse, instituted in the Kingdom of *England* and Dominions of *Wales*'.[44] Another, directed against Lord Cottington in particular, was power of 'prohibition to all others whatsoever to intermeddle with that business, either by imitating, or any other ways altering the said Offices, without permission and Deputation from the said Samuel Hartlib'.

In fact, Hartlib's hopes in setting up his Office of Address were never realized, and he did not even publish the proposed third tract on the Office of Communications.

There can be little doubt that the small group of men referred to by Boyle as the 'Invisible College' consisted of the founder-members of a 'philosophical college' which failed to materialize—the Office of Address envisaged by Hartlib and his collaborators. This whole project was itself only one of a number of unsuccessful attempts, both in this country and on the Continent, to found 'pansophic' colleges according to the concept of Comenius, Hartlib and Dury. The course of these efforts, which persisted through several decades, is discussed in relation to the Royal Society, in the following chapter. It may be said here, what is clear from the evidence, that Hartlib and his associates did not foreshadow the purpose of the Royal Society; and it is that fact, rather than a question of identity which is significant in this background.

44 In the preface entitled 'An other Memorial on the behalf of Master Hartlib, and his negotiations for the general good of the Kingdom'. This preface does not appear in every copy.

4

THE ROYAL SOCIETY
AND 'PANSOPHIA'

Although the Oxford experimental club, as such, was not interested in Hartlib's 'pansophic' schemes, Hartlib and his associates showed considerable interest in this club. Hartlib himself sometimes had news of its work through friends and acquaintances, Boyle being a particular source of information.[1] This interest increased as the society became more prominent, and was sometimes expressed in a proprietary tone which has puzzled historians and has even led a few to suppose that somehow the Royal Society must owe its origin to Hartlib and his associates.

As on the question of Gresham College's relationship to the Royal Society, the answer here has hitherto been sought in marginal details with no essential bearing on the problem. The solution is to be found in two major considerations: first, an examination of the fundamental misunderstanding by Hartlib and his collaborators of Bacon's concept of science, together with their confusion of that plan with another plan of Bacon's for improving academic education in general; and

[1] See, for example, *Notes and Records of the Royal Society of London*, vol. 10, no. 2, pp. 126–8, 1953, containing entries from Hartlib's 'Ephemerides', published by Professor G. H. Turnbull.

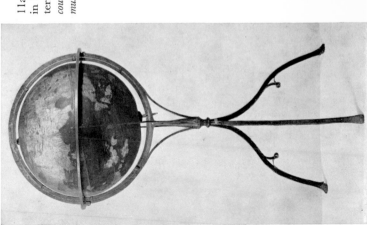

11a. The Nuremberg globe, made in 1492, and now the oldest terrestrial globe in existence. *By courtesy of the Germanisches National-museum, Nuremberg.*

11b. The island Antilia. Detail from the Nuremberg globe (from E. G. Ravenstein, *Martin Behaim. His life and his Globe). By courtesy of the Bodleian Library, Oxford.*

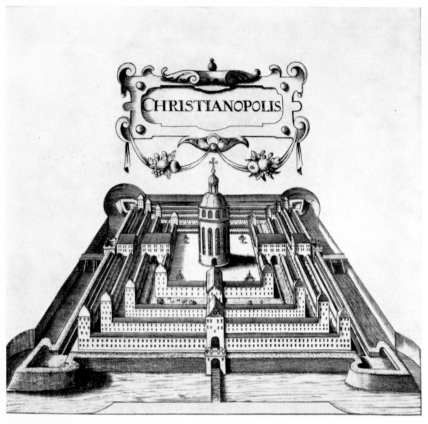

12. Johann Valentin Andreae's utopian city Christianopolis, from his *Reipublicae Christianopolitanae Descriptio* (1619). *By courtesy of the Bodleian Library, Oxford.*

secondly, in an investigation of the real aims and source of their own projects.

That they had confused Bacon's suggestions for improving academic knowledge in general, as it was then taught in the universities, with his plan for reconstructing the system of natural sciences, becomes clear as the evidence is analysed. In order to understand the reason for this confusion of two quite different proposals, it is important to know what this group's attitude to scientific knowledge really was; and to examine the substance of the passage in Bacon's *De Augmentis Scientiarum* on which their misconception was based.

In his own treatise on the reform of Natural Philosophy, published in 1633,[2] Comenius had condemned the Aristotelian philosophy as 'defective in many parts, and many ways intricate, full of turnings and windings, and partly also erroneous' and 'unprofitable for Christians'.[3] But what Comenius wanted to put in its place was equally remote from genuine science. His concept of science was one against which Bacon had specifically warned—an approach which depended on Scriptural interpretations for the explanation of purely physical phenomena, and carried with it no means of development.

In the same treatise Comenius complained that Bacon had provided a key, but had not unlocked the door to man's understanding of the physical universe. Like the pseudo-scientists the alchemists, Comenius wanted an all-embracing formula which would unlock nature at one stroke. So, baffled and disappointed, he turned sadly from Bacon's New Philosophy with the brief comment:

> Yet it grieved me . . . that I saw most noble *Verulam* present us indeed with a true key of Nature, but not open the secrets of Nature, onely shewing us by a few examples, how they were to be opened; and leave the rest to depend on observations and inductions continued for severall ages.[4]

Instead, therefore, of following Bacon's concept of science, Comenius continued to follow an inclination, typical of this

---

[2] J. A. Comenius, *Physicae ad Lumen Divinum Reformatae, Synopsis, Philodidacticorum & Theodicactorum, censurae exposita*, Leipzig, 1633. An English translation of this was published in London in 1651, entitled *Naturall Philosophie Reformed*—'Being a view of the WORLD in generall, and of the particular *Creatures* therein conteined; grounded upon *Scripture Principles*'.

[3] Ibid., Preface.   [4] Ibid.

H

group, towards vague metaphysical disquisition based on interpretations of Scriptural passages, as he indicated here:

> Yet I saw nevertheless, that my hopes were not quite left in sus-
> pense: in as much as I perceived my minde so enlightened by the
> light which it received from those severall sparks, now grown
> welnigh to a torch, that some great secrets of Nature, and very
> obscure places of Scripture, (the reason of which I knew not
> before) were now plain, as if of their own accord, to the exceed-
> ing great content of my mind.[5]

This group's interest in Bacon's recommendations had one
specific and persistent issue—the aim of setting up 'universal
colleges' in England which would embody their 'pansophic'
ideas. In a suggestion made by Bacon in the preface to the
second book of the *De Augmentis Scientiarum* they thought they
recognized the kind of project which was not only congenial
to them, but in addition had the advantage of being indigenous, a factor which was not unimportant when they were
approaching sponsors for the project in England, as distinct
from similar projects which they hoped to inaugurate on the
Continent. But, as will presently be seen, Bacon's intentions
on this point were misunderstood; and a further complication
of the situation is that in practice this group did not distinguish
between these proposals of Bacon's and his proposals for a
scientific institution. So the pre-Royal Society club at Oxford,
and later, the more formal, though nameless society in London,
and even the Royal Society proper, being 'Baconian', were
looked on by Hartlib and his associates as a practical start to
their 'pansophic' aspirations in England.

In his general review of the state of learning, Bacon had
pointed out in the preface to the second book of the *De Augmentis
Scientiarum*,[6] published in 1623, what he had already said in
The Advancement of Learning,[7] published in 1605—that colleges
throughout Europe were devoted to 'professory learning',
which was too limited to meet the various needs of a wide education. Academic learning, he said, should be both wider in its
range and deeper and more solid in its particular application:

[5] J. A. Comenius, *Physicae ad Lumen Divinum Reformatae, Synopsis, Philodidacticorum & Theodicactorum, censurae exposita.*
[6] Francis Bacon, *De Augmentis Scientiarum* II: *Works*, vol. IV, pp. 285-6.
[7] Ibid., *The Advancement of Learning* II: vol. III, pp. 323-4.

First therefore, among so many noble foundations of colleges in Europe, I find it strange that they are all dedicated to professions, and none left free to the study of arts and sciences at large. For if . . . any man think that Philosophy and Universality are idle and unprofitable studies, he does not consider that all arts and professions are from thence supplied with sap and strength. And this I take to be a great cause, which has so long hindered the more flourishing progress of learning; because these fundamental knowledges have been studied but in passage, and not drunk deeper of. . . . Neither is it to be forgotten that this dedication of colleges and societies to the use of professory learning has not only been inimical to the growth of the sciences [i.e. the 'disciplines' in general],[8] but has also been prejudicial to states and governments. For hence it proceeds that princes when they have to choose men for business of state, find a wonderful dearth of able men around them; because there is no collegiate education designed for these purposes, where men naturally so disposed and affected might (besides other arts) give themselves especially to histories, modern languages, books of policy and civil discourse; whereby they might come better prepared and instructed to offices of state.[9]

This was the suggestion for founding colleges which Hartlib and Comenius had adopted, though their interpretation of 'Universality' was not what Bacon had intended.

Nor had they any idea of putting Bacon's scientific proposals into action, for they were temperamentally incapable of thinking in those terms. All their projects reveal the kind of intellectual cleavage which Bacon had seen to be fatal to the development of science: on the one hand a view of the physical universe which was vague, distorted, and, above all, incapable of correction or progress because it was not rooted in scientific method; on the other hand various practical projects of a limited kind, concerned with such matters as husbandry, methods of school-teaching, and the haphazard collection and dissemination of inventions and discoveries, whether proved or merely speculative.

In his exposition of 'Pansophia',[10] which he sent to Hartlib

---

[8] See above, p. 35.   [9] Above, p. 208, note 6.
[10] This treatise was first published at Oxford in 1637 (under the title *Conatuum Comenianorum Praeludia: Porta Sapientiae Reserata, sive Pansophiae Seminarium*) by Samuel Hartlib, to whom Comenius had sent the manuscript to read.

in 1636, Comenius showed conclusively that the plans for establishing 'Pansophia' were not concerned with scientific knowledge at all. He again expressed his disappointment in Bacon's failure to provide an immediate, easy or guaranteed solution, and said in so many words that Bacon's concept of science was of little use to 'Pansophia', which, he declared, was much larger than the mere study of natural phenomena. He contrasted Bacon's 'rule for studying Philosophy' with 'The rule for building up Pansophia'. Under the first of these two headings he said:

> In his examination of nature, most noble Verulam seemed to have discovered a rule, that of skilfully wrought induction, which certainly was hidden, but has been revealed as a way of inquiring into nature. But, in fact, because this method demands the continuous labour of many men and many centuries, and thus seems burdensome, and furthermore, uncertain because of its somewhat doubtful success, the result is that the splendid discovery is despised by many as useless. To us indeed it brings little help regarding the construction of Pansophia, because (as I have said) it has been directed only towards revealing the secrets of nature, whereas we consider things in their entirety. Therefore we shall need another rule, absolutely universal, which perhaps our merciful God will not disdain to reveal to us when we seek for it. His purpose in hiding himself is that he may be sought; he wishes to be sought that he may be found.[11]

Comenius then expounded 'The rule for building up Pansophia', beginning:

> What, in answer to our urgent prayers and inquiries our Lord God has revealed and granted us to understand, I will now unfold. . . . Indeed I will unfold the whole matter in some Aphorisms.[12]

His arrangement of the ensuing disquisition in aphorisms gives it a superficial resemblance to the *Novum Organum*, but the content has no bearing on the development of science.

In this treatise Comenius acknowledged his debt to various persons, concerning his idea of 'Pansophia'. Among others, he

[11] Translated from the text (under the title *Pansophiae Praeludium*) in Comenius's own edition of his collected works, *Didactica Opera Omnia*, Amsterdam, 1657, Part I, 432, section 63.

[12] Ibid., 432–3, section 64.

mentioned Bacon,[13] but said that the principal influence had been Johann Valentin Andreae,[14] a German; and on another occasion Comenius said that he owed 'almost the very elements' of his 'pansophic' ideas to Andreae.[15] This information is very revealing in that it relates these 'pansophic' projects to their real source and inspiration.

Andreae's own 'Pansophia', so to say, in which the practice of 'the Reformed Protestant Religion' was the first consideration, and, within that, the pursuit of various aspects of learning, had been set out in two publications issued respectively in 1619 and 1620. These were *Reipublicae Christianopolitanae Descriptio*, an exposition of his ideal commonwealth, with the College at the centre—'the innermost shrine of the city . . . the centre of activity of the State'—and *Christianae Societatis Imago; Christiani Amoris Dextra Porrecta*, which gave information about the organization, administration and ambitions of the envisaged society.

Andreae's 'Christianopolis' will be considered in more detail when the similarity to it of a later scheme, which the sponsor attempted to persuade the Royal Society to adopt, is discussed.[16] At this point, however, it is important to notice that Andreae, writing some fifteen years after Bacon had published his *Advancement of Learning* (though before the publication of the *Novum Organum* and the *New Atlantis*), reflected the influence which this work had on him; and it is of particular significance that the manifestation of this influence appeared in the same misrepresented notion of a 'pansophic' college as it did with Comenius and Hartlib. In other words (and to place the events in chronological order), Andreae's projected institution, whose nucleus society he called 'Antilia',[17] was the prototype of that later advocated by the 'pansophic' group led by Comenius and Hartlib. This is clear, first, from Andreae's own texts, particularly *Christianae Societatis Imago*,[18] which is permeated by

[13] *Didactica Opera Omnia*, Part I, 442, section 97.

[14] Ibid.

[15] In a letter to Magnus Hesenthaler, quoted by Felix Held, *Christianopolis, An Ideal State of the Seventeenth Century* [Urbana], 1914, pp. 103–4.

[16] Below, pp. 226–7.

[17] See below, pp. 222 ff.

[18] This treatise was thought to have been lost since the seventeenth century, until Professor G. H. Turnbull, in *Hartlib, Dury and Comenius*, London, 1947, p. 74, mentioned that two manuscript copies of it were among Hartlib's

precepts and phrases from *The Advancement of Learning*, especially those relating to Bacon's suggested colleges and to Bacon's recommendation for greater communication between universities throughout Europe;[19] and, secondly, this is confirmed in an address to Hartlib, placed before the text in the English translation of *Christianae Societatis Imago*, which was made at Hartlib's request by a friend and supporter, John Hall, in 1647.[20] Hall referred this treatise back to the passages in *The Advancement of Learning* in which Bacon had originally advocated these colleges and the development of international intellectual communication:

> Your self (who were acquainted with some members of this *Society* in *Germanie*) can witnesse tis more then an *Idæa*; and tis a great deal of pitty both that warre *discontinued* it where it was first instituted: and that it is not again reviv'd among such minds, as have wholly *espoused* themselves to great and publick endeavours.
>
> They who are pleased to consider what the results of *associated* labours are, in comparison of *sequestered*, & assigne the increase of the Jesuits to this cause, will easily wish that which the Excellent Lord *Verulam* did some years before,[21] *Talis cum sis utinam noster esses* [They (the Jesuits) are so good that I wish they were on our side];[22] for as tis observ'd in the great work of *Providence*, that Commodities are *dispers'd* into severall Countries to occasion mutual relief and consequently *Commerce*, why may we not judge

[19] Francis Bacon, *The Advancement of Learning* II: *Works*, vol. III, pp. 323–4 and 327. This recommendation, like that for the colleges themselves, is repeated in *De Augmentis Scientiarum* II: *Works*, vol. IV, pp. 285–6 and 289.
[20] It was published under the title *A Modell of a Christian Society; The Right Hand of Christian Love Offered*. The diminutive volume in the Bodleian Library (less than 3¾ in. × 2 in. × ½ in.) is probably the only copy now in existence.
[21] 'Before' in that Bacon first made this observation in *The Advancement of Learning*, published in 1605 (see below, note 22), while Andreae's *Christianae Societatis Imago* was published in 1620.
[22] Francis Bacon, *Advancement of Learning* I: *Works*, vol. III, p. 277; and *De Augmentis Scientiarum* I: *Works*, vol. I, p. 445. This reference to the Jesuits is one of a number in which Bacon expressed his high regard for their scholarship, their contribution to knowledge and the international character of their institution.

---

papers, then in his charge. In fact, the published English translation of it (below, p. 212 and note 20) survived in the Bodleian Library; but this publication has been overlooked, and Andreae's debt to Bacon's *Advancement of Learning* accordingly minimized.

it of minds? since one Countrey can neither *engrosse* all great spirits, nor one great spirit all knowledge.[23]

The identity of 'Antilia', which has not hitherto been established,[24] would be of no more than passing interest in its context of these 'pansophic' schemes, were it not that this continental prototype of the 'pansophic' college was immediately recognized as such in a scheme concerning the Royal Society, put forward in December 1660. This scheme would have altered the nature of the as yet nameless Royal Society, for the aim was to incorporate it by Royal Charter according to the concept of 'Pansophia'. The circumstances in which this plan was made, and the terms of it, are discussed later, at the appropriate chronological point.[25]

Meantime it was in this aberrant approach to Bacon that his suggestion for colleges to study 'Universality' continued to be taken up by Hartlib, Comenius and their supporters. In 1636 Hartlib wrote to Comenius that there would

> have to be founded at this juncture a college such as the illustrious Bacon desired, dedicated to all studies of the world, of men whose care was to bring about augmentations, worthy of the human race, in the sciences and arts.[26]

On 7/17 February 1641 Comenius wrote to Hartlib that now was the time for the plans of Verulam to be heard and his wishes carried out. Comenius begged Hartlib to read again the preface to Book II of the *De Augmentis Scientiarum* (in which, as discussed above, Bacon urged the founding of colleges for 'Philosophy and Universality'). Comenius thought that the supplications Bacon had addressed to King James, might even more appropriately be transferred to King Charles. Verulam had desired a Universal College of learned men, said Comenius, and he and Hartlib also considered such a college necessary for universal restoration, together with universal books, 'the lamps of human pansophia', and universal schools, 'the candelabra of those lamps'. Comenius wanted the chief men in England,

---

[23] J. A. Andreae, *A Modell of a Christian Society*, translated by John Hall, London, 1647, in a letter to Samuel Hartlib from the translator, placed before the text.

[24] See below, pp. 221–4.   [25] Below, pp. 227–31.

[26] Quoted by Robert Fitzgibbon Young, *Comenius in England, 1641–1642*, London, 1932, p. 36.

or the King, or both, to be solicited for this purpose, and thought that a college should be founded in London, of six or seven men, to correspond with learned men throughout the world for the increase of inventions and discoveries.[27]

In September 1641, at Hartlib's pressing invitation, Comenius came to England. Their project was approved by various prominent persons, and for a brief period even received the consideration of Parliament, Chelsea College being named as a possible building for the purpose; 'so that', said Comenius,

> nothing seemed more certain than that the plan of the great Verulam respecting the opening somewhere of a Universal College, wholly devoted to the advancement of the sciences could be carried out.[28]

The plan fell through, owing, said Comenius, to the outbreak of war in Ireland. But while still in England he wrote his *Via Lucis*, another exposition of 'Pansophia',[29]

> a scheme which can state all things of this or any future age, hidden or revealed, in an order inviolable and in fact never broken, with such clearness that no man who surveys them with attentive mind can fail to understand all things, or to give them his genuine assent.[30]

The book was not published until 1668, the year after Sprat's *History*, whose publication had clearly prompted Comenius to publish then. His dedication to the Royal Society has an unmistakable proprietary tone, and was virtually a claim of priority; he considered that the Society had simply taken up where his group had left off. His reference to the 'territory'[31] offered his group in 1641 was presumably to Chelsea College, which Sprat had mentioned in the *History* as having been presented to the Royal Society:

> . . . the *College* at *Chelsey*, which the *King* has bestow'd on them; where they have a large *Inclosure*, to serve for all *Experiments* of

[27] Quoted by G. H. Turnbull, *Hartlib, Dury and Comenius*, 1947, p. 350.
[28] J. A. Comenius, *Didactica Opera Omnia*, Amsterdam, 1657, Part II, Introduction (and Robert Fitzgibbon Young, *Comenius in England, 1641–1642*, pp. 52–5).
[29] Ibid.
[30] J. A. Comenius, *The Way of Light*, translated by E. T. Campagnac, Liverpool, 1938, Dedication, p. 7.
[31] Below, p. 215.

Gardening and *Agriculture*: and by the neighbourhood of the *River* they have excellent opportunity of making all *Trials* that belong to the Water.[32]

Comenius commented:

It is not unfitting that a book entitled *The Way of Light* should be sent to you, who are the ministers of Light, to you, illustrious men whose labour in bringing the light of Natural Philosophy from the deeper wells of Truth is coming to be proclaimed and published throughout Europe. It is the more appropriate since the work was conceived in that country where the territory offered to us for the search for Light and Truth has passed into your keeping, according to that Word of Christ (applicable in its proper sense to this occasion): Others have laboured and you have entered into their labours. Pray, accept what may be to your purpose, so that these studies may come back to the source from which they sprang.[33]

When, in the text itself of the *Via Lucis*, written in 1641–2, Comenius described his 'Universal College' or 'College of Light', he referred to Bacon's proposed colleges:

When Bacon saw so many colleges nobly founded throughout Europe and all assigned to certain definite professions, he expressed a very just surprise that none were dedicated to the free and universal study of the Arts and Sciences: he was convinced that the real reason why a happier advance of learning had hitherto been checked among mankind was to be found precisely in this, that no one has concerned himself with Universal matters. The world will be wise if it takes better forethought for the study of wisdom in this sense.[34]

Comenius went on to give his own interpretation of what 'this sense' was. The 'College of Light' was to be a religious foundation whose members would 'be bound by the ties of sacred laws' whether they were 'grouped together or scattered' in various parts of the world. They were to be 'the teachers of mankind', but Comenius did not state what work they would do, except that 'they must give themselves up wholly and with-

[32] Thomas Sprat, *History*, p. 434.
[33] J. A. Comenius, *The Way of Light*, trans. E. T. Campagnac, 1938, Dedication, p. 3.
[34] Ibid., p. 169.

I

out reserve to advancing the glory of God and promoting the welfare of men'.[35] They were to set up schools and try to convert others to their religious beliefs:

> Further, they will see to it that schools are set up in every nation, town and village, and upon this matter they will give advice to the magistrates and other persons who are in power and authority. And they will make it their business to ensure the proper management of the Schools and will prevent abuses from creeping in, and keep them from going to sleep. Moreover, when they have settled things satisfactorily within their own borders they will take thought for spreading the light of wisdom to neighbouring peoples also, so long as there are any left who ought to be saved from the dominion of darkness; and for this purpose they will be at pains to have definite and effective methods for convincing and converting Jews, Mahometans, idolaters and others.[36]

Comenius added a footnote, as it were, to this explanation of the 'Universal College':

> ... the College of Light may be first established with one man and then a second, who have become acquainted with the mystery of Light—and this, not that they may take for themselves any advantage or superiority over others, but that they may set an example to others. For a beginning must be made with individuals, since the whole complement (of the College), however vast the number to which it may spread, must have its origin with a unit, and then rise to two and to three and so onwards, since every unit has an equal perfection with any other in itself and in regard to the whole.[37]

Comenius's real preoccupation, as he made very clear in this treatise, was not scientific truth, but a religious 'reformation', both for the individual and for mankind in general—an aspiration which was chiliastic in nature, and repetitious in exposition, abounding in vague metaphysical terms. In the dedication of 1668 Comenius rebuked the Royal Society for what he considered its materialism and lack of missionary zeal, and, addressing Charles II as Founder, urged him to turn the Society's attention to religion, 'because it is the salvation of the whole world that we seek'.[38]

[35] J. A. Comenius, *The Way of Light*, trans. E. T. Campagnac, 1938, pp. 169–74. See note 33.   [36] Ibid., p. 175.   [37] Ibid., pp. 222–3.
[38] Ibid., Dedication, pp. 24–5. See also below, p. 233.

While Comenius was in England in 1641, Hartlib himself published a brief utopia entitled *A Description of the Famous Kingdome of Macaria*, in the form of a dialogue between a Scholar and a Traveller (presumably himself and Comenius), addressing it to Parliament. In it the Traveller said:

> I heare that they are generally bent to make a good reformation, but that they have some stops and hinderances, so that they cannot make such quick dispatch as they would; and if any experience which I have learned in my long travels may stand them in stead, I would willingly impart it for the publick good.[39]

Hartlib went on to give a generalized and vague account of 'the Kingdome of Macaria'. The government was by 'a Great Councell, like to the Parliament in England', and had 'five under Councels': of Husbandry, Fishing, Trade by Land, Trade by Sea, and for new Plantations. They also had a 'house or College of experience'

> where they deliver out yeerly such medicines as they find out by experience; and such as shall be able to demonstrate any experiment for the health or wealth of men, are honourably rewarded at the publike charge, by which their skill in Husbandry, Physick, and Surgerie, is most excellent.[40]

In his tortuous exposition of the religious policy of 'Macaria', Hartlib unconsciously expressed his own doubts about the success of an imposed religion. This religion, while capable of proof 'by invincible arguments', so that all dissension was silenced, at the same time admitted to the existence of 'those who are of contrarie minds'.

> Their Religion consists not in taking notice of severall opinions and sects, but is made up of infallible tenets, which may be proved by invincible arguments, and such as will abide the grand test of extreme dispute; by which meanes none have power to stirre up

---

[39] Samuel Hartlib, *A Description of the Famous Kingdome of Macaria*, London, 1641, p. 2. Hartlib took the name Macaria from Sir Thomas More's *Utopia*, where he mentions 'the Macarians, a people that lie not far from Utopia'. (More himself, deriving 'Macaria' from 'μακαριος' (blessed or happy), indicated the utopian connotation of this word in ancient Greek literature.)

[40] Samuel Hartlib, *A Description of the Famous Kingdome of Macaria*, pp. 3–5.

Schismes and Heresies; neither are any of their opinions ridiculous to those who are of contrarie minds.[41]

The Scholar declared:

> I have read over Sr. *Thomas Mores Vtopia*, and my Lord *Bacons New Atlantis*, which hee called so in imitation of *Plato*'s old one, but none of them giveth mee satisfaction, how the Kingdome of England may be happy, so much as this discourse, which is briefe and pithy, and easie to be effected, if all men be willing.[42]

In 1646 Comenius was still hoping for a 'Universal College' to be started in England. Writing to Hartlib on 25 May (N.S.) he asked whether there was any chance of establishing the 'Collegium Lucis' ('College of Light') in England.[43] Hartlib's own unsuccessful proposals for his Office of Address, published in 1647 and 1648 (referred to above, in the previous chapter),[44] obviously constituted a version of the 'pansophic' college.

In 1658, Hartlib, still clinging to hopes of Parliamentary support for his plans for a 'reformed Church and State', thought he saw in John Wilkins, now married to Cromwell's sister, one with the influence, qualities and disposition needed to preside over a scheme which would have resembled his Office of Address for Communications,[45] the dominant part of that version of the 'pansophic' college. In a letter to Boyle dated 16 December 1658, Hartlib said:

> I am wondrous glad that you have written of the present protectors intentions for countenancing and advancing of universal useful learning in due time. I had, by the last post out of Germany, in my learned letters, some passages of special importance tending that way: I mean about the care of magistrates, for ordering and improving of learning, how it may be rightly constituted to work out, without any noise and disturbance, a real reformation and advancement in all manner of literature. . . . My humble and faithful service to the doctor [Wilkins], . . . letting him know, that I hope to see him not only made provost of Eton college, . . . but likewise president of the forementioned standing council of universal learning. I hope likewise, that the Lord will make your

[41] Samuel Hartlib, *A Description of the Famous Kingdome of Macaria*, p. 7.
[42] Ibid., p. 9.
[43] Quoted by G. H. Turnbull, *Hartlib, Dury and Comenius*, 1947, pp. 371–2.
[44] Above, pp. 200–5.   [45] Above, pp. 202 ff.

worthy self eminently instrumental for carrying on that design, upon that, or any other the like favourable either public or private occasions.[46]

In another letter to Boyle on 15 November 1659, Hartlib again expressed his longing to realize his 'pansophic' aspirations. His *cri de cœur* was occasioned by a treatise written by John Beale, a friend and supporter, entitled 'A free discovery of the true, lawful, holy and divine expedient for the propagation of the gospel, and establishment of an universal peace all over the world'. Hartlib said:

> The truth is, I design all such and the like works or tracts be printed upon the charges of *Macaria*, whose scope it is most professedly to propagate religion, and to endeavour the reformation of the whole world. But it is scarce one day (or hour in the day) or night being brim full with all manner of objects of that publick and most universal nature, but my soul is crying out,
>
> *Phosphore! redde diem, quid gaudia moraris?*
> *Phosphore, redde diem!*[47]

But by 15 October 1660 Hartlib was giving up hope of establishing a real 'Macaria'. In a letter of that date to John Worthington he admitted this, and at the same time provided an important piece of information linking that project in England with similar, earlier attempts on the Continent. Hartlib said:

> We were wont to call the desirable Society by the name of Antilia, and sometimes by the name of Macaria: but name & thing is as good as vanished.[48]

But 'Antilia' was destined to make one last appearance, and that a dramatic one, only two months later, when a scheme closely resembling it was confided to Hartlib. The proposal was an attempt to incorporate the former Oxford experimental science club (by then meeting in London, but still nameless) under Royal Charter as a 'pansophic' college, and so realize the long-frustrated hopes of Hartlib and Comenius.

[46] Robert Boyle, *Works*, ed. Thomas Birch, 1744, vol. V, p. 282.
[47] Ibid., p. 293.
[48] *The Diary and Correspondence of Dr. John Worthington*, ed. James Crossley (Chetham Society Publications, vol. XIII), Manchester, 1847, vol. I, p. 211.

The first evidence of this plan is on the occasion when the author of it, Bengt Skytte, a Swedish nobleman, approached Hartlib. Skytte had come to London in April 1659 in the hope of promoting one of his favourite projects, the foundation of a great Protestant alliance of States, which would be under Swedish leadership.[49] Skytte, a Senator in the Swedish Parliament, who had the confidence of the King, Karl Gustav, was well known for his interest in schemes for advancing learning.[50] In this he followed his father, Johan Skytte, who had been a friend and admirer of Francis Bacon,[51] and who in 1642, while Chancellor of Uppsala University, had been a member of the influential group which sponsored Comenius's stay in Sweden, for the purpose of improving teaching methods in the schools.[52] Among those in Sweden who protected Comenius's interests was Johan Matthiae, Bishop of Strengnäs, a protégé of Johan Skytte's.[53] Matthiae was the leader there of the scheme for reconciliation among Protestants,[54] which John Dury, one of Comenius's collaborators, had made his life work.[55] When Dury was in Sweden in 1636–8, Bengt Skytte had publicly advocated Dury's scheme for 'church peace'.[56]

Bengt Skytte had joined the experimental science club while he was in London,[57] and hoped to use this means to establish a 'pansophic' institution for learning on a grandiose scale. In a letter dated 17 December 1660 to his friend John Worthington, Hartlib said that Skytte had already sent him two documents and intended to call on him personally in the near future. Although Skytte had not explained these papers in detail, merely proffering them for Hartlib's examination pending their meeting, Hartlib was able to deduce their context from what he had seen:

I rec^d the papers without any explication, so that I do but guess that one of the papers contains the propositions which were made

[49] Fritz Arnheim, 'Freiherr Benedikt Skytte (1614–1683)', *Festschrift zu Gustav Schmollers 70. Geburtstag. Beiträge zur brandenburgischen und preussischen Geschichte*, Leipzig, 1908, p. 80.
[50] *The Diary and Correspondence of John Worthington*, op. cit., vol. I, p. 246.
[51] Fritz Arnheim, op. cit., p. 91.
[52] J. A. Comenius, *Didactica Opera Omnia*, 1657, Part II, Introduction.
[53] Fritz Arnheim, op. cit., p. 68.   [54] Ibid.
[55] Above, pp. 196–7.   [56] Fritz Arnheim, op. cit., p. 73.
[57] See Hartlib's letter, below, p. 221 and note 60.

to his Majesty by the Lord Skytte, and the other a draught for the royal grant or patent wch is desired for the establishing this foundation. Thus much is certain, that there is a meeting every week of the prime virtuosi, not only at Gresham College, in term time, but also out of it, at Mr. Ball's chambers in the Temple. They desired his Maj[esty's] leave that they might thus meet or assemble y^mselves at all times, wch is certainly granted. Mr. Boyle, Dr. Wilkins, Sr Paul Neale, Viscount Brouncker are some of the members.[58]

Hartlib considered that this society was the embryo from which Skytte's ambitious scheme, as set out in the two papers, might be realized:

I look upon this society as a previous introduction of the grand design here represented.[59]

Hartlib gave a further indication of the nature of Skytte's plan and of his own attitude to it and to the society originated by Wilkins, when he compared Skytte's plan to 'Antilia'. At the beginning of the same letter to John Worthington, Hartlib said that Skytte's proposal was practically the same as 'the other Antilia':

In the letter [of 10 December] I answered not so fully as now I shall, that passage in your last, Nov. 29, about Antilia. For since I have rec^d some other papers, that have been confided to me, holding forth almost the same things as the other Antilia (for be not offended if I continue to use this mystical word) but, as I hope, to better purpose. At least, the authors and founders walking in the light, we shall know from time to time how this proposed affair is managed by them. Lord Skytte, a Swedish nobleman, of a senatorian rank in that kingdom, is one of the prime gentlemen, who it seems hath devoted the spending of his life and estate after this manner. His Excellency (for so he is called) sent me word that he would shortly wait upon me...[60]

In the letter of 10 December 1660, referred to in the above passage, Hartlib had told Worthington what he meant by 'Antilia':

The word Antilia I used because of a former society, that was really begun almost to the same purpose a little before the Bohem-

[58] *The Diary and Correspondence of John Worthington*, op. cit., vol. I, pp. 246–8.
[59] Ibid., pp. 248–9.   [60] Ibid., pp. 245–6.

ian wars. It was as it were a tessera of that society, used only by the members thereof. I never desired the interpretation of it. It was interrupted and destroyed by the following Bohemian and German wars.

Hartlib went on to say that 'Antilia' was the name 'wch I had used to give that society, wch I know was real' [61] (that is, not merely a projected society, as some evidently thought). Hartlib used almost the same words when, in answer to a letter of 4 February 1660, he sent John Evelyn a copy of Andreae's *Christianae Societatis Imago; Christiani Amoris Dextra Porrecta* in John Hall's translation, entitled *A Modell of a Christian Society* [etc]:

> Honoured Sir, . . . Here I present you with the model of the Christian Society really begun in Germany: but the cursed Bohemian wars did destroy so noble and Christian a design . . . [62]

The society which was later named Antilia by its members originated, as Hartlib said, in Germany shortly before the beginning of the Thirty Years War in 1618. The founder was the Lutheran theologian and pastor Johann Valentin Andreae— at that time deacon at the little town of Vaihingen in Würtemberg—whose society of about thirty persons had been drawn from many parts of Germany and beyond. Andreae's aim was to establish a society throughout the German states, with international associations, under the patronage of a German prince. The society, to which Andreae referred formally as his 'Christian Union', was dedicated to the practice of the 'Reformed Protestant Religion' and to the cultivation of learning.

Andreae made several detailed references to this group and its intended development, particularly in letters to Prince August, Duke of Brunswick and Lüneburg. In a letter to him dated 27 June 1642, Andreae described the society, whose original scheme, he said, was later printed in 1620 (*Christianae*

---

[61] *The Diary and Correspondence of John Worthington*, vol. I, p. 239. For the derivation of the name Antilia, see below, pp. 224–5.

[62] *The Diary and Correspondence of John Evelyn*, ed. William Bray, London [1906], p. 598. (This edition is distinct from the three-volume edition prepared by William Bray and published in London in 1906, which does not contain this letter.) These words are also almost the same as those used by John Hall when referring to Andreae's society in the letter to Samuel Hartlib, quoted above, p. 212.

Societatis Imago). It had always been hoped that Prince August himself would become the head of the projected organization, but the group had been broken up early in the German wars, and even the copies of the book had been burnt to ashes. Dispersed and unable to correspond, most of the members had either died or had become disheartened. Eight years after the disruption of the society, on renewing contact at Nuremberg with some of the most faithful and zealous members, Andreae contracted his Christian Union to four, naming the others as Johann Saubert, Michael Baier (a patrician) and Christopher Leibnitz, all of Nuremberg.[63] In his autobiography Andreae mentions two visits to Nuremberg in which he renewed acquaintance with these faithful friends—the first occasion in the summer of 1624 and the second in the spring of 1628. With the help of these supporters Andreae produced a new manifesto in the hope of establishing the projected society: *Verae Unionis in Christo Jesu Specimen*, published in 1629.[64] He enclosed this publication and *Christianae Societatis Imago; Christiani Amoris Dextra Porrecta* with the above letter to Prince August of 27 June 1642.

In another letter to Prince August dated 19 March 1645, Andreae explained that various symbols or names had been used to indicate the hoped-for society. One name, given to the project (in the group's first phase) by his friend Wilhelm Wense, on the suggestion of Tobias Adami, was 'Civitas Solis',[65] after Campanella's utopia, then still in manuscript. Tobias Adami had visited Campanella in Italy, became his friend, and later published a number of his manuscripts, some of which he translated from the Italian into Latin and German. Adami published Campanella's *Civitas Solis* at Frankfurt in 1623. But by the time Andreae revived his society, that name had been

---

63 The letter, which is in Latin, is published in *Jana Amosa Komenského: Korrespondence*, ed. Jan Kvačala, Prague, vol. II, 1902, pp. 75–6.
64 J. V. Andreae, *Vita*, ed. F. H. Rheinwald, Berlin, 1849, pp. 104 and 108–11.
65 The letter, in German, is now in the Herzog August Bibliothek, Wolfenbüttel: Cod-Guelf. 65.1 Extr. Andreae had already given this information about the group's first phase, in his funeral eulogy on Wense in 1642, when he also stated that the society was Lutheran. (The funeral eulogy is quoted by R. Pust, 'Ueber Valentin Andreaes Anteil an der Societätsbewegung des 17. Jahrhunderts', *Monatshefte der Comenius-Gesellschaft*, Berlin, 1905, Band XIV, pp. 241–3.)

dropped. *Civitas Solis* had been published during the period of the society's disruption, and it is not surprising that when this Lutheran group took up the threads again at Nuremberg (without Wense and Adami) they preferred not to retain the name derived from Campanella, a Roman Catholic and an Italian. Instead they continued under a name with an indigenous connotation.[66] In the above letter of 19 March 1645 Andreae went on to say that the name of the group at Nuremberg was Antilia, towards whose realization he had directed his *Verae Unionis in Christo Jesu Specimen*, though he had never been successful in reaching a proper constitution. Samuel Hartlib was in correspondence with some of those concerned in various attempts to realize Antilia at that time.[67]

Antilia, as the expression of a Protestant utopia remained unrealized, but for decades it continued to inspire new attempts from Andreae's followers. J. A. Pöhmer of Nuremberg tried to put Antilia into practice with Heinrich Hein, an old friend of Andreae's. In 1636 Pöhmer wrote to Andreae that it was Hein who had introduced him to Andreae's *Christiani Amoris Dextra Porrecta* 'that unique and most perfect Idea of a truly Philosophical Society'. In November 1640, in answer to Andreae's request for information about their Antilian project, Pöhmer said: 'You will have no need of an interpreter in order to understand the meaning of this name, this project of Antilia, for it does not differ much from that delineation of the Christian-philosophical Society which you put before us in *Porrecta Amoris Christiani Dextera* or *Christianopolis*'. In a further letter Pöhmer thanked Andreae for an invitation to join his Christian Union, and discussed 'the real and primary aim of Antilia'.[68]

The name 'Antilia' itself was an expression of utopian aspiration which in Nuremberg had particular associations. For the island 'Antilia' appeared prominently on Martin Behaim's famous Nuremberg globe of 1492, placed to the south-west of Portugal, far out in the Atlantic Ocean. On the globe Behaim, himself a native of Nuremberg, had inscribed the 'history' of the island, acquired by him during his Portuguese travels and

---

[66] Below, pp. 224–5.
[67] See G. H. Turnbull, *Hartlib, Dury and Comenius*, 1947, pp. 11 and 69–73.
[68] These letters, which are in Latin, are published in *Jana Amosa Komenského: Korrespondence*, ed. Jan Kvačala, Prague, vol. II, 1902, pp. 8–9, 65–6 and 71–3.

voyages. The globe, which had been commissioned by the Nuremberg City Council 'for the honour and enjoyment of the commonalty',[69] had remained on view in the Town Hall for over a hundred years, until the beginning of the seventeenth century.[70] It still survives in Nuremberg, where it is now in the Germanic National Museum.

The legend of Antilia, which was inscribed on the globe in German, depicted a situation whose implications were not lost on Andreae and his group, which from the first had contained a zealous Nuremberg element—that of a Christian society which was both a refuge and a spiritual stronghold, consisting of a number of 'cities' united under one head. Martin Behaim had related that when 'the heathen of Africa' (the Moors) conquered and over-ran Spain in the eighth century, the Archbishop of Oporto 'with six other bishops, and other Christians' took refuge on the island of Antilia or Septe Citade (Seven Cities), and inhabited it.[71] In Andreae's ideal state Christianopolis, literally 'the Christian city' (which is further considered below), an inhabitant says:

> when the world raged against the good, and drove them out of her boundaries, religion, an exile, gathering about her the comrades whom she regarded the most faithful, after crossing the sea and examining various places, finally chose this land in which to establish her followers. Later she built a city which we call Christianopolis, and desired that it should be the home, or, if you prefer, the stronghold of honesty and excellence.[72]

Andreae, like Plato,[73] Sir Thomas More[74] and Campanella,[75] to all of whom he was indebted in the description of his utopia, saw his ideal society as an end in itself. Bacon, on the other

[69] E. G. Ravenstein, *Martin Behaim. His Life and his Globe*, London, 1908, p. 71.

[70] Ibid., p. 59. (By a slip Ravenstein said sixteenth instead of seventeenth century.)

[71] Ibid., p. 77.

[72] J. V. Andreae, *Reipublicae Christianopolitanae Descriptio*, Chapter III. See below, p. 226, note 77.

[73] Plato's Atlantis is described in the *Timaeus* and the *Critias*. (See also above, p. 61 and note 169.)

[74] The *Utopia* was first published, in Latin, at Louvain in 1516.

[75] Tommaso Campanella, *Civitas Solis*. This was first published in 1623, but Andreae had read it in manuscript when it was brought from Italy by his friend Tobias Adami.

hand, had a specific aim in his New Atlantis. Although his society was to have the spiritual and social virtues which he considered desirable, the actual purpose of his proposed institution was to build up a new system of natural sciences.

The first of Andreae's publications which describe his ideal society was his utopian *Reipublicae Christianopolitanae Descriptio*, published in 1619. He probably meant this to represent society at large, reformed according to his ideals, rather than a particular community, for in the second of these publications, *Christiani Societatis Imago* [etc.], he said:

> Moreover this society is not to dissolve any order of life, neither calls any man (unlesse upon great necessity) from his own vocation and course of life, but it leaves the body any where, onely knits the minds in Christ . . .[76]

It was, however, the description of the republic of Christianopolis which had engaged Skytte's attention, particularly its self-sufficiency and material assets (which he translated into terms of autonomy and privilege for the members of his proposed 'Royal Society'), and it was this model that Hartlib recognized in Skytte's scheme.

Andreae's Christianopolis[77] is a community of about four hundred persons, of whom many are in family units comprising two hundred and sixty-four homes. Its buildings, the most prominent elegantly colonnaded, are arranged on a compact plan, the College being 'the centre of activity of the State'. To meet the practical needs of the community, fields and meadows, together with the appropriate buildings, are available for growing crops and rearing animals. Water (both 'spring water and flowing water') is plentiful and there is a moat stocked with fish. Open spaces contain wild animals which are hunted for use. Many useful and some ornamental crafts are practised.

The College has particular regard for the practical side of learning. Besides a library, archives and its own printing press (over which it exercises religious and moral censorship), it

[76] J. V. Andreae, *A Modell of a Christian Society*, trans. John Hall, 1647, p. 10.

[77] J. V. Andreae, *Reipublicae Christianopolitanae Descriptio*, Strasbourg, 1619 (translated by Felix Held, *Christianopolis, An Ideal State of the Seventeenth Century* [Urbana], 1914).

has a laboratory 'fitted out with most ingenious ovens and with contrivances for uniting and dissolving substances'. There is also a pharmacy which 'is for them a veritable miniature of all nature'. Anatomy is studied by the dissection of animals. The 'hall of physics' shows natural history 'painted on the walls in detail and with the greatest skill'. Pictorial art, sculpture and architecture are studied, and there is a collection of mathematical instruments, including 'the very valuable telescope recently invented'. Astronomy and astrology are both practised.

In general there is a decided interest in practical and useful knowledge at a utilitarian level, but the underlying concept of science is still medieval.

Hartlib had given a clear indication of the nature of Skytte's proposals for the potential Royal Society, based on his reading of the two papers sent him by Skytte. But the text of the documents was not disclosed, and except for some comments on the scheme made at the time by Hartlib's friend and correspondent, John Beale, in an hitherto unpublished letter,[78] no more was heard of the papers for nearly three hundred years, until they were recently recovered.

Although the recovered documents are not signed or dated, which is not surprising, as the proposed charter was never realized, circumstantial evidence that they do indeed contain Skytte's project for a 'Royal Society' charter is overwhelming. The evidence is of three kinds: contemporary reference to the papers or to the plan set out in them; the circumstances and context in which the recovered papers were found; and the internal evidence of the text itself, particularly in its marked similarity to another charter devised by Skytte. This evidence will be considered in order.

Hartlib's references to the scheme show that it consisted of two documents, the first containing propositions addressed to the King, the second a draft of a royal patent for the foundation of the proposed institution;[79] and that the plan itself resembled Andreae's 'Antilia'.[80] Further information about it comes from John Beale's letter of 3 January 1660/61 to Hartlib,[81] in which Beale showed that he had observed a connexion between Skytte's proposed institution and the Anglican Church: that Charles II was to be its patron and founder, not

---

[78] Below, p. 228.   [79] Above, pp. 220–1.   [80] Above, p. 221.
[81] British Museum MS. Add. 6271, fol. 10ʳ. See below, p. 228.

only in his role as head of the State, but also as head of the Church of England:

> I doe highly approve of the Lord Skytts Designe towards practical Philosophy: and doe much rejoyce to hear from all persons, That his Maj^{tie} is not only a sonne of Art as He is a sonne of the Church Catholique; but as he is head of the Churches of thiese greate Islands, soe is he allso Head and founder, the great Patron of those noble Arts and Sciences, wch will make him a Sharer of the Glory of Solomon.

It will presently be seen that all these references by Hartlib and Beale relate to the recovered documents.

The circumstances and context in which the documents were found are additional evidence of their identity. A draft of the proposed royal patent itself, which was the second of the two papers, survives in two copies made from Worthington's papers, while still in the possession of his son, by John Ward.[82] Worthington's papers also included both sides of the correspondence between himself and Hartlib on the subjects of Skytte's scheme and of Antilia.[83] In 1667, Worthington, as he himself described, had charge of Hartlib's papers for a time, when he spent several days re-arranging them.[84] He presumably removed these letters of his to Hartlib, and put them in the relevant place among his own papers. Beale's letter to Hartlib referring to Skytte's scheme (in a copy made in 1688 by Worthington's son) was also copied out by Ward from Worthington's papers.

Under the heading 'Antilia', John Ward had copied from Worthington's correspondence references to Antilia and to Skytte's scheme, as well as the texts of other documents connected with Skytte—including the draft of the proposed Royal

---

[82] See above, Part Two, Chapter 2 for John Ward's account of Gresham College and its professors.

[83] These extracts from Worthington's papers (which are among John Ward's papers) are in British Museum MSS. Add. 6271, ff. 6–15 and Add. 6269. The extracts in the latter manuscript appear to be derived from the former, with some abridgments, and with additions from correspondence between Hartlib and Worthington which had already been published by Worthington's son.

[84] *The Diary and Correspondence of Dr. John Worthington*, ed. James Crossley (Chetham Society Publications, vol. XXXVI), Manchester, 1855, vol. II, Part I, p. 230.

Charter, which he placed immediately after Beale's letter referring to 'the Lord Skytts Designe'. Another copy of this proposed Royal Charter has since been found among Hartlib's papers,[85] where, folded with it, and, as the contents show, belonging to it, are three copies of a list of propositions to King Charles for the foundation of this institution.

Further evidence of Skytte's authorship is found in the form and content of the scheme itself. In 1936 Herr Anders Grape, Librarian of the University Library, Uppsala, surmised that Skytte's plan for the Royal Society must have been similar to the plan for a 'Universal University', an institute of 'Sciences and Arts', which Skytte later proposed to Frederick William, Prince Elector of Brandenburg;[86] and this surmise appears to be justified. The scheme in the recovered papers is essentially the same as Skytte's Brandenburg scheme of 1667,[87] with some variations according to the time and place. To put it another way, the Brandenburg scheme, which Skytte put forward seven years after his unsuccessful attempt in London, was a slightly adapted form of his unrealized 'Royal Society' plan. Although the Brandenburg 'Royal Charter' setting out the conditions for this foundation was signed by the Elector,[88] it came to nothing. Immediately after the Elector had given his assent, Skytte tried to make special conditions, and demanded that he should run the whole project. The Elector then decided that it had got out of proportion, and dropped it.[89]

[85] Hartlib's papers, the property of Lord Delamere, were then in the charge of the late Professor G. H. Turnbull. That the text of Skytte's proposed royal patent and the list of propositions might be found among Hartlib's papers was a logical guess. I wrote to Professor Turnbull describing Ward's copy of the 'royal patent' document in the British Museum, and asked whether he had a similar one, together with a list of 'propositions to the King'. He had. Charles II is referred to in both documents by such formal titles as 'His Serene Highness the King of Great Britain', etc., and once, in the 'propositions' (which obviously precede the 'charter'), as 'King Charles'. All the copies of these documents, both in the British Museum and among Hartlib's papers, are in Latin.

[86] Anders Grape, 'Comenius, Bengt Skytte och Royal Society', *Lychnos*, Uppsala, 1936.

[87] The text of Skytte's Brandenburg scheme, whose proposed 'Royal Charter' actually bears the Elector's signature, and of the further conditions set out by Skytte and signed by him, is given in full, in the original Latin, by J. C. C. Oelrichs, *Commentationes historico-literariae*, Berlin, 1751, pp. 12–25.

[88] Above, note 87.   [89] Fritz Arnheim, op. cit., pp. 88 ff.

Skytte had planned his institution as a centre of learning and culture resembling Andreae's Christianopolis. The 'college' in both the Brandenburg and the 'Royal Society' schemes was to be a residential establishment whose members, native and foreign, would, with their families, constitute a permanent community; it would also be a centre for visiting scholars. It was to be virtually a state within a state under the direct authority and protection of the Prince Elector of Brandenburg in the one case, and of the King of England in the other. Each of these proposed institutions was planned on a lavish scale, with a taste for the luxurious quite untypical of Hartlib's projects. In the Brandenburg plan the institute was to be 'a palace of palaces', while in the 'Royal Society' plan it was to be 'a palace', and, in both, members and their families were to have special exemption from taxes and levies. The 'Royal Society' charter, somewhat less ambitious than Skytte's final Brandenburg scheme, was nevertheless on a grandiose scale. It was to provide for 'buildings, domiciles, courts, colonnades, preserves, pastures, tillage, lands, waters and rivers, hunting, fishing and all appertaining revenues'. It was to grant a printing press, over which the Governors were to exercise censorship 'to suppress seditious matter and to see that nothing injurious to piety is printed'. The Governors were also responsible for purchasing 'the more famous books, paintings, sculptures and rare objects of art or nature' and they were to 'seek out from various regions unusual or useful arts and sciences, buy them up with college funds, and apply them to its welfare and increase'.

The charter claimed for the members, their families, and possessions, all the privileges enjoyed by the Court, or (with a tardy gleam of realism, considering the precarious standing of the Court at the time of the Restoration) the privileges which it might later possess:

> We receive into our royal grace and favour and protection all the aforementioned individuals, their families, and all their goods and chattels severally. We decree that their domicile should enjoy the same rights and privileges as our own Royal Court possesses, or can in future time possess. Moreover, that the personnel of this College should have the same rights and privileges as our own courtiers and members of the Royal Household. To the Governors of the College we grant over the members therein the same juris-

diction as the Master of the Royal Household and other functionaries excise over our Court and courtiers.

In both schemes there were to be two Governors (*bini Directores*), the 'Royal Society' charter specifying 'one from among our own subjects, the other a foreigner'. It seems extremely likely that Skytte had himself in mind as the foreign Governor, particularly in the light of his great reluctance to return to Sweden on the rise to power of his enemies during his absence in England, on the death at that time of King Karl Gustav.[90] In fact Skytte's personal dilemma and the timing of this scheme suggest that he would have preferred exile in England if he could have secured a congenial position of high standing and remuneration under the direct protection of the Sovereign—an attempt which he certainly made later in Brandenburg.

In connexion with the proposed settling of foreigners in the college, the 'Royal Society' plan, both in the propositions to the King and in the charter itself, gave assurances that this was to be an Anglican foundation:

> There must be no public practice of religion other than according to the rites of the Church of England. Let freedom of conscience be allowed to those of different creed and ritual, but they must abstain from public practice and argument and from all other harmful devices for spreading to others their opinions and observances.

Skytte's plan was in accord with the project of 'pansophia' advocated by Comenius and Hartlib, and was welcomed by Hartlib as such. In the light of Royal Society policy, it is easy to see why this plan would have been unacceptable to the Society, on scientific, and even on religious grounds. Moreover, although the Society may have hoped for more than nominal support from Charles II, it was realized that no great revenues would be forthcoming. Apart from major considerations of policy, however, it is unlikely that Skytte would have been allowed to take over the role of negotiator with the King, a part already embarked on with some success by Sir Robert Moray.[91] In any case, Skytte's personal ambitions may well have been suspect.

90 Fritz Arnheim, op. cit., pp. 80–1.   91 Above, p. 131, note 10.

Yet the decision to reject Skytte's plan could hardly have been automatic in the Society, for at least Boyle, who in 1660 already stood high in the esteem of his colleagues, supported the proposition. Hartlib said:

> Lord Skytte desires to come to me to confer about his design. He is one of the virtuosi. . . . Mr. Boyle, one of them, . . . offers to contribute to it.[92]

But the Society, as a body, did not want it. On 2 April 1661 Hartlib wrote to Worthington:

> There becomes nothing of Lord Skytte's business, & I believe the other virtuosi will not have it that it should go forward.[93]

Hartlib himself, worn out by illness and poverty in what he believed to be a great cause, died little more than a year later. Skytte returned to Sweden, and is heard of no more on the English scene. But the Royal Society was not to escape reproach for its wilful resistance to such projects. One expression of disappointment came from John Worthington, who had been a confidant of Hartlib for many years, until his death. Writing to Henry More on 5 February 1667/8, a few months after Sprat's *History* had been published, Worthington said:

> I see some there are in the world, scattered in corners, who are of a better and finer spirit. All are not materialistic and for nothing but what gratifies externall sense, or what sense doth reach; though the writer of the History of the R. Society is perfect Hylobares: and there are many more such; that is the way now in request.[94]

Hylobares, a character in Henry More's *Divine Dialogues*, is described as 'A young, witty, and well-moralized *Materialist*' in contrast to Philotheus, 'A zealous and sincere Lover of God and *Christ*, and of the whole Creation'.[95]

Public rebuke came from Comenius himself. In the dedication to the Royal Society of his *Via Lucis*, mentioned earlier,[96]

[92] *The Diary and Correspondence of John Worthington*, op. cit., vol. I, p. 257.
[93] Ibid., pp. 295–6.
[94] Ibid. (Chetham Society Publications, vol. CXIV), 1886, vol. II, Part II, p. 265.
[95] Henry More, *Divine Dialogues*, London, 1668, facing p. 1.
[96] Above, pp. 214, 216.

he not only indicated a claim to priority but considered it his business to caution the Society on its supposed deviation from the proper course. While congratulating it on its scientific achievement, he warned it that unless its religious policy were altered it would

> ... win the derision, if not of men ... yet of God himself and the Angels. And your work will be a Babylon turned upside down, building not towards heaven, but towards the earth.[97]

Addressing the King as Founder of the Royal Society, Comenius urged him to 'set an example of wisdom', for, he said:

> ... since our aims are world-wide, because it is the salvation of the whole world that we seek, we need not a fragment of a ship, but a whole ship for carrying Light, Peace and Truth abroad to all the continents and islands of the world.[98]

Comenius sent four copies of the book to the Royal Society: one each for the President (Viscount Brouncker), the two Secretaries (John Wilkins and Henry Oldenburg) and the Royal Society itself.[99] The Society sent back a courteous though non-committal acknowledgment of the gift.[100]

Yet it is possible that in the last few months before his death Hartlib himself saw the importance of the Royal Society's scientific policy. In a letter to John Worthington, written on 26 August 1661,[101] Hartlib quoted at length from a letter he had received from his friend and supporter, John Beale, who earlier had 'highly approved' of Skytte's scheme.[102] Beale expressed astonishment at the progress made by the 'virtuosi' in so short a time, seen especially in Boyle's first publications. Hartlib quoted Beale as saying:

> Tis my great joy that Mr. B[oyle] is so far engaged to give us the rest of his notes and following experiments. In these he hath obliged all the intelligent inhabitants of this world, and hath given us hope, that we shall shortly complete humane sciences.[103]

[97] J. V. Comenius, *The Way of Light*, trans. E. T. Campagnac, Liverpool, 1938, Dedication, p. 19.   [98] Ibid., pp. 24–5.
[99] Letter Book, vol. II, p. 202. The letter is dated 7/17 May 1668.
[100] Ibid., p. 217; and Journal Book, vol. III, p. 214, which records the Society's order to reply to the letter.
[101] *The Diary and Correspondence of John Worthington*, op. cit., vol. I, pp. 365–7.
[102] Above, p. 228.
[103] *The Diary and Correspondence of John Worthington*, op. cit., vol. I, p. 369.

Hartlib further quoted Beale, who had turned to Francis Bacon for guidance in 'philosophical experiments':

> ... but of this I complained, that in the progress of late years we had not brought his experiments or added our own, to any degree of ripeness. And this was indeed my discouragement. Now I confess I am surprised with wonder at the present advancement, & I dare promise our posterity, that knowledge shall in this following age abound in very great perfection, & to the best of noble operations.[104]

Beale's admiration for the Royal Society, and wish to be of service to it, soon brought him honorary membership—on 7 January 1662/3—and the offer of a Fellowship,[105] to which he was elected a fortnight later.[106] By that time Hartlib was dead: and with him had died, too, the impetus for establishing a 'pansophic' college in England.

So ends the story of the persistent efforts to found a 'Baconian' institution which would have taken no account of Bacon's scientific postulates. As with the other erroneous sources to which the Royal Society has been ascribed, careful examination of this one serves to illuminate, even more clearly, the unique character of the Royal Society.

[104] *The Diary and Correspondence of John Worthington*, op. cit., vol. I, pp. 371-3.
[105] Journal Book, vol. I, p. 128.   [106] Ibid., p. 133.

CONCLUSION

At the time of the inception of the Royal Society, the entire structure of the natural sciences, still dominated by the Aristotelian philosophy, which prevailed in the universities, was antiquated, unrealistic and sterile. Individual discoveries—even those of a major order—together with utilitarian inventiveness, had failed to produce new sciences. Experimental investigations of natural phenomena were spasmodic, unrelated, often impeded by an admixture of superstitious practices, and lacked organization in any comprehensive sense.

Examination of contemporary evidence both inside and outside the Royal Society shows that the Society's central purpose—putting into action the vision of Francis Bacon—was to cut away the whole existing system of natural sciences, and deliberately to begin the process of creating new sciences in which an organized body of related inductive knowledge, capable of continuous, unlimited development, could be built up, for the long-term benefit of mankind.

Francis Bacon's dominant role in this metamorphosis has been unrecognized by historians of science for three main reasons: first, his contribution to science has primarily been sought in the actual scientific content of his works, which is negligible; secondly, misunderstanding of his text has led to misconceptions about his theory of induction, and to its rejection as unworkable; and thirdly, the assumption has been made, in retrospect, that the emergence of an embryo system of modern sciences in the second half of the seventeenth century was purely spontaneous and inevitable.

In fact, Bacon's contribution was not scientific but philosophical in nature. Yet so profound was his concept in its perception, scope and foresight, that in action its effect was dynamic, as he had predicted. His concept embraced the entire range of nature in its working, both in its uninhibited manifestations and under controlled conditions created by the experimenter. The structure of 'the New Philosophy' was to be a comprehensive and expanding system of related inductive sciences, and to this vast theme Bacon brought a powerful imagination.

The fundamental precepts which Bacon laid down were permanent principles governing the successful establishment and continued growth of the sciences. His insistence, for example, that while particular sciences must be evolved as such, they must not develop in isolation, but in relation to contiguous sciences, is justified increasingly as scientific knowledge progresses. The present spectacular advance in molecular biology is only one of the effective results of combining the resources of physical, chemical and biological knowledge, in solving problems. This advance also provides an outstanding vindication of Bacon's dictum that the study of the internal structures of both organic and non-organic matter was essential, and of his belief that scientific investigation should involve not only static analysis, nor even analysis at particular stages, but also the study of continuous processes in action, especially those subtle processes beyond the reach of sense-perceptions.

Among the more serious misunderstandings about Bacon's concept of science is the widely held belief that Bacon failed to take into account the factor of intuition in scientific research —the informed hunch—when in fact this element, supported by the existing framework of 'hard' knowledge, and carried forward by the innate intelligence of the investigator, using practical means of verification, was a vital ingredient in his theory of induction.

Since the chief obstacle to the reform of the sciences was the academic system in the universities, it was here that action was most needed, and it was in fact within Oxford University that the originators of the Royal Society, led by John Wilkins, who had just been appointed Warden of Wadham College, 'first conceiv'd it in their minds, and practis'd some little draught of it'.[1]

[1] Thomas Sprat, *History*, p. 53.

The universities, as such, fearing the undermining of traditional learning, not only in the natural sciences, but in the whole academic system, were strongly opposed to the Royal Society. Notwithstanding this, the Society, especially after its establishment as a royal foundation, took on a leading role in the development of science.

In its aim of building up new sciences, the Royal Society welcomed into its ranks those artisans who showed a talent for disinterested scientific investigation, as distinct from a merely utilitarian approach to knowledge. But these were relatively few, the majority of Fellows being those whose very lack of experience in a particular craft, or even in a profession, ensured an uncommitted mind. Sufficient leisure for sustained work was also desirable, so it was inevitable that those who were able to respond were chiefly 'Gentlemen, free, and unconfin'd'.[2]

The Royal Society followed Francis Bacon, too, in his recommendations on the style of language best suited to the needs of the new sciences. Superseding the verbosity of the Aristotelian style, this was to be simple, direct and functional to the point of starkness, the conscious creation of a technical language. Though not without some influence on the mainstream of the language, the idiom of science remained distinct from it. The cultural language, itself reacting against a previous form—the cadenced structure of Renaissance prose—was not chiefly characterized by plainness but by flexibility. These two idioms, the scientific and the literary, never fused into a single form, and diverged to such a degree that they are now often regarded as the expressions of two cultures.

The importance of the early Royal Society is not confined to its example and immense influence in the scientific field. Its religious policy, also derived from Francis Bacon as part of its whole concept, was outstanding in that age. At a time when strong official discrimination was directed against all non-Anglicans, especially Roman Catholics, and debarred them from public office and the professions, the Royal Society was the only learned society which admitted men of all denominations on equal terms. While upholding Christian principles, the Society insisted on the right of the individual to follow his conscience in religious practice. In thus dissociating itself, as a body, from the religious policy then practised by the

2 Thomas Sprat, History, p. 67.

Establishment, the Royal Society represented a highly-civilized advance towards the full liberty of the subject.

A theory that the Royal Society was an expression of 'the Puritan ethic' is seen to be untenable. The Society, both in its initial stage at Oxford, and later as an established institution in London after the Restoration, was opposed to the claims of party interest, whether political or religious. Repudiating the limits set by provincialism and nationalism, the Society sought the co-operation of Europe and the civilized world at large.

In its concept of science the Royal Society was distinct from preceding societies. Although earlier societies with an interest in 'the New Philosophy' had helped to create an atmosphere in which the prototype of the Royal Society could establish itself and flourish, none of those societies constituted the model on which the Royal Society was formed. And notwithstanding the failure of some Fellows to grasp the essential principles of its scientific policy, and a degree of dilettantism, the element which may be called the leaven in the lump, which constituted a genuine and important distinction of function, prevailed; and this was achieved largely through the control exercised by the Society's Council.

Some societies which, individually, according to various theories, have been thought to constitute the Royal Society's origin, have been discussed. Thus Theodore Haak's club in London, which John Wallis once claimed to be the prototype of the Royal Society, is shown to be different in nature from the Royal Society. It is here shown that Wallis later dropped the claim that the Royal Society originated in Haak's club during the Civil War, and maintained, in an account which entirely agrees with Sprat's, that the Royal Society originated at Oxford, soon after the end of the Civil War.

Gresham College, according to one theory not only the location, but the inspiration of the embryo Royal Society, is seen to be neither the one nor the other; nor did Gresham College ever make any such claim.

On the other hand Samuel Hartlib and Comenius did show a proprietary interest in the Royal Society, though on mistaken grounds, the error being a fundamental one of concept, based on a misunderstanding of Bacon's intentions. Their persistent efforts to found 'pansophic' colleges included support for an attempt, in 1660, to incorporate by Royal Charter the as yet unnamed Royal Society, according to 'pansophic' ideas. These took no account either of the Society's scientific policy or of its stand on religious freedom.

That the activities of the Royal Society enormously accelerated the development of the natural sciences is generally accepted; but that this was the working out of a conscious, deliberately-conceived ideal has been lost to sight, and with it the real significance of the early Royal Society's contribution to science. Perhaps, paradoxically, it is some measure of the originators' success that what they had pioneered came to be taken for granted. Those succeeding generations for which the Society had so tenaciously struggled to build a sound foundation for a new '*Systeme* of *Natural Philosophy*',[3] failed to see that strenuous action had ever been necessary, supposing that this undertaking was the unpremeditated, inevitable product of its age.

Such an assumption takes no account of the effort and effectiveness of man's conscious role in the course of history. For in the context of its time this concept of science was not merely a difference of degree; it was a difference in kind—one of the great formative acts of the human intellect and will, and a significant turning-point in the story of man's relationship with his physical environment. Scientific investigation had been thrust forward into a new era of coherence and growth, where no philosophic stops in the mind qualified in advance its limitless potential; and the following three centuries have borne witness to the unprecedented rate of its expansion.

[3] Thomas Sprat, *History*, p. 327.

INDEX